Y0-ALM-327

Presented to:

Mom

From:

Eric + Mindy

Date:

Xmas 2017

Jesus Always

Embracing Joy *in* His Presence

Sarah Young

THOMAS NELSON
Since 1798

Jesus Always: Embracing Joy in His Presence

© 2016 by Sarah Young

All rights reserved. No portion of this book may be reproduced, stored in a retrieval system, or transmitted in any form or by any means—electronic, mechanical, photocopy, recording, scanning, or other—except for brief quotations in critical reviews or articles, without the prior written permission of the publisher.

Published in Nashville, Tennessee, by Thomas Nelson. Thomas Nelson is a registered trademark of HarperCollins Christian Publishing, Inc.

Thomas Nelson titles may be purchased in bulk for educational, business, fund-raising, or sales promotional use. For information, please e-mail SpecialMarkets@ThomasNelson.com.

Unless otherwise noted, Scripture quotations are taken from the Holy Bible, New International Version®, NIV®. Copyright © 1973, 1978, 1984 by Biblica, Inc.® Used by permission of Zondervan. All rights reserved worldwide. www.zondervan.com. The "NIV" and "New International Version" are trademarks registered in the United States Patent and Trademark Office by Biblica, Inc.®

Other Scripture quotations are from the following sources:

The Amplified® Bible (AMP). Copyright © 1954, 1958, 1962, 1964, 1965, 1987 by The Lockman Foundation. Used by permission. (www.Lockman.org). The ESV® Bible (The Holy Bible, English Standard Version®) (ESV). Copyright © 2001 by Crossway, a publishing ministry of Good News Publishers. Used by permission. All rights reserved. The Good News Translation in Today's English Version—Second Edition (GNT). Copyright 1992 by American Bible Society. Used by permission. The Holman Christian Standard Bible® (HCSB). Copyright © 1999, 2000, 2002, 2003, 2009 by Holman Bible Publishers. Used by permission. HCSB® is a federally registered trademark of Holman Bible Publishers. The King James Version (KJV). Public domain. *The Message* (MSG). Copyright © by Eugene H. Peterson 1993, 1994, 1995, 1996, 2000, 2001, 2002. Used by permission of Tyndale House Publishers, Inc. The New American Standard Bible® (NASB). Copyright © 1960, 1962, 1963, 1968, 1971, 1972, 1973, 1975, 1977, 1995 by The Lockman Foundation. Used by permission. (www.Lockman.org). The New Century Version® (NCV). © 2005 by Thomas Nelson. Used by permission. All rights reserved. The NET Bible® (NET). Copyright © 1996–2006 by Biblical Studies Press, L.L.C. http://netbible.com. All rights reserved. The New King James Version® (NKJV). © 1982 by Thomas Nelson. Used by permission. All rights reserved. The *Holy Bible*, New Living Translation (NLT). © 1996, 2004, 2007, 2013 by Tyndale House Foundation. Used by permission of Tyndale House Publishers, Inc., Carol Stream, Illinois 60188. All rights reserved. The Revised Standard Version of the Bible (RSV). Copyright 1946, 1952, and 1971 National Council of the Churches of Christ in the United States of America. Used by permission. All rights reserved. The Living Bible (TLB). Copyright © 1971. Used by permission of Tyndale House Publishers, Inc., Carol Stream, Illinois 60188. All rights reserved.

Any Internet addresses, phone numbers, or company or product information printed in this book are offered as a resource and are not intended in any way to be or to imply an endorsement by Thomas Nelson, nor does Thomas Nelson vouch for the existence, content, or services of these sites, phone numbers, companies, or products beyond the life of this book.

ISBN 978-0-7180-9541-3 (large deluxe)
ISBN 978-0-7180-9338-9 (custom)

Printed in China

17 18 19 20 21 DSC 6 5 4 3 2

*I dedicate this book to Jesus—
my Lord and my God, my Savior and Friend.*

Then will I go to the altar of God, to

God, my joy and my delight.

—Psalm 43:4

You will show me the path of life;

In Your presence is fullness of joy;

At Your right hand are pleasures forevermore.

—Psalm 16:11 NKJV

Though you have not seen him [Jesus], you love him;

and even though you do not see him now, you believe in him

and are filled with an inexpressible and glorious joy.

—1 Peter 1:8

Acknowledgments

I am blessed to work with a very talented team: Jennifer Gott, my editorial project manager, has worked valiantly on the production of this book—wearing a variety of hats quite effectively. I'm thankful for Kris Bearss, my editor who knows my work wonderfully well and edits my writing with just the right touch. Finally, I'm grateful for my publisher, Laura Minchew, who has an abundance of creative ideas—and shepherds my publishing so well.

Introduction

Writing *Jesus Always* has been a marathon for me. I began working on it in September 2012, while I was still living in Perth, Western Australia. In 2013 my husband and I moved back to the US—a complicated international move from one side of the planet to the other. I lived out of suitcases for half a year, staying in seven different homes, moving back and forth between some of them multiple times. Needless to say, I didn't get much writing done during that six-month period.

When we finally settled into our permanent home in Tennessee, I was delighted to be able to start writing again. Working on *Jesus Always* became my top priority: I chose to postpone many worthwhile activities in order to complete the book. It was a pleasure and a privilege to be able to set aside large blocks of time for focusing on Jesus and His Word.

Jesus Always is designed to increase your Joy and strengthen your relationship with Jesus. If you belong to Him, your story has an indescribably happy ending—no matter what is happening in your life right now. And just knowing that your story finishes so wondrously well can fill your present earth-journey with Joy. If you do not yet know Christ as your Savior, be assured that I'm praying for you every day—that you will ask Him to forgive all your sins and give you the glorious gift of eternal life. Then you too can experience the amazing Joy of being Jesus' beloved friend.

I have been contending with impaired health for many

years—since August 2001. In my quest to find healing, I've gone to a number of doctors and tried a variety of medical treatments. I continue to have significant limitations in my life, yet I have found Joy in my journey.

My inability to be "out and about" very much has given me more time to focus on Jesus and enjoy His Presence. It has also provided opportunities to spend time with precious friends and acquaintances. I no longer drive because of the chronic vertigo I've had since 2008. As a result, caring friends have driven me to various places, often staying with me during long waits for doctors. Spending time with these wonderful people has been a source of much pleasure for me.

Leading a quiet life helps me look for and find little treasures that brighten my day: a cardinal or blue jay in flight, a "coincidence" reminding me that God is at work in the details of my life. I try to take time every day to jot down in a notebook a few of the recent blessings I've received. I call it my "Thanks Book," but it could just as easily be called my "Joy Book." Looking for good things and thanking God for them cheers me up and changes my perspective, helping me see my life through a grid of gratitude.

I love the story of a weak, old coal miner whose body had been ravaged by his many years of hard labor in the mines. In his humble home there was a table with a small bowl of thin porridge on it. Holding a piece of bread in his coal-stained hand, he was ready to eat his meager meal. But first he knelt beside the table, joyfully exclaiming over and over again: "All this, and Jesus too! All this, and Jesus too!"

This story inspires me and helps me grasp the beautiful truth that having Jesus in my life means I am blessed beyond belief! I'm convinced that thankfulness is one of the most important ingredients in a joyful heart.

I enjoy singing this short, simple song in the morning: "This is the day that the Lord has made. We will rejoice and be glad in it." It helps me approach the day as a precious gift from God—remembering that every breath I breathe is from Him.

The subtitle of *Jesus Always* is *Embracing Joy in His Presence*. We embrace Joy by embracing Jesus—loving Him, trusting Him, staying in communication with Him. We can choose to live this way even during our most challenging times. In fact, the more difficult our circumstances, the brighter our gladness will shine—in vivid contrast to the dark backdrop of adversity. Thus we make the Light of Jesus' Presence visible to people around us.

I consider the Bible a priceless treasure; it is the only inspired, inerrant, unchanging Word of God. I enjoy reading it—pondering *the depth of the riches of the wisdom and knowledge of God*. During the last five years, memorizing Scripture has become increasingly precious to me. It's so comforting to have God's Word in my heart all the time—guiding and encouraging me day and night.

As in all my devotional writing, *Jesus Always* is written from the perspective of Jesus speaking to you, the reader. Because I revere the Bible, I always endeavor to make my writing consistent with biblical truth. I include Scripture in the devotions (indicated with italics), and each entry is followed by three or four Bible references. I encourage you to look up and read these scriptures carefully; they are words of Life!

A few of the devotions in this book reflect ideas found in *Dear Jesus* or *Jesus Lives*. These have been included in *Jesus Always* to increase the "Joy-quotient" in the book.

Ever since the publication of *Jesus Calling*, I have prayed daily for people who are reading my books. Over the years, these prayers have become longer, covering a wide range of topics. Even when I've been hospitalized, I have not missed a day of praying for readers. I consider this a God-given responsibility and a rewarding privilege. I am delighted to add *Jesus Always* readers to this precious community. One of my most heartfelt daily prayers is that the Lord will bring many readers into His kingdom of *inexpressible and glorious Joy*!

Dear reader, as you make your way through the pages of this book, I long for you to embrace the Joy of a close relationship with Jesus. He is with you at all times, and in His Presence there is *fullness of Joy*.

BOUNTIFUL BLESSINGS!

Sarah Young

January

*Your word is a lamp to guide my feet
and a light for my path.*

Psalm 119:105 NLT

January 1

D0 NOT DWELL ON THE PAST. *See, I am doing a new thing!* As you begin a fresh year, rejoice that I am continually working newness into your life. Don't let recent disappointments and failures define you or dampen your expectations. This is the time to make a fresh start! I am a God of unlimited creativity; expect Me to do surprising things in this year that stretches out before you.

Today is a precious gift. The present moment is where I meet with you, beloved. So seek My Face throughout *this day that I have made.* I have carefully prepared it for you—with tender attention to every detail. I want you to *rejoice and be glad in it.*

Search for signs of My loving Presence as you journey along *the path of Life.* Look for the little pleasures I have strewn alongside your pathway—sometimes in surprising places—and thank Me for each one. Your thankfulness will keep you close to Me and help you find Joy in your journey.

> "Forget the former things; do not dwell on the past. See, I am doing a new thing! Now it springs up; do you not perceive it? I am making a way in the desert and streams in the wasteland."—ISAIAH 43:18–19

> *This is the day that the LORD has made; let us rejoice and be glad in it.*—PSALM 118:24 ESV

> *You will show me the path of life; in Your presence is fullness of joy; at Your right hand are pleasures forevermore.*—PSALM 16:11 NKJV

January 2

I AM YOUR JOY! These four words can light up your life. Since I am always with you, *the Joy of My Presence* is continually accessible to you. You can open up to My Presence through your trust in Me, your love for Me. Try saying, "Jesus, You are my Joy." My Light will shine upon you and within you as you *rejoice in Me*, your Savior. Ponder all I have done for you and all that I am to you. This will lift you up above your circumstances.

When you became My follower, I empowered you to rise above the conditions in your life. I filled you with My Spirit, and this Holy Helper has limitless Power. I promised that *I will come back and take you to be with Me* in heaven—*that you may be where I am* forever. Whenever your world is looking dark, brighten your perspective by focusing on Me. Relax in My Presence, and hear Me saying, "Beloved, I am your Joy!"

> *Surely you have granted him eternal blessings and made him glad with the joy of your presence.*—PSALM 21:6

> *Rejoice in the Lord always. Again I will say, rejoice!*—PHILIPPIANS 4:4 NKJV

> *"And if I go and prepare a place for you, I will come back and take you to be with me that you also may be where I am."*—JOHN 14:3

January 3

Be still, and know that I am God. Most Christians are familiar with this command, but not so many take it seriously. Yet for those who *do*, blessings flow like *streams of living water.* As these believers sit in stillness—focusing on Me and My Word—their perception of Me expands and their troubles shrink in importance.

I want *you* to share in these blessings, beloved. Take time, take time with Me. While you rest in My Presence, I untangle your thoughts and help you view things more biblically. Remember: *My Word is a lamp to guide your feet and a light for your path.* Biblical thinking illuminates the path before you so you can find your way.

It's crucial to know not only that *I am God* but that *I made you and you are Mine.* You are a *sheep of My pasture.* Sheep have very limited understanding of what their shepherd is doing for them, but they follow him anyway. Similarly, as My "sheep," your job is to trust Me and follow wherever I lead.

> "Be still, and know that I am God; I will be exalted among the nations, I will be exalted in the earth!"—Psalm 46:10 NKJV

> "Whoever believes in me, as the Scripture has said, streams of living water will flow from within him."—John 7:38

> Your word is a lamp to guide my feet and a light for my path.—Psalm 119:105 NLT

> Know that the Lord is God. It is he who made us, and we are his; we are his people, the sheep of his pasture.—Psalm 100:3

January 4

Find Joy in Me, for I am your Strength. It is vital to keep your Joy alive, especially when you're in the throes of adversity. Whenever you are struggling with difficulties, you need to guard your thoughts and spoken words carefully. If you focus too much on all the things that are wrong, you will become increasingly discouraged—and your strength will be sapped. As soon as you realize what is happening, stop this hurtful process immediately. Turn to Me, asking Me to help you with all your struggles.

Take time to praise Me: Speak or sing words of worship. Read scriptures that help you rejoice in Me.

Remember that your problems are temporary but *I* am eternal—and so is your relationship with Me. As you find Joy in Me, delighting in *My unfailing Love* for you, your strength will increase. This is *the Joy of the Lord,* which is yours for all time and throughout eternity!

Nehemiah said, "Go and enjoy choice food and sweet drinks, and send some to those who have nothing prepared. This day is sacred to our Lord. Do not grieve, for the joy of the Lord is your strength."—Nehemiah 8:10

Shout with joy to God, all the earth! Sing the glory of his name; make his praise glorious! Say to God, "How awesome are your deeds! So great is your power that your enemies cringe before you."—Psalm 66:1–3

Let the morning bring me word of your unfailing love, for I have put my trust in you. Show me the way I should go, for to you I lift up my soul.—Psalm 143:8

January 5

LET *MY CONSOLATION*—My comfort—*bring Joy to your soul*. When anxiety is welling up within you, come to Me and *pour out your heart*. Then sit quietly in My Presence while I comfort you, helping you see things from My perspective. I remind you of your heavenly destination, for you are indeed on your way to Glory! I infuse My Joy and Peace into your heart, mind, and soul.

When you are joyful, this changes the way you view the world around you. Even though you see much darkness, you can also see the Light of My Presence continuing to shine. Moreover, the Joy in your soul gives you buoyancy, enabling you to rise above the countless problems in your life. Once you have gained this perspective, you will discover that you can comfort others in the midst of their troubles. They will find in you the consolation that you have found in Me. Thus your Joy becomes contagious, "infecting" those around you with Joy in *their* souls!

When anxiety was great within me, your consolation brought joy to my soul.—PSALM 94:19

Trust in him at all times, O people; pour out your hearts to him, for God is our refuge.—PSALM 62:8

Praise be to the God and Father of our Lord Jesus Christ, the Father of compassion and the God of all comfort, who comforts us in all our troubles, so that we can comfort those in any trouble with the comfort we ourselves have received from God.—2 CORINTHIANS 1:3–4

January 6

IT IS POSSIBLE for My followers to be joyful and afraid at the same time. When an angel told the women who came to My tomb that I had risen from the dead, they were *"afraid yet filled with joy."* So do not let fear keep you from experiencing the Joy of My Presence. It is not a luxury reserved for times when your problems—and the crises in the world—seem under control. My loving Presence is yours to enjoy today, tomorrow, and forever!

Do not give in to joyless living by letting worries about the present or the future weigh you down. Instead, remember that *neither the present nor the future, nor any powers, nor anything else in all creation, will be able to separate you from My Love.*

Talk with Me about your fears, expressing your thoughts and feelings freely. Relax in My Presence and entrust all your concerns to Me. Then ask Me to bless you with My Joy, which *no one can take from you.*

So the women hurried away from the tomb, afraid yet filled with joy, and ran to tell his disciples.—MATTHEW 28:8

For I am convinced that neither death nor life, neither angels nor demons, neither the present nor the future, nor any powers, neither height nor depth, nor anything else in all creation, will be able to separate us from the love of God that is in Christ Jesus our Lord.—ROMANS 8:38–39

"So also you have sorrow now, but I will see you again, and your hearts will rejoice, and no one will take your joy from you."—JOHN 16:22 ESV

January 7

THE MORE OFTEN YOU TURN your thoughts to Me, the more you will enjoy My *perfect Peace*. This is a challenging goal, but it is also a glorious gift. I, *the Shepherd of your soul,* am always accessible to you.

You can train your mind to turn from other things and focus on Me. When you experience something beautiful, thank Me for it. When a loved one brings you joy, remember that I am the Source of this pleasure. Post reminders of My Presence in your home or car or office. It's also wise to memorize Scripture since it is ultimately about Me.

Turning your thoughts to Me demonstrates your trust in Me. Even undesired things such as pain and problems can be reminders to communicate with Me. Focusing on My Presence protects you from getting stuck on problems—going over and over them in your mind without making any progress.

Be creative in finding new ways to turn your thoughts toward Me. Thus you can enjoy the wondrous gift of My Peace.

He will keep in perfect peace all those who trust in him, whose thoughts turn often to the Lord!—ISAIAH 26:3 TLB

For you were continually straying like sheep, but now you have returned to the Shepherd and Guardian of your souls.—1 PETER 2:25 NASB

Do not be anxious about anything, but in everything, by prayer and petition, with thanksgiving, present your requests to God. And the peace of God, which transcends all understanding, will guard your hearts and your minds in Christ Jesus.—PHILIPPIANS 4:6–7

January 8

IN ME YOU CAN DISCOVER *Joy inexpressible and full of Glory*! You will not find this kind of pleasure anywhere else; it is available only in your relationship with Me. So trust Me, beloved, and walk confidently along your life-path. As we journey together, you will encounter many obstacles—some of which are quite painful. Expect these difficulties each day, and don't let them throw you off course. Refuse to let adversity keep you from enjoying Me. In My Presence deep sorrow can coexist with even deeper Joy.

Your life with Me is an adventure, and there are always some dangers involved in adventurous journeys. Ask Me to give you courage so that you can face your troubles boldly. Keep your hope fully fastened on Me and on the heavenly reward that awaits you. Your Joy will expand astronomically—beyond anything you could possibly imagine—when you reach your eternal home. There you will see Me *face to Face*, and your Joy will know no bounds!

. . . Whom having not seen you love. Though now you do not see Him, yet believing, you rejoice with joy inexpressible and full of glory. —1 PETER 1:8 NKJV

. . . Sorrowful, yet always rejoicing; poor, yet making many rich; having nothing, and yet possessing everything. —2 CORINTHIANS 6:10

Now we see but a poor reflection as in a mirror; then we shall see face to face. Now I know in part; then I shall know fully, even as I am fully known. —1 CORINTHIANS 13:12

January 9

I AM YOUR TREASURE! Sometimes you feel frazzled—pulled this way and that by people and circumstances around you. Your yearning for meaning and deep connection drives you into more and more activity. Even when your body is still, your mind tends to race—anticipating future problems and searching for solutions. You need to remember that *all the treasures of wisdom and knowledge are hidden in Me*. Remind yourself of this glorious truth frequently, whispering: "Jesus, You are my Treasure. In You I am complete."

When you prize Me above all else, making Me your *First Love*, you are protected from feeling fragmented. Whenever you find your thoughts straying, you can train your mind to return to the One who completes you. This gives focus to your life and helps you stay close to Me. Living near Me, enjoying My Presence, involves seeking to *obey My commands*. I am telling you this *so that My Joy may be in you and that your Joy may be complete*.

> *My purpose is that they may be encouraged in heart and united in love, so that they may have the full riches of complete understanding, in order that they may know the mystery of God, namely, Christ, in whom are hidden all the treasures of wisdom and knowledge.*—COLOSSIANS 2:2–3

> *"Nevertheless I have this against you, that you have left your first love."*—REVELATION 2:4 NKJV

> *"If you obey my commands, you will remain in my love, just as I have obeyed my Father's commands and remain in his love. I have told you this so that my joy may be in you and that your joy may be complete."*—JOHN 15:10–11

January 10

Beware of overthinking things—obsessing about unimportant matters. When your mind is idle, you tend to go into planning mode: attempting to figure things out and make various decisions before you really need to do so. This is an unproductive way of trying to grasp control, and it's a waste of your precious time. Often, you end up changing your mind or forgetting what you decided. There is a time for planning, but it's definitely not *all* the time—or even most of it.

Seek to live in the present moment, where My Presence awaits you continually. Refresh yourself in My nearness, letting My Love soak into your innermost being. Relax with Me, putting aside problems so you can be attentive to Me and receive more of My Love. *Your soul thirsts for Me*, but often you don't realize what you're really longing for: awareness of My Presence. Let Me *lead you beside quiet waters* and *restore your soul*. Just as lovers don't need to say much to communicate deeply, so it is in your relationship with Me—the Lover of your soul.

> *And I pray that you, being rooted and established in love, may have power, together with all the saints, to grasp how wide and long and high and deep is the love of Christ, and to know this love that surpasses knowledge—that you may be filled to the measure of all the fullness of God.*—Ephesians 3:17–19

> *O God, You are my God; early will I seek You; my soul thirsts for You; my flesh longs for You in a dry and thirsty land where there is no water.*—Psalm 63:1 NKJV

> *He makes me lie down in green pastures, he leads me beside quiet waters, he restores my soul. He guides me in paths of righteousness for his name's sake.*—Psalm 23:2–3

January 11

There is a time for everything, and a season for every activity under heaven. When you seek My Face and My will—searching for guidance—I may show you the next step on your journey without revealing the appointed time for you to take that step. Instead of going full speed ahead as soon as you know what is next, you must wait until I show you *when* I want you to go forward.

There is a season for everything. This means that even the most fulfilling times in life must eventually give way to something new. Whereas some of My followers "champ at the bit" to forge ahead into new territory, others hold back even when I am clearly directing them to go forward. Moving from a comfortable season of life into a new situation can feel scary—especially to those who dislike change. However, I want you to trust Me enough to cling to Me and follow wherever I lead, *whenever* I choose. *Your times are in My hands.*

> *There is a time for everything, and a season for every activity under heaven.*—Ecclesiastes 3:1

> *"See, I am doing a new thing! Now it springs up; do you not perceive it? I am making a way in the desert and streams in the wasteland."*—Isaiah 43:19

> *Therefore, if anyone is in Christ, he is a new creation; old things have passed away; behold, all things have become new.*—2 Corinthians 5:17 nkjv

> *My times are in your hands.*—Psalm 31:15

January 12

Do not be terrified or discouraged, *for I am with you wherever you go.* It's easy for My followers to feel frightened and pessimistic when the mainstream voices in this world speak so heavily against them. Looking at this life through godless, biased lenses will indeed pull you down. Christian courage is the antidote to this poisonous input, and it is nourished by the knowledge that I am always with you.

It is crucial to remember that what you can see of reality is only a very small piece of the whole. When Elijah was deeply discouraged, he said he was the *only one* who had remained faithful. Yet there were thousands in Israel who had not bowed down to Baal. Elijah was blinded by his isolation and his discouragement. Similarly, Elisha's servant was terrified because he couldn't see what Elisha saw: *horses and chariots of fire all around* to protect them from enemy forces.

Beloved, not only am I with you, but I have unlimited resources to help you. So look beyond the way things appear, and *take courage!*

"Have I not commanded you? Be strong and courageous. Do not be terrified; do not be discouraged, for the Lord your God will be with you wherever you go."—Joshua 1:9

[Elijah] replied, "I have been very zealous for the Lord God Almighty. The Israelites have rejected your covenant, broken down your altars, and put your prophets to death with the sword. I am the only one left, and now they are trying to kill me too."—1 Kings 19:14

And Elisha prayed, "O Lord, open his eyes so he may see." Then the Lord opened the servant's eyes, and he looked and saw the hills full of horses and chariots of fire all around Elisha.—2 Kings 6:17

But Jesus immediately said to them: "Take courage! It is I. Don't be afraid."—Matthew 14:27

January 13

All things are possible with Me! Let these powerful words light up your mind and encourage your heart. Refuse to be intimidated by the way things look at the moment. I am training you to *live by faith, not by sight.*

The sense of sight is a spectacular gift from Me, to be used joyfully and gratefully. However, it's easy to be mesmerized by all the visual stimulation surrounding you—and forget about Me. Faith is a type of vision that connects you to Me. Instead of being so focused on the visible world, *dare* to trust in Me and My promises.

Live close to Me, your Savior and Friend, but remember: I am also infinite God. When I lived on your planet, *My miraculous signs revealed My Glory, and My disciples put their faith in Me.* I continue to do miracles in your world, according to My will and purposes. Seek to align your will with Mine and to see things from My perspective. Exert your faith to ask for big things, and *watch in hope for Me* to work.

> Jesus looked at them and said, "With man it is impossible, but not with God. For all things are possible with God."—Mark 10:27 esv

> We live by faith, not by sight.—2 Corinthians 5:7

> This, the first of his miraculous signs, Jesus performed at Cana in Galilee. He thus revealed his glory, and his disciples put their faith in him.—John 2:11

> As for me, I watch in hope for the Lord, I wait for God my Savior; my God will hear me.—Micah 7:7

January 14

You are fully known. I know absolutely everything about you, and I love you with perfect, *unfailing Love.* Many people are searching for greater self-understanding and self-acceptance. Underlying their search is a desire to find someone who truly understands them and accepts them as they are. I am the Someone who can fully satisfy this deep-seated longing. It is in your relationship with Me that you discover who you really are.

I encourage you to be real with Me—dropping all pretenses and opening yourself fully to Me. As you draw near, utter these inspired words: *"Search me, O God, and know my heart; test me, and know my anxious thoughts."* In the Light of My holy gaze, you will see things you need to change. But don't despair; I will help you. Continue resting in My Presence, receiving My Love that flows freely into you through your openness to Me. Take time to let this powerful Love soak in deeply—filling up your empty spaces and overflowing into joyous worship. Rejoice greatly, for you are fully known and forever loved!

For now we see indistinctly, as in a mirror, but then face to face. Now I know in part, but then I will know fully, as I am fully known. —1 Corinthians 13:12 HCSB

The Lord delights in those who fear him, who put their hope in his unfailing love. —Psalm 147:11

Search me, O God, and know my heart; test me and know my anxious thoughts. See if there is any offensive way in me, and lead me in the way everlasting. —Psalm 139:23–24

January 15

THE CHRISTIAN LIFE is all about trusting Me: in good times *and* in hard times. I am Lord over all your circumstances, so I want to be involved in every aspect of your life. You can quickly connect with Me by affirming your confidence in Me here and now. When your world seems dark and you trust Me anyway, My Light shines brightly through you. Your display of transcendent faith weakens spiritual forces of evil. And My supernatural Light showing through you blesses and strengthens people around you.

Clinging to Me in the dark requires you to persistently exert your willpower. But while you're grasping onto Me, remember: My hand has an eternal grip on yours—I will never let go of you! Moreover, My Spirit helps you keep hanging on. When you feel on the verge of giving up, cry out for His assistance: "Help me, Holy Spirit!" This brief prayer enables you to tap into His limitless resources. Even when your circumstances look dark and threatening, My Light is still *shining on* in surpassing splendor!

> *But if we walk in the light, as he is in the light, we have fellowship with one another, and the blood of Jesus, his Son, purifies us from all sin.*—1 JOHN 1:7

> *Trust in him at all times, O people; pour out your hearts to him, for God is our refuge.*—PSALM 62:8

Your hand shall lead me, and Your right hand shall hold me.—PSALM 139:10 NKJV

And the Light shines on in the darkness, for the darkness has never overpowered it [put it out or absorbed it or appropriated it, and is unreceptive to it].—JOHN 1:5 AMP

January 16

When things are not going your way, refuse to get flustered. Stop what you're doing and take some deep breaths. *Seek My Face*—spend a few moments enjoying My Presence. Tell Me about the matters that are frustrating you. I will help you see things from My perspective and sort out what is really important. Moreover, I will open up the way before you as you press on in trusting dependence, remaining in communication with Me.

Your desire to feel in control is often the culprit behind your frustration. You plan your day and expect others to behave in ways that expedite your plans. When that doesn't happen, you face a choice: to resent the situation or to trust Me. Remember that *I am in control* and *My ways are higher than yours—as the heavens are higher than the earth*. Instead of getting agitated about setbacks to your schedule, use them as reminders: I am your Savior-God, and you are My beloved follower. Relax in My sovereign control, *trusting in My unfailing Love*.

When You said, "Seek My face," my heart said to You, "Your face, Lord, I will seek."—Psalm 27:8 NKJV

"For as the heavens are higher than the earth, so are My ways higher than your ways, and My thoughts than your thoughts."—Isaiah 55:9 NKJV

Why are you so downcast, O my soul? Why so disturbed within me? Put your hope in God, for I will yet praise him, my Savior and my God.—Psalm 43:5

But I trust in your unfailing love; my heart rejoices in your salvation.—Psalm 13:5

January 17

I brought you out into a spacious place. I rescued you because I delighted in you. You are in a spacious place of salvation—saved from being a *slave to sin*. Your salvation is the greatest, most lavish gift you could ever receive. Never stop thanking Me for this infinitely precious gift! In the morning when you awaken, rejoice that I have adopted you into My royal family. Before you go to sleep at night, praise Me for My glorious grace. Live in ways that help others see Me as the fountainhead of abundant, never-ending Life.

I delighted in you, not because of worthiness in you. Rather, I *chose* to delight in you and lavish My Love on you. Since your best efforts could never be sufficient to save you, I clothed you in My own perfect righteousness. Wear this *clothing of salvation* gratefully—with overflowing Joy. Remember that you are royalty in My kingdom, where Glory-Light shines eternally. *Live as a child of Light,* securely robed in radiant righteousness.

> He brought me out into a spacious place; he rescued me because he delighted in me.—Psalm 18:19

> Jesus replied, "I tell you the truth, everyone who sins is a slave to sin."—John 8:34

> I am overwhelmed with joy in the Lord my God! For he has dressed me with the clothing of salvation and draped me in a robe of righteousness. I am like a bridegroom dressed for his wedding or a bride with her jewels.—Isaiah 61:10 NLT

> For you were once darkness, but now you are light in the Lord. Live as children of light.—Ephesians 5:8

January 18

I AM ALWAYS DOING SOMETHING NEW in your life. So try to keep an open mind when you encounter things you have not seen before—or even imagined.

Do not recoil from the unfamiliar without even taking time to determine whether it might be from Me. Consider the trapeze artist: She must leave the safety of the swing she is on in order to move toward her goal. As she abandons the security of where she was, she will be briefly in flight—until she connects to the next trapeze.

At times *you* may feel as if you're "in flight" when you experience newness that feels uncomfortable. The temptation is to just criticize the changes and cling to the familiar. Instead of this knee-jerk response, come to Me in prayer. Tell Me your concerns, and ask Me to help you see the situation from My viewpoint. *I am always with you, and I hold you by your right hand. I guide you with My counsel*—helping you discern the best way to respond and go forward.

> *"Neither is new wine put into old wineskins. If it is, the skins burst and the wine is spilled and the skins are destroyed. But new wine is put into fresh wineskins, and so both are preserved."*—MATTHEW 9:17 ESV

> *The name of the* LORD *is a strong tower; the righteous run to it and are safe.*—PROVERBS 18:10 NKJV

> *"Come to me, all you who are weary and burdened, and I will give you rest."*—MATTHEW 11:28

> *Yet I am always with you; you hold me by my right hand. You guide me with your counsel, and afterward you will take me into glory.*—PSALM 73:23–24

January 19

I call you by name and lead you. I know you—I know every detail about you. You are never a number or statistic to Me; My involvement in your life is far more personal and intimate than you can comprehend. So *follow Me* with a glad heart.

After My resurrection, when Mary Magdalene mistook Me for the gardener, I spoke one word: *"Mary."* Hearing Me say her name, she recognized Me and *cried out in Aramaic, "Rabboni!" (which means Teacher).*

Beloved, I also speak *your* name in the depths of your spirit. When you read your Bible, try inserting your name into appropriate passages. Remember: *I called you out of darkness into My marvelous Light.* I chose to set My *everlasting Love* upon you. Take time to "hear" Me speaking to you personally in Scripture, reassuring you of My Love. The unshakable knowledge that I love you forever provides a firm foundation for your life. It strengthens you so that you can follow Me faithfully and joyfully—*proclaiming My praises* as you journey through your life.

> *"The watchman opens the gate for him, and the sheep listen to his voice. He calls his own sheep by name and leads them out. . . . My sheep listen to my voice; I know them, and they follow me."*—John 10:3, 27

> *Jesus said to her, "Mary." She turned toward him and cried out in Aramaic, "Rabboni!" (which means Teacher).*—John 20:16

> *But you are a chosen generation, a royal priesthood, a holy nation, His own special people, that you may proclaim the praises of Him who called you out of darkness into His marvelous light.*—1 Peter 2:9 nkjv

> *The Lord has appeared of old to me, saying: "Yes, I have loved you with an everlasting love; therefore with lovingkindness I have drawn you."*—Jeremiah 31:3 nkjv

January 20

Remember that *the fruit of the Spirit* includes Joy. Even in the midst of *severe suffering*, My Spirit can give you this wondrous gift. Feel free to ask Him to fill you with Joy—as often as you need. He resides in the deepest depths of your being, so His work within you is very effective. You cooperate with Him by saturating your mind with Scripture and asking Him to illuminate it to you.

One way the Holy Spirit increases your Joy is to help you think My thoughts. The more you see things from My perspective, the more accurately you view your life. You need not only to *know* biblical truth but to tell yourself the truth over and over each day.

The world continually assaults your mind with lies and deceptions, so you must be diligent to recognize falsehood, dispel it, and replace it with biblical teaching. The most glorious, life-changing truth is the gospel: I have died (to save all who *believe in Me*). I have risen. I will come again. *Rejoice in Me always*!

> *But the fruit of the Spirit is love, joy, peace, patience, kindness, goodness, faithfulness, gentleness and self-control. Against such things there is no law.*—Galatians 5:22–23

> *You became imitators of us and of the Lord; in spite of severe suffering, you welcomed the message with the joy given by the Holy Spirit.*—1 Thessalonians 1:6

> *"For God so loved the world, that he gave his only Son, that whoever believes in him should not perish but have eternal life."*—John 3:16 esv

> *Rejoice in the Lord always. Again I will say, rejoice!*—Philippians 4:4 nkjv

January 21

To enjoy My Presence more fully, you need to think less and less about yourself. This is not an arbitrary demand; it's the secret to living *more abundantly.* Self-forgetfulness is a delightful way to live!

Try to become aware of how much time you spend thinking about yourself. Take a look at your mind's contents. Though your thoughts are not visible to other people unless you choose to share them, I see each and every one. When you realize your thinking is unworthy of Me, make every effort to change the subject. If you're struggling with a self-centered idea that recurs again and again, try connecting it to a favorite scripture or a brief prayer. This forms a bridge for your attention—away from yourself and toward Me. For example, praying "I love You, Lord" can quickly direct your focus to Me.

If you have to repeat this process many times, don't be discouraged. You are training your mind to *seek My Face,* and this endeavor is pleasing to Me. *Seek Me,* beloved, *and live* abundantly.

"The thief does not come except to steal, and to kill, and to destroy. I have come that they may have life, and that they may have it more abundantly."—John 10:10 nkjv

When You said, "Seek My face," my heart said to You, "Your face, Lord, I will seek."—Psalm 27:8 nkjv

This is what the Lord says to the house of Israel: "Seek me and live."—Amos 5:4

January 22

I AM WORTHY of *all* your confidence, *all* your trust. There are people and things that deserve *some* of your confidence and trust, but only *I* deserve all of it. In a world that seems increasingly unsafe and unpredictable, I am the Rock that provides a firm foundation for your life. More than that, I am *your* Rock in whom you can *take refuge*—for I am *your God*.

You must not let your circumstances define your sense of security. Though it is natural for you to want to be in control of your life, I can empower you to live supernaturally, resting in My sovereign control. I am *a well-proved help in trouble*, and I am always present with you. I help you face unwelcome changes, and even catastrophic circumstances, without fear.

Instead of letting anxious thoughts roam freely in your mind, lasso them by voicing your hope in Me. Then bring those captive thoughts into My Presence, where I will disarm them. *Whoever trusts in Me is kept safe.*

The Lord is my rock, my fortress and my deliverer; my God is my rock, in whom I take refuge. He is my shield and the horn of my salvation, my stronghold. —Psalm 18:2

God is our Refuge and Strength [mighty and impenetrable to temptation], a very present and well-proved help in trouble. Therefore we will not fear, though the earth should change and though the mountains be shaken into the midst of the seas. —Psalm 46:1–2 AMP

We demolish arguments and every pretension that sets itself up against the knowledge of God, and we take captive every thought to make it obedient to Christ. —2 Corinthians 10:5

Fear of man will prove to be a snare, but whoever trusts in the Lord is kept safe. —Proverbs 29:25

January 23

I AM THE JOY THAT NO ONE CAN TAKE away from you. Savor the wonders of this gift, spending ample time in My Presence. Rejoice that this blessing is yours—I am yours—for all eternity!

Many things in this world can bring you pleasure for a while, but they are all passing away because of death and decay. In Me you have a matchless Treasure—Joy in the One who is *the same yesterday, today, and forever.* No one can take this pleasure away from you, for I am faithful and I never change.

Whenever you feel joyless, the problem is not in the Source (Me) but in the receiver. You may be so focused on other things—either pleasures or difficulties in your life—that you're neglecting your relationship with Me. The remedy is twofold: Remember that I am your *First Love*, and seek to put Me first in your life. Also, ask Me to increase your receptivity to My Presence. *Delight yourself in Me*, beloved, and receive Joy in full measure.

> "So with you: Now is your time of grief, but I will see you again and you will rejoice, and no one will take away your joy."—JOHN 16:22

> Jesus Christ is the same yesterday, today, and forever.—HEBREWS 13:8 NKJV

> "Nevertheless I have this against you, that you have left your first love."—REVELATION 2:4 NKJV

> Delight yourself in the LORD and he will give you the desires of your heart.—PSALM 37:4

January 24

I AM YOUR STRENGTH! When you begin a day feeling weak and weary, it's all right. Your weakness can be a reminder of your need for Me. Remember that I am with you continually—ready to help you as you go along your way. Take My hand in joyful trust, letting Me guide you and *strengthen you*. I delight in helping you, My child.

Whenever you feel inadequate for the task ahead, stop and think about your resources. I, *your Strength*, am infinite: I never run out of anything. So when you work in collaboration with Me, don't set limits on what you expect to accomplish. I will give you what you need to keep moving forward, step by step. You may not reach the goal as quickly as you'd like, but you will get there in my perfect timing. Refuse to be discouraged by delays or detours. Instead, trust that I know what I'm doing—and just take the next step. Perseverance and trust in Me make a potent combination!

> *But I will sing of your strength, in the morning I will sing of your love; for you are my fortress, my refuge in times of trouble. O my Strength, I sing praise to you; you, O God, are my fortress, my loving God.*—PSALM 59:16–17

> *I can do all things through Christ who strengthens me.*—PHILIPPIANS 4:13 NKJV

> *Do you not know? Have you not heard? The LORD is the everlasting God, the Creator of the ends of the earth. He will not grow tired or weary, and his understanding no one can fathom. He gives strength to the weary and increases the power of the weak.*—ISAIAH 40:28–29

January 25

Though the mountains be shaken and the hills be removed, yet My unfailing Love for you will not be shaken nor My covenant of Peace be removed. Nothing on earth seems as enduring or immovable as soaring, majestic mountains. When you stand on their heights, breathing in that rarified air, you can almost smell eternity. Yet My Love and My Peace are even *more* enduring than the greatest mountain on earth!

Think deeply about *My unfailing Love.* One of the meanings of "unfailing" is *inexhaustible.* No matter how needy you are or how many times you fail Me, My supply of Love for you will never run low. Another meaning of "unfailing" is *constant.* I do not love you more on days when you perform well, nor do I love you less when you fail badly.

I Myself am your Peace. Live close to Me so you can enjoy this supernatural Peace. Come freely into My Presence, beloved, even when you're feeling bad about yourself. Remember who I am: *the Lord who has compassion on you.*

> "Though the mountains be shaken and the hills be removed, yet my unfailing love for you will not be shaken nor my covenant of peace be removed," says the Lord, who has compassion on you.—Isaiah 54:10

> "Lift up your eyes to the heavens, look at the earth beneath; the heavens will vanish like smoke, the earth will wear out like a garment and its inhabitants die like flies. But my salvation will last forever, my righteousness will never fail."—Isaiah 51:6

> For He Himself is our peace, who has made both one, and has broken down the middle wall of separation.—Ephesians 2:14 NKJV

January 26

Relax, My child. I'm in control. Let these words wash over you repeatedly, like soothing waves on a beautiful beach, assuring you of My endless Love. You waste a lot of time and energy trying to figure out things before their time has come. Meanwhile, I am working to prepare the way before you. So be on the lookout for some wonderful surprises—circumstances that only *I* could have orchestrated.

Remember that you are My beloved. I am on your side, and I want what is best for you. Someone who is loved by a generous, powerful person can expect to receive an abundance of blessings. *You* are loved by the King of the universe, and I have good plans for you. As you look ahead into the unknown future, relax in the knowledge of who you are—*the one I love.* Cling to My hand, and go forward with confidence. While you and I walk together along *the path of Life,* your trust in Me will fill your heart with Joy and your mind with Peace.

> "For I know the plans I have for you," declares the Lord, "plans to prosper you and not to harm you, plans to give you hope and a future." —Jeremiah 29:11

> About Benjamin he said: "Let the beloved of the Lord rest secure in him, for he shields him all day long, and the one the Lord loves rests between his shoulders." —Deuteronomy 33:12

> You will show me the path of life; in Your presence is fullness of joy; at Your right hand are pleasures forevermore. —Psalm 16:11 NKJV

January 27

WALK WITH ME in close, trusting Love-bonds of joyful dependence. "Joyful dependence" may sound like an oxymoron, but it is the most fulfilling way to live. When you delight in relying on Me, you are living according to My perfect design for you.

The relationship I offer you is full of *glorious riches*: I am totally trustworthy, and I reach out to you with *unfailing Love*. I am closer than the very air you are breathing. I rejoice when you seek to live in trusting reliance on Me. This strengthens our relationship—building more and more bonds of affection between us.

A happily married man and woman are connected by much more than law and morality. Their warm memories of shared experiences create ties that draw them close and keep them committed to each other. Dear one, I want you to know that I am totally committed to *you*! I can fill your heart with loving memories as you *walk in the Light of My Presence*, joyfully depending on Me.

> *And my God will meet all your needs according to his glorious riches in Christ Jesus.*—PHILIPPIANS 4:19

> *But I am like an olive tree flourishing in the house of God; I trust in God's unfailing love for ever and ever.*—PSALM 52:8

> *Blessed are those who have learned to acclaim you, who walk in the light of your presence, O LORD. They rejoice in your name all day long; they exult in your righteousness.*—PSALM 89:15–16

January 28

I made you a little lower than the heavenly beings and crowned you with glory and honor. You were made for greatness, beloved. Never doubt your personal significance, for *I created you in My own image*—in My likeness. I formed you with a magnificent brain that can communicate with Me, think rationally, create wonderful things, and much more. I gave you *dominion over the fish of the sea, the birds of the air, and every living thing that moves on the earth.* Of everything I created, only mankind is made in My likeness. This is a glorious privilege and responsibility; it makes every moment of your life meaningful.

One of your chief purposes in life is to glorify Me. I *crowned you with glory* so that you can *reflect My Glory*: lighting up this dark world and helping others come to know Me. I also want you to enjoy Me. I created you with unlimited capacity for pleasure in knowing Me. This Joy you find in Me here and now is a tiny foretaste of the eternal delights awaiting you in heaven.

You made him a little lower than the heavenly beings and crowned him with glory and honor.—Psalm 8:5

So God created man in His own image; in the image of God He created him; male and female He created them. Then God blessed them, and God said to them, "Be fruitful and multiply; fill the earth and subdue it; have dominion over the fish of the sea, over the birds of the air, and over every living thing that moves on the earth."—Genesis 1:27–28 nkjv

And we, who with unveiled faces all reflect the Lord's glory, are being transformed into his likeness with ever-increasing glory, which comes from the Lord, who is the Spirit.—2 Corinthians 3:18

January 29

You will seek Me and find Me when you seek Me with all your heart. I don't expect perfection in this pursuit; it's not about that at all. It is the effort itself that pleases Me—when you keep on seeking Me even though it's so difficult. Actually, the intensity of this challenging search blesses you. As you strive to find Me in your moments, your focus is on Me. While you trudge toward Me through countless distractions, your awareness of Me increases. Even if you don't feel close to Me, you find yourself communicating with Me. So there is a sense in which your efforts to find Me are self-fulfilling: I am richly present in your striving. As a result, you feel more alive—more awake and real—when you are actively pursuing Me.

Your willingness to pour yourself into this glorious quest delights My heart. This joyful journey is all about *perseverance*. As long as you continue seeking Me, you are on the right path. Moreover, your success is certain: *I will be found by you!*

> "You will seek me and find me when you seek me with all your heart. I will be found by you . . . and will bring you back from captivity. I will gather you from all the nations and places where I have banished you . . . and will bring you back to the place from which I carried you into exile."—JEREMIAH 29:13–14

> Therefore, since we are surrounded by such a great cloud of witnesses, let us throw off everything that hinders and the sin that so easily entangles, and let us run with perseverance the race marked out for us.—HEBREWS 12:1

> We also glory in tribulations, knowing that tribulation produces perseverance.—ROMANS 5:3 NKJV

> For this very reason, make every effort to add to your faith goodness; and to goodness, knowledge; and to knowledge, self-control; and to self-control, perseverance; and to perseverance, godliness.—2 PETER 1:5–6

January 30

I am making everything new! This is the opposite of what is always happening in your world of death and decay. Every day that you live means one less day remaining in your lifespan on this earth. Actually, this is very good news for My followers. At the end of each day, you can tell yourself: "I'm one step closer to heaven."

The world is in such a desperately fallen condition that there is only one remedy for it: making *everything* new. So do not be discouraged when your efforts to improve matters are unsuccessful. All things—including your efforts—are tainted by the Fall. Although I want you to endeavor to do your best, in dependence on Me, your world needs much more than a tune-up or an overhaul. It needs to be made completely new! And this is absolutely guaranteed to happen at the end of time, for *My words are trustworthy and true.*

You have good reason to rejoice, beloved, because I will make everything—including you—new and gloriously perfect!

> *He who was seated on the throne said, "I am making everything new!" Then he said, "Write this down, for these words are trustworthy and true."*—Revelation 21:5

> *For to me, to live is Christ, and to die is gain.*—Philippians 1:21 NKJV

> *We know that the whole creation has been groaning as in the pains of childbirth right up to the present time. Not only so, but we ourselves, who have the firstfruits of the Spirit, groan inwardly as we wait eagerly for our adoption as sons, the redemption of our bodies.*—Romans 8:22–23

January 31

STRENGTH AND JOY *are in My dwelling place.* So the closer to Me you live, the stronger and more joyful you will be.

Invite Me to permeate your moments with My Presence. This helps you view people from a positive perspective. Whenever you're around someone who irritates you, don't focus on that person's flaws. Instead, gaze at *Me* through the eyes of your heart, and those irritants will wash over you without harming you—or hurting others. Judging other people is a sinful snare that draws you away from Me. How much better it is to *be joyful in Me, your Savior*!

The more you focus on Me, the more I can strengthen you. In fact, *I am your Strength.* You can train your mind to stay aware of Me even when other things are demanding your attention. I created you with an amazing brain that is able to be conscious of several things at once. Create a permanent place for Me in your mind, and My Light will shine on all your moments.

> *Splendor and majesty are before him; strength and joy in his dwelling place.* —1 CHRONICLES 16:27

> *"Judge not, that you be not judged."* —MATTHEW 7:1 NKJV

> *Yet I will rejoice in the LORD, I will be joyful in God my Savior. The Sovereign LORD is my strength; he makes my feet like the feet of a deer, he enables me to go on the heights.* —HABAKKUK 3:18–19

February

*Behold, God is my salvation,
I will trust and not be afraid;
For the Lord God is my strength and song,
And He has become my salvation.*

Isaiah 12:2 NASB

February 1

I am the Living One *who sees you*. I am more fully, gloriously alive than you can imagine. Someday you will see Me *face to Face* in all My Glory, and you will be awestruck! Now, though, *you see through a glass, darkly*. Your view of Me is obscured by your fallen condition. Nonetheless, I see *you* with perfect clarity. I know everything about you, including your most secret thoughts and feelings. I understand how broken and weak you are: *I remember that you are dust*. Yet I choose to love you with everlasting Love.

The gift of My Love was indescribably costly. I endured unspeakable suffering to save you from an eternity of agony. *I became sin for you so that in Me you might become the righteousness of God*. Ponder this wondrous truth: My righteousness is now yours! This gift of infinite value has been yours ever since you trusted Me as the God-Man who saved you from your sins. Rejoice that *the living One who sees you* perfectly is the Savior who loves you always!

> *So she called the name of the Lord Who spoke to her, You are a God of seeing, for she said, Have I [not] even here [in the wilderness] looked upon Him Who sees me [and lived]? Or have I here also seen [the future purposes or designs of] Him Who sees me? Therefore the well was called Beer-lahai-roi [A well to the Living One Who sees me]; it is between Kadesh and Bered.*—Genesis 16:13–14 AMP

> *For now we see through a glass, darkly; but then face to face: now I know in part; but then shall I know even as also I am known.*—1 Corinthians 13:12 KJV

> *For he knows how we are formed, he remembers that we are dust.*—Psalm 103:14

> *God made him who had no sin to be sin for us, so that in him we might become the righteousness of God.*—2 Corinthians 5:21

February 2

I AM YOUR *EVER-PRESENT HELP*. Many people stumble out of bed in the morning and head straight for the coffee pot. Though they are not yet thinking clearly, they are awake enough to move toward something that will help unscramble their thoughts. I perform a similar function for you when your mind stumbles in My direction. Ask Me to clear out the confusion so you can communicate deeply with Me. You have this amazing capacity because I created you *in My own image.*

As you wait in My Presence, I not only unscramble your thoughts, I straighten your path through the day. I am sovereign over every aspect of your life, so opening up the way before you is no problem for Me. Some people assume they don't have time to begin their day with Me. They don't realize how much I can facilitate their activities—removing obstacles and giving insights that save time. When you spend precious moments with Me, I compensate you generously: I clarify your thinking and smooth out the circumstances of your life.

God is our refuge and strength, an ever-present help in trouble.—PSALM 46:1

So God created man in His own image; in the image of God He created him; male and female He created them.—GENESIS 1:27 NKJV

Ah, Sovereign LORD, you have made the heavens and the earth by your great power and outstretched arm. Nothing is too hard for you.—JEREMIAH 32:17

We wait in hope for the LORD; he is our help and our shield.—PSALM 33:20

February 3

G<small>LORY IN</small> M<small>Y HOLY</small> N<small>AME</small>; *let the hearts of those who seek Me rejoice.* To "glory" in something is to give it praise and honor. Jesus is *the Name that is above every name*—it represents *Me* in all My sinless perfection. As My follower, you can whisper, speak, or sing My Name with confidence that I am listening. This draws you closer to Me and helps you find strength in My Presence. It also serves to drive away your spiritual enemies.

I'm delighted that you take time to seek Me, desiring to know Me better. Come freely into My loving Presence, letting your heart *rejoice in Me.* Remember that you are on *holy ground,* and breathe in the rarified air of My holiness. Release cares and concerns while you rest in the splendor of My Glory. Let My joyous Presence envelop you—permeating you through and through. As you delight in My nearness, time seems to slow down, enhancing your enjoyment of Me. Thank Me for these moments of sweet intimacy.

> *Glory in his holy name; let the hearts of those who seek the L*<small>ORD</small> *rejoice.* —P<small>SALM</small> 105:3

> *For this reason also, God highly exalted Him, and bestowed on Him the name which is above every name, so that at the name of Jesus* <small>EVERY KNEE WILL BOW</small>, *of those who are in heaven and on earth and under the earth, and that every tongue will confess that Jesus Christ is Lord, to the glory of God the Father.* —P<small>HILIPPIANS</small> 2:9–11 <small>NASB</small>

> *Rejoice in the Lord always. I will say it again: Rejoice! Let your graciousness be known to everyone. The Lord is near.* —P<small>HILIPPIANS</small> 4:4–5 <small>HCSB</small>

> *"Do not come any closer," God said. "Take off your sandals, for the place where you are standing is holy ground."* —E<small>XODUS</small> 3:5

February 4

It is good to proclaim My Love in the morning and My faithfulness at night. Proclaiming this Love is exceedingly good for you. When you declare the wonders of My loving Presence, you are strengthened and encouraged. This glorious blessing flows into you more fully as you speak these words out loud. Let this delightful declaration fill you with *Joy inexpressible and full of Glory!*

Ponder some of the qualities of My amazing Love: It is sacrificial, unfailing, priceless, boundless—*reaching to the heavens.* It shines so brightly that it can carry you through your darkest days. When you get to the end of each day, it is time to proclaim My faithfulness that *reaches to the skies.* Look back over the day, and notice how I helped you navigate your way through it. The more difficulties you encountered, the more help I made available to you. It is good to give voice to My great faithfulness, especially at night, so that you can *lie down and sleep in peace.*

> *It is good to praise the Lord and make music to your name, O Most High, to proclaim your love in the morning and your faithfulness at night.*—Psalm 92:1–2

> *. . . Whom having not seen you love. Though now you do not see Him, yet believing, you rejoice with joy inexpressible and full of glory.*—1 Peter 1:8 nkjv

> *Your love, O Lord, reaches to the heavens, your faithfulness to the skies. Your righteousness is like the mighty mountains, your justice like the great deep. O Lord, you preserve both man and beast. How priceless is your unfailing love! Both high and low among men find refuge in the shadow of your wings.*—Psalm 36:5–7

> *I will lie down and sleep in peace, for you alone, O Lord, make me dwell in safety.*—Psalm 4:8

FEBRUARY 5

THE JOY I GIVE YOU transcends your circumstances. This means that no matter what is happening in your life, it is possible to be joyful in Me. The prophet Habakkuk listed a series of dire circumstances that he was anticipating, then he proclaimed: *"Yet I will rejoice in the Lord, I will be joyful in God my Savior."* This is transcendent Joy!

I am training you to view your life from a heavenly perspective—through eyes of faith. When things don't go as you had hoped, talk with Me. *Seek My Face* and My guidance. I will help you discern whether you need to work to change the situation or simply accept it. Either way, you can teach yourself to say: "I can still rejoice in *You*, Jesus." This short statement of faith—expressing your confidence in Me—will change your perspective dramatically. As you practice doing this more and more, your Joy will increase. This training also prepares you to handle the difficulties awaiting you on your pathway toward heaven. *Rejoice in Me always.*

> *Though the fig tree does not bud and there are no grapes on the vines, though the olive crop fails and the fields produce no food, though there are no sheep in the pen and no cattle in the stalls, yet I will rejoice in the LORD, I will be joyful in God my Savior.*—HABAKKUK 3:17–18

> *Seek the LORD and His strength; seek His face continually.*—PSALM 105:4 NASB

> *Rejoice in the Lord always. I will say it again: Rejoice!*—PHILIPPIANS 4:4

February 6

Rejoice that I have clothed you with *garments of salvation*. This *robe of righteousness* is yours forever and ever! Because I am your Savior, My perfect righteousness can never be taken away from you. This means you don't need to be afraid to face your sins—or to deal with them. As you become aware of sin in your life, confess it and receive My forgiveness in full measure.

It is essential also to forgive yourself. Self-hatred is not pleasing to Me, and it is very unhealthy for you. I urge you to take many looks at *Me* for every look at your sins or failures. I am the perfect antidote to the poison of self-loathing.

Since you are already precious in My sight, you don't have to prove your worth by trying to be good enough. I lived a perfect life on your behalf because I knew that you could not. Now I want you to live in the glorious freedom of being My fully forgiven follower. Remember that *there is no condemnation for those who belong to Me*.

I delight greatly in the Lord; my soul rejoices in my God. For he has clothed me with garments of salvation and arrayed me in a robe of righteousness, as a bridegroom adorns his head like a priest, and as a bride adorns herself with her jewels.—Isaiah 61:10

And she will bring forth a Son, and you shall call His name Jesus, for He will save His people from their sins.—Matthew 1:21 nkjv

If we confess our sins, He is faithful and just to forgive us our sins and to cleanse us from all unrighteousness.—1 John 1:9 nkjv

Therefore, there is now no condemnation for those who are in Christ Jesus, because through Christ Jesus the law of the Spirit of life set me free from the law of sin and death.—Romans 8:1–2

FEBRUARY 7

Do not fear, for I am with you. I will uphold you with My righteous right hand. Let these words enfold you like a warm blanket, sheltering you from the coldness of fear and discouragement. When trouble seems to be stalking you, grip My hand tightly and stay in communication with Me. You can *trust and not be afraid,* for *I am your Strength and Song.* My powerful Presence is with you always. You face *nothing* alone! Moreover, I have promised to *strengthen you and help you.*

My strong hand supports you in both good times and bad. When things are going well in your life, you may not be attentive to My sustaining Presence. But when you are *walking through the valley of the shadow of death,* you become keenly aware of your neediness. During these difficult times, holding onto Me keeps you standing—and able to put one foot in front of the other. As you endure this adversity patiently—in trusting dependence on Me—I bless you with abundant Joy in My Presence.

> *"So do not fear, for I am with you; do not be dismayed, for I am your God. I will strengthen you and help you; I will uphold you with my righteous right hand."*—Isaiah 41:10

> *Behold, God is my salvation, I will trust and not be afraid; for the Lord God is my strength and song, and He has become my salvation.*—Isaiah 12:2 nasb

> *Yea, though I walk through the valley of the shadow of death, I will fear no evil; for You are with me; Your rod and Your staff, they comfort me.*—Psalm 23:4 nkjv

February 8

My Love will never let you go! It has an eternal grip on you. You live in a world that is unpredictable and unsafe in many ways. As you look around, you see landscape littered with broken promises.

However, My Love is a promise that will never be broken. *Though the mountains be shaken and the hills be removed, yet My unfailing Love for you will not be shaken.* The prophet Isaiah is painting a picture of dire circumstances: quaking mountains and disappearing hills. No matter *what* is happening, My Love is unshakable. You can build your life on it!

Sometimes My children believe I care for them but still find it difficult to receive My Love in full measure. I want you to learn *to grasp how wide and long and high and deep is My Love for you.* Ask My Spirit to empower you *to know this Love that surpasses knowledge.* Break free from faulty self-images so you can view yourself as I see you—radiant in *My righteousness*, wrapped in luminous Love.

> "Though the mountains be shaken and the hills be removed, yet my unfailing love for you will not be shaken nor my covenant of peace be removed," says the Lord, who has compassion on you.—Isaiah 54:10

> I pray that out of his glorious riches he may strengthen you with power through his Spirit in your inner being, so that Christ may dwell in your hearts through faith. And I pray that you, being rooted and established in love, may have power, together with all the saints, to grasp how wide and long and high and deep is the love of Christ, and to know this love that surpasses knowledge—that you may be filled to the measure of all the fullness of God.—Ephesians 3:16–19

> I will greatly rejoice in the Lord, my soul shall be joyful in my God; for He has clothed me with the garments of salvation, He has covered me with the robe of righteousness, as a bridegroom decks himself with ornaments, and as a bride adorns herself with her jewels.—Isaiah 61:10 NKJV

February 9

Rejoice that I understand you completely and love you with perfect, unending Love. Many people are afraid that anyone who comes to know them fully will look down on them or even reject them. So they strive to keep others at a safe distance, disclosing only the parts of themselves they think are acceptable. This way of interacting with others tends to feel safer, but it leads to loneliness.

Be thankful that there is One who sees straight through your defenses and pretenses. There is no hiding from Me! I know absolutely *everything* about you. So rest in the wonder of being *fully known*—yet delighted in! You don't have to work at trying to earn My Love. The truth is, nothing could ever *stop* Me from loving you. Because you are Mine—bought with My blood—you are accepted and treasured forever. You need to tell yourself this truth over and over, till it seeps into your inner being and changes the way you view yourself. Self-acceptance is the path to self-forgetfulness, which is the royal road to Joy!

> *Oh give thanks to the Lord, for he is good, for his steadfast love endures forever! . . . Whoever is wise, let him attend to these things; let them consider the steadfast love of the Lord.*—Psalm 107:1, 43 esv

> *Now we see but a poor reflection as in a mirror; then we shall see face to face. Now I know in part; then I shall know fully, even as I am fully known.*—1 Corinthians 13:12

> *For the Lord takes delight in his people; he crowns the humble with salvation. Let the saints rejoice in this honor and sing for joy on their beds.*—Psalm 149:4–5

> *Having predestined us to adoption as sons by Jesus Christ to Himself, according to the good pleasure of His will, to the praise of the glory of His grace, by which He made us accepted in the Beloved.*—Ephesians 1:5–6 nkjv

February 10

Come to Me, and I will ease, relieve, and refresh your soul. Approach Me confidently, dear one, knowing that I have perfect understanding of you and everything that concerns you. Tell Me your troubles candidly; let the Light of My Face shine on them and illuminate your thinking. Then rest with Me, slowly inhaling the beauty of My Presence. You can feel safe and secure in *My everlasting arms.* As you spend precious time with Me, let Me ease and relieve your soul.

Your soul is the most important part of you because it is eternal. The New Testament Greek word for "soul" is sometimes translated "life." When you are *heavy-laden and overburdened,* you may feel as if the life is draining out of you. But I offer wonderfully nourishing care for this vital part of you. *I restore your soul*—helping you to rest and see things from My perspective. As I am refreshing you, relax and feel My Life flowing into you. *Your soul finds rest in Me alone.*

> "Come to Me, all you who labor and are heavy-laden and overburdened, and I will cause you to rest. [I will ease and relieve and refresh your souls.]"—MATTHEW 11:28 AMP

> The eternal God is your dwelling place, and underneath are the everlasting arms.—DEUTERONOMY 33:27 ESV

> He makes me lie down in green pastures, he leads me beside quiet waters, he restores my soul. He guides me in paths of righteousness for his name's sake.—PSALM 23:2–3

> My soul finds rest in God alone; my salvation comes from him.—PSALM 62:1

February 11

Be joyful always; pray continually. The way to rejoice at all times is to find moment-by-moment pleasure in your relationship with Me—the Lover of your soul. This relationship is so full of comfort and encouragement that it's possible to *be joyful in hope* even when you're in the midst of adversity.

Give thanks in all circumstances. There is immense Power in praying, "Thank You, Jesus." These three words are appropriate for all times and in every situation because of My great sacrifice for you. I encourage you to praise Me for every good thing as soon as you become aware of it. This practice adds sparkle to your blessings—heightening your Joy.

When you are feeling sad or discouraged, it is still a good time to thank Me. This demonstrates your trust in Me and brightens your perspective. To enhance your gratefulness, ponder specific things about *Me* that delight you—My continual Presence, My lavish grace, *My unfailing Love*. Thanking Me in all circumstances strengthens your relationship with Me and helps you live more joyfully!

Be joyful always; pray continually; give thanks in all circumstances, for this is God's will for you in Christ Jesus.—1 Thessalonians 5:16–18

Be joyful in hope, patient in affliction, faithful in prayer.—Romans 12:12

In him we have redemption through his blood, the forgiveness of sins, in accordance with the riches of God's grace that he lavished on us with all wisdom and understanding.—Ephesians 1:7–8

Let the morning bring me word of your unfailing love, for I have put my trust in you. Show me the way I should go, for to you I lift up my soul.—Psalm 143:8

February 12

I OFFER YOU *INEXPRESSIBLE and glorious Joy*—straight from heaven itself! This *triumphant, heavenly Joy* can be found only in Me. It is easy to slide, ever so gradually, from delighting in Me to living for the next spiritual "high." Sometimes I bless you with a taste of heaven's splendor, but the primary purpose of these experiences is to whet your appetite for the next life. Do not underestimate the brokenness of the world you inhabit. Your enjoyment of My Presence will always intermingle with the sorrows of living in this fallen world—until *I take you into Glory*.

Someday you will see Me face to Face, but for now *you love Me without having seen Me. You believe in Me even though you do not see Me*. This love for Me is not irrational or whimsical. It's a response to My boundless passion for you, dramatically displayed on the cross and verified by My resurrection. You worship a risen, living Savior! *Blessed are those who have not seen Me and yet have believed.*

> *Without having seen Him, you love Him; though you do not [even] now see Him, you believe in Him and exult and thrill with inexpressible and glorious (triumphant, heavenly) joy.*—1 PETER 1:8 AMP

> *Yet I am always with you; you hold me by my right hand. You guide me with your counsel, and afterward you will take me into glory.*—PSALM 73:23–24

> *We love Him because He first loved us.*—1 JOHN 4:19 NKJV

> *Jesus said to him, "Thomas, because you have seen Me, you have believed. Blessed are those who have not seen and yet have believed."*—JOHN 20:29 NKJV

February 13

In My Presence there is *fullness of Joy.* As you peer into My Presence—remembering who I Am in all My Power and Glory—ponder also My eternal commitment to you. *Nothing in all creation will ever be able to separate you from Me!* Your relationship with Me has been rock-solid secure ever since you confessed your sinfulness and received My forgiveness. You are My beloved in whom I delight; *this* is your permanent identity.

You can find Joy even in this broken world, because *I have set eternity in your heart.* Spend time refreshing yourself in My Presence, where you can relax and learn to *delight yourself in Me* above all else. As the Love-bonds between us grow stronger, so does your desire to help others enjoy this amazing Life you have found in Me. When your love for Me overflows into other people's lives, there is abundant Joy both in heaven and on earth! As you go along this *path of Life*, I will lead you—and I'll bless you with *pleasures forevermore.*

You will show me the path of life; in Your presence is fullness of joy; at Your right hand are pleasures forevermore. —Psalm 16:11 nkjv

Neither height nor depth, nor anything else in all creation, will be able to separate us from the love of God that is in Christ Jesus our Lord. —Romans 8:39

He has made everything beautiful in its time. He has also set eternity in the hearts of men; yet they cannot fathom what God has done from beginning to end. —Ecclesiastes 3:11

Delight yourself in the Lord and he will give you the desires of your heart. —Psalm 37:4

February 14

Let My unfailing Love be your comfort. One definition of "comfort" is a person or thing that makes you feel less upset or frightened during a time of trouble. Because you live in such a broken world, trouble is never far away. There are many sources of comfort in the world, yet only one of them is unfailing: My Love! Other sources will help you *some* of the time, but My tender Presence is with you *all* of the time.

My perfect, inexhaustible Love is not just a *thing* that makes you feel less upset; it's also a *Person. Nothing in all creation can separate you from Me.* And *I* am inseparable from My Love.

As My cherished follower, you can turn to Me for comfort at all times. Since you have this boundless Source of blessing—*Me*—I want you to be a blessing in the lives of other people. You *can comfort those in any trouble with the comfort you have received from Me.*

> *May your unfailing love be my comfort, according to your promise to your servant.*—Psalm 119:76

> *"These things I have spoken to you, that in Me you may have peace. In the world you will have tribulation; but be of good cheer, I have overcome the world."*—John 16:33 nkjv

> *For I am convinced that neither death nor life, neither angels nor demons, neither the present nor the future, nor any powers, neither height nor depth, nor anything else in all creation, will be able to separate us from the love of God that is in Christ Jesus our Lord.*—Romans 8:38–39

> *Praise be to the God and Father of our Lord Jesus Christ, the Father of compassion and the God of all comfort, who comforts us in all our troubles, so that we can comfort those in any trouble with the comfort we ourselves have received from God.*—2 Corinthians 1:3–4

February 15

I AM YOUR SHEPHERD—*to guide and shield you.* A good shepherd cares about his sheep and understands them very well. My care for you is wonderfully complete: I love you with perfect, *unfailing Love.* I know *everything* about you—your weaknesses and limitations, your struggles and sins, your strengths and abilities. So I am able to shepherd you exceptionally well.

I have designed you to walk through this perilous world in trusting dependence on Me. I lovingly go before you and open up the way, carefully preparing the path you will follow. I remove many dangers and obstacles from the road ahead, and I help you handle the difficulties that remain.

Even when you walk through the darkest valley, you need not be afraid, for I am close beside you. Enjoy My nearness, beloved, and communicate with Me. I will guide you carefully through this day and all your days. *For I am your God for ever and ever; I will be your Guide even to the end.*

The Lord is my Shepherd [to feed, guide, and shield me], I shall not lack.—PSALM 23:1 AMP

In your unfailing love you will lead the people you have redeemed. In your strength you will guide them to your holy dwelling.—EXODUS 15:13

Even when I walk through the darkest valley, I will not be afraid, for you are close beside me. Your rod and your staff protect and comfort me.—PSALM 23:4 NLT

For this God is our God for ever and ever; he will be our guide even to the end.—PSALM 48:14

February 16

Before you begin a task—large or small—take time to pray about it. By doing so, you acknowledge your need for Me and your trust that I will help you. This enables you to go about your work in dependence on Me. There are many benefits to this practice. I can guide your mind as you think things out and make decisions. Just knowing I am involved in what you're doing gives you confidence, reducing stress. It's wise to thank Me often for My help and to keep asking Me to *guide you along the best pathway*.

Though the Bible instructs you to *pray continually*, at times you ignore this teaching. When you're feeling rushed, you find it hard to slow down enough to seek My perspective on the work at hand. However, diving in and forging ahead on your own is actually counterproductive. When you request My involvement *before* you begin, I can point you in the right direction—saving precious time and energy. I delight in helping you with everything, even simple tasks, because you are *My beloved*.

Whatever you do, do your work heartily, as for the Lord rather than for men.—Colossians 3:23 nasb

The Lord says, "I will guide you along the best pathway for your life. I will advise you and watch over you."—Psalm 32:8 nlt

Pray continually.—1 Thessalonians 5:17

I am my beloved's, and my beloved is mine. He feeds his flock among the lilies.—Song of Songs 6:3 nkjv

FEBRUARY 17

YOU CAN FIND JOY in the most unexpected places. However, this requires effort: searching for the good and refusing to let your natural responses blind you to what is there. I will help you respond in a *supernatural* way, giving you eyes that see beyond the obvious and discover treasure hidden in your troubles. Simply ask Me.

Living joyously is a choice. Since you inhabit such a sinful, broken world, you must choose gladness many times daily. This is especially true during difficult times. When something happens that breaks the pattern of comfort and happiness in your life, you are being put to the test. Such trials can both prove and strengthen your faith, which is *much more precious than gold.* I am training you to *consider it pure Joy whenever you face trials of many kinds.*

I made the agonizing choice to *endure the cross for the Joy set before Me*—the eternal pleasure of *bringing My followers to Glory.* Choose Joy, beloved, by *fixing your eyes on Me* and looking for treasures in your trials.

In this you greatly rejoice, though now for a little while, if need be, you have been grieved by various trials, that the genuineness of your faith, being much more precious than gold that perishes, though it is tested by fire, may be found to praise, honor, and glory at the revelation of Jesus Christ.—1 PETER 1:6–7 NKJV

Consider it pure joy, my brothers, whenever you face trials of many kinds.—JAMES 1:2

Let us fix our eyes on Jesus, the author and perfecter of our faith, who for the joy set before him endured the cross, scorning its shame, and sat down at the right hand of the throne of God.—HEBREWS 12:2

For it was fitting for Him, for whom are all things and by whom are all things, in bringing many sons to glory, to make the captain of their salvation perfect through sufferings.—HEBREWS 2:10 NKJV

February 18

In My Presence you can find *fullness of Joy, perfect Peace,* and *unfailing Love.* Walk with Me along *the path of Life*—enjoying My company each step of the way. Because I am always by your side, the Joy of My Presence is yours for the taking!

I will keep you in perfect Peace as you *fix your thoughts on Me.* Stay in communication with Me through your spoken words, thoughts, and songs. Spend ample time absorbing My Word—letting it speak into your heart, where it changes the way you think and live. As you ponder who I really am, My Light shines warmly into your mind, helping you live in My Peace.

Beloved, I want you to flourish in My Presence—*like an olive tree flourishing in the house of God.* As the sunlight of My Presence nourishes you, you are able to produce abundant fruit in My kingdom. And the more you *trust in My unfailing Love,* the more you will realize how utterly secure you are.

> *You will show me the path of life; in Your presence is fullness of joy; at Your right hand are pleasures forevermore.*—Psalm 16:11 NKJV

> *You will keep in perfect peace all who trust in you, all whose thoughts are fixed on you!*—Isaiah 26:3 NLT

> *But I am like an olive tree flourishing in the house of God; I trust in God's unfailing love for ever and ever.*—Psalm 52:8

February 19

Set Me before you continually; keep your eyes on Me. *I am at your right hand*, close by your side. This is the most reliable source of Joy: knowing that I am always near. Seek to strengthen your awareness of My Presence so you can enjoy Me in your moments and feel more secure.

Communicating with Me—in silent prayers, in whispers, in spoken words, in shouts of praise—is the best way to stay attentive to Me. I want you to be real with Me in your prayers. Instead of worrying or obsessing about things, turn those thoughts toward Me. Talk with Me about whatever is on your mind. I will show you *My* way to handle the person or situation that concerns you.

Study and meditate on Scripture. Let it saturate your heart and mind, changing your way of thinking. Permeate your prayers with biblical concepts and content. As you stay in close communication with Me, the Joy of My Presence is yours!

I have set the Lord continually before me; because He is at my right hand, I will not be shaken.—Psalm 16:8 nasb

My lips will shout for joy when I sing praise to you— I, whom you have redeemed.—Psalm 71:23

Don't worry about anything; instead, pray about everything. Tell God what you need, and thank him for all he has done.—Philippians 4:6 nlt

Satisfy us in the morning with your unfailing love, that we may sing for joy and be glad all our days.—Psalm 90:14

February 20

Don't think of prayer as a chore. Instead, view it as communicating with the One you adore. *Delight yourself in Me*; this will draw you irresistibly into communion with Me. Remember all that I am to you, all I have done for you. I love you with perfect, everlasting Love, and *I take great delight in you*. Let My tenderness embrace you, convincing you that you are indeed My beloved. Rejoice in the One who will never let you go!

Often the easiest way to start talking with Me is to thank Me for being your Savior, Redeemer, and Friend. You can also give thanks for things that are happening in your life, your family, your church, and beyond. These grateful prayers connect you with Me and ease the way into other prayers.

You can talk freely with Me since I know everything about you and your circumstances. I never reject you because the penalty for your sins has been paid in full—with My blood. Trust Me enough to *pour out your heart to Me, for I am your Refuge*.

Delight yourself in the Lord and he will give you the desires of your heart.—Psalm 37:4

"The Lord your God is with you, he is mighty to save. He will take great delight in you, he will quiet you with his love, he will rejoice over you with singing."—Zephaniah 3:17

You are my God, and I will praise You; You are my God, I will exalt You. Oh, give thanks to the Lord, for He is good! For His mercy endures forever.—Psalm 118:28–29 nkjv

Trust in him at all times, O people; pour out your hearts to him, for God is our refuge.—Psalm 62:8

February 21

Put on the armor of Light. To wear this bright, protective covering, you have to *put aside deeds of darkness.* You live in a world where darkness is prevalent all around you. You need My Light-armor to help you see things clearly—protecting you from being led astray by the worldliness that surrounds you.

I want you to *walk in the Light* with Me. Make every effort to live close to Me, aware of My loving Presence. Just as you put clothes on your body, you can also *clothe yourself with Me.* Such nearness to Me will help you make good decisions. Sometimes, though, you will make bad choices that lead you into sin. Do not despair when this happens. Because I am your Savior, I have made provision for *all* your sin. Moreover, the blood I shed on the cross *cleanses you* and keeps you walking in the Light.

If you confess your sins, I forgive you and cleanse you from all unrighteousness. I am *faithful and just*, and I delight in your nearness to Me.

> *The night is nearly over; the day is almost here. So let us put aside the deeds of darkness and put on the armor of light.*—Romans 13:12

> *But if we walk in the light as He is in the light, we have fellowship with one another, and the blood of Jesus Christ His Son cleanses us from all sin.*—1 John 1:7 nkjv

> *Clothe yourselves with the Lord Jesus Christ, and do not think about how to gratify the desires of the sinful nature.*—Romans 13:14

> *If we confess our sins, He is faithful and just to forgive us our sins and to cleanse us from all unrighteousness.*—1 John 1:9 nkjv

February 22

One of My names is *Wonderful Counselor*. I understand you far, far better than you understand yourself. So come to *Me* with your problems and insecurities, seeking My counsel. In the Light of My loving Presence you can see yourself as you really are: radiantly lovely in My brilliant righteousness. Though My righteousness is perfect, you will continue to struggle with imperfections—yours and others'—as long as you live in this world. Still, your standing with Me is secure. *Nothing in all creation can separate you from My Love*!

A good counselor helps you recognize truth and live according to it. *Actually, I was born and came into the world to testify to the truth*. So be open and honest when you bring Me your concerns. Also, fill your mind and heart with My Word, which contains absolute truth.

A *wonderful* counselor is not only extremely good at helping people but also able to inspire delight or pleasure. *Delight yourself in Me*, beloved, *and I will give you the desires of your heart*.

For a child will be born to us, a son will be given to us; and the government will rest on His shoulders; and His name will be called Wonderful Counselor, Mighty God, Eternal Father, Prince of Peace. —Isaiah 9:6 nasb

For I am convinced that neither death nor life, neither angels nor demons, neither the present nor the future, nor any powers, neither height nor depth, nor anything else in all creation, will be able to separate us from the love of God that is in Christ Jesus our Lord. —Romans 8:38–39

Pilate said, "So you are a king?" Jesus responded, "You say I am a king. Actually, I was born and came into the world to testify to the truth. All who love the truth recognize that what I say is true." —John 18:37 nlt

Delight yourself in the Lord and he will give you the desires of your heart. —Psalm 37:4

February 23

I AM THE WORD OF LIFE—*eternal Life*. I have always existed: I am *that which was from the beginning*. Moreover, I am divine. As the apostle John wrote, *"The Word was God."* This divine Word brings Life to all who believe in Me.

From the beginning of creation, words have been associated with life. Originally, the earth was formless, empty, and dark. Then I said, *"Let there be light," and there was light*. I spoke everything into existence, including all the plants and animals. Finally, I spoke mankind into being.

The Life I offer you is *eternal*. It begins when you trust Me as your only Savior—but it never ends. You can enjoy immense freedom through knowing *there is no condemnation* for you. I have forever *set you free from the law of sin and death*! The best response to this glorious gift is grateful Joy—delighting in the One who loves you perfectly *and* eternally. Remember that I am always near you, closer than the air you breathe.

That which was from the beginning, which we have heard, which we have seen with our eyes, which we have looked at and our hands have touched—this we proclaim concerning the Word of life. The life appeared; we have seen it and testify to it, and we proclaim to you the eternal life, which was with the Father and has appeared to us.—1 JOHN 1:1–2

In the beginning was the Word, and the Word was with God, and the Word was God.—JOHN 1:1 NKJV

In the beginning God created the heavens and the earth. Now the earth was formless and empty, darkness was over the surface of the deep, and the Spirit of God was hovering over the waters. And God said, "Let there be light," and there was light.—GENESIS 1:1–3

Therefore, there is now no condemnation for those who are in Christ Jesus, because through Christ Jesus the law of the Spirit of life set me free from the law of sin and death.—ROMANS 8:1–2

February 24

Morning by morning I awaken you and open your understanding to My will. I'm always mindful of you, beloved. I never sleep, so I'm able to watch over you while you're sleeping. *When you wake up* in the morning, *I am still with you.* As you become aware of My loving Presence, I help you become more alert—smoothing out the tangles in your mind and enabling you to see Me more clearly. I invite you to spend time enjoying My Presence and nourishing your soul with My Word. When you respond to My Love-call by *drawing nearer to Me,* I am delighted.

This time dedicated to Me blesses and strengthens you immensely. I open your understanding to My Word—enabling you to comprehend Scripture and apply it to your life. As you make plans for your day, I help you discern My will. This collaboration with Me empowers you to handle *whatever* comes your way as you go through the day. I am training you to *trust Me at all times*—in all circumstances.

> *The Lord God has given me his words of wisdom so that I may know what I should say to all these weary ones. Morning by morning he wakens me and opens my understanding to his will.* —Isaiah 50:4 TLB

> *How precious are your thoughts about me, O God. They cannot be numbered! I can't even count them; they outnumber the grains of sand! And when I wake up, you are still with me!* —Psalm 139:17–18 NLT

> *Draw near to God and He will draw near to you. Cleanse your hands, you sinners; and purify your hearts, you double-minded.* —James 4:8 NKJV

> *Trust in him at all times, O people; pour out your hearts to him, for God is our refuge.* —Psalm 62:8

February 25

THE LIGHT OF MY GLORY is shining on you, beloved. Look up to Me with worship in your heart. Let the radiance of My Love fall upon you and soak into the depths of your being. Savor these moments alone with Me. I am using them to make you more like Me. The more you keep your gaze on Me—in quiet times *and* busy times—the better you can *reflect My Glory* to other people.

Staying conscious of Me when you're busy can be quite a challenge. But I have created you with an amazing mind that can function on more than one "track." Practicing My Presence involves dedicating one track to your relationship with Me. This practice has many benefits: When you are aware that I am present with you, you're less likely to do or say something that's displeasing to Me. When you're struggling with difficult circumstances or painful feelings, awareness of My Presence offers courage and comfort. I can use *everything* in your life for good—*transforming you into My likeness with ever-increasing Glory.*

> *Let us fix our eyes on Jesus, the author and perfecter of our faith, who for the joy set before him endured the cross, scorning its shame, and sat down at the right hand of the throne of God.* —HEBREWS 12:2

> *And we, who with unveiled faces all reflect the Lord's glory, are being transformed into his likeness with ever-increasing glory, which comes from the Lord, who is the Spirit.* —2 CORINTHIANS 3:18

And we know that God causes everything to work together for the good of those who love God and are called according to his purpose for them. —ROMANS 8:28 NLT

February 26

Man looks at the outward appearance but I look at the heart. The ability to see is a great gift. I grant glimpses of My Glory via visual beauty in nature. Great paintings, sculptures, and cinematography can also help awaken your soul. Rejoice in these glorious gifts, but do not become enslaved to appearances. I am primarily interested in the condition of your heart, and I work to create beauty in it.

It is vital to set aside time for nourishing your heart. *Above all else, guard your heart, for it is the wellspring of life.* A wellspring is a source of abundant supply. Since you belong to Me, My own Life flows through you! However, to keep this Life flowing abundantly, you must protect your heart from evil influences and nourish it with Bible study and prayer.

Aligning your priorities with My teaching can be very freeing. When you don't like the way things look in your world, close your eyes and gaze at who I am. Remember that I am *Immanuel—God with you.*

But the Lord said to Samuel, "Do not consider his appearance or his height, for I have rejected him. The Lord does not look at the things man looks at. Man looks at the outward appearance, but the Lord looks at the heart." —1 Samuel 16:7

Above all else, guard your heart, for it is the wellspring of life. —Proverbs 4:23

"The virgin will be with child and will give birth to a son, and they will call him Immanuel"—which means, "God with us." —Matthew 1:23

February 27

I came into the world as a Light so that no one who believes in Me should stay in darkness. I did not just *bring* light into the world; I Myself am *the Light that keeps on shining in the darkness.* Since I am infinite and all-powerful, nothing can extinguish this illumination!

When you believed in Me, you became a *child of Light*, and the brightness entered into your inner being. This helps you see things from My perspective—both things in the world and things in your heart. This illumination of the contents of your heart can be very uncomfortable. However, when it leads to repentance and walking in My ways, it is the road to freedom.

Rejoice in your brightened perspective. *The god of this age has blinded the minds of unbelievers so that they cannot see the Light of the gospel of My Glory.* But because you are My cherished one, you have *the Light of the knowledge of My Glory* shining in your heart. Rejoice greatly!

> "I have come into the world as a light, so that no one who believes in me should stay in darkness."—John 12:46

> And the Light shines on in the darkness, for the darkness has never overpowered it [put it out or absorbed it or appropriated it, and is unreceptive to it].—John 1:5 AMP

> For you are all children of light, children of the day. We are not of the night or of the darkness.—1 Thessalonians 5:5 ESV

> The god of this age has blinded the minds of unbelievers, so that they cannot see the light of the gospel of the glory of Christ, who is the image of God. . . . For God, who said, "Let light shine out of darkness," made his light shine in our hearts to give us the light of the knowledge of the glory of God in the face of Christ.—2 Corinthians 4:4, 6

February 28

You are no stranger to Me, dear one. *Before I formed you in the womb I knew you.* My knowledge of you has continued without interruption: through your entrance into this world and onward throughout your life. I delight in transforming you more and more into the one I created you to be, much as a skilled potter delights in the work he is creating.

One implication of My uninterrupted Presence with you is that you are never alone. I am training you to be increasingly aware of Me, but I understand that you are human and your attention span is limited. Sometimes when you are suffering, you may feel as if you're alone or abandoned. However, I suffered alone on the cross so that you would *never* have to be alone in your struggles. *You are always with Me; I hold you by your right hand.*

The last enemy you will face is death, but My crucifixion and resurrection have decimated that foe! So trust Me to guide you through your life, and *afterward take you into Glory.*

> "Before I formed you in the womb I knew you, before you were born I set you apart; I appointed you as a prophet to the nations."—Jeremiah 1:5

> Your eyes saw my unformed body. All the days ordained for me were written in your book before one of them came to be.—Psalm 139:16

> Yet I am always with you; you hold me by my right hand. You guide me with your counsel, and afterward you will take me into glory.—Psalm 73:23–24

February 29

I CALLED YOU OUT OF DARKNESS into My marvelous Light. I brought you not only *out of darkness* but *into* My royal family. I clothed you with My personal *robe of righteousness*, making you fit for My kingdom. You are one of *My own special people*: You belong to Me, and I delight in you.

I have chosen to use imperfect ones like you to *proclaim My praises*. I know you cannot do this as well as you would like. Actually, without My help it is impossible for you to do. This gap between My call on your life and your ability to respond is part of My plan. It heightens your awareness of your utter insufficiency. Because you are Mine, I allow you to connect your inability to My boundless sufficiency. Instead of focusing on your inadequacy, work on staying close to Me. In everything you do, consciously rely on My help, living in the joyous wonder of self-forgetfulness. As you look to Me for all you need, your face will reflect the Light of My surpassing Glory.

> But you are a chosen generation, a royal priesthood, a holy nation, His own special people, that you may proclaim the praises of Him who called you out of darkness into His marvelous light. —1 PETER 2:9 NKJV

> I delight greatly in the LORD; my soul rejoices in my God. For he has clothed me with garments of salvation and arrayed me in a robe of righteousness, as a bridegroom adorns his head like a priest, and as a bride adorns herself with her jewels. —ISAIAH 61:10

> "I am the vine, you are the branches. He who abides in Me, and I in him, bears much fruit; for without Me you can do nothing." —JOHN 15:5 NKJV

> And we, who with unveiled faces all reflect the Lord's glory, are being transformed into his likeness with ever-increasing glory, which comes from the Lord, who is the Spirit. —2 CORINTHIANS 3:18

March

From the fullness of his grace we have all received one blessing after another.

JOHN 1:16

March 1

I give you Joy in your journey through the world. This sparkling gift is not a luxury; it's a necessity! There are bumps in the road ahead, as well as sharp curves, ascents, and descents. Without Joy in your heart, you will *become weary and discouraged.*

Joy is not dependent on the circumstances in your life. It can transcend them all! This is why impoverished people are often more joyful than those who have material wealth. Sick—and even dying—people can also be joyful when they're trusting in Me as Savior, Lord, and Friend.

Seek to spread Joy in the world around you. Let My Light reflect from your demeanor—through your smiles, your laughter, your words. The Holy Spirit will equip you to do this as you give Him space in your life. Ask Him to fill you with contagious delight. Concentrate on staying close to Me, and I will lead you along *the path of Life. In My Presence there is fullness of Joy.*

> *For consider Him who endured such hostility from sinners against Himself, lest you become weary and discouraged in your souls.*—Hebrews 12:3 nkjv

> *Though the fig tree does not bud and there are no grapes on the vines, though the olive crop fails and the fields produce no food, though there are no sheep in the pen and no cattle in the stalls, yet I will rejoice in the Lord, I will be joyful in God my Savior.*—Habakkuk 3:17–18

> *You make known to me the path of life; in your presence there is fullness of joy; at your right hand are pleasures forevermore.*—Psalm 16:11 esv

March 2

My paths are beyond tracing out! Come to Me with humility in your heart, bowing before My infinite intelligence. Relinquish your demand to understand; accept the fact that many things are simply beyond your comprehension. Because I am infinite and you are finite, the limitations of your mind make it impossible for you to understand much of what happens in your life—and in the world. So it's vital to make room for *mystery* in your worldview.

You are privileged to know many things that were formerly mysteries—things that had *been kept hidden for ages and generations*. The New Testament is full of revelations that came through My incarnation, life, death, and resurrection. You are immeasurably blessed to have this priceless knowledge!

Nonetheless, the ways I work in your world are often mysterious to you—beyond tracing out. This presents you with a choice: to resent My ways or to bow before Me in wonder and worship. Marvel at *the depth of the riches of My wisdom and knowledge*!

> Oh, the depth of the riches of the wisdom and knowledge of God! How unsearchable his judgments, and his paths beyond tracing out!—Romans 11:33

> Trust in the Lord with all your heart; do not depend on your own understanding.—Proverbs 3:5 nlt

> . . . *The mystery that has been kept hidden for ages and generations, but is now disclosed to the saints.*—Colossians 1:26

March 3

My Love chases after you every day of your life. So look for signs of My tender Presence as you go through this day. I disclose Myself to you in a vast variety of ways—words of Scripture just when you need them, helpful words spoken through other people, "coincidences" orchestrated by My Spirit, nature's beauty, and so on. My Love for you is not passive; it actively chases after you and leaps into your life. Invite Me to open the eyes of your heart so you can "see" Me blessing you in myriad ways—both small and great.

I want you not only to receive My bountiful blessings but to take careful note of them. Treasure them and *ponder them in your heart.* Thank Me for these ways I show up in your life; write some of them down so you can enjoy them again and again. These signs of My Presence strengthen you and prepare you for difficulties on the road ahead. Remember that *nothing in all creation can separate you from My Love.*

Your beauty and love chase after me every day of my life. I'm back home in the house of God for the rest of my life.—Psalm 23:6 msg

Your word I have hidden in my heart, that I might not sin against You.—Psalm 119:11 nkjv

But Mary treasured up all these things and pondered them in her heart.—Luke 2:19

Neither height nor depth, nor anything else in all creation, will be able to separate us from the love of God that is in Christ Jesus our Lord.—Romans 8:39

March 4

Blessed are all those who wait for Me! Waiting patiently does not come easily to you, but it is nonetheless very good for you. You long to plan ahead, make definitive decisions, and make things *happen*. There is a time for that, but this is not the time. Now is a time for sitting in My Presence, trusting Me with your whole being. This discipline will bring a wealth of blessings your way.

Some of the good things I offer you reside in the future. While you obediently wait on me, you are building up equity for those not-yet blessings. Because they are veiled in the mystery of the future, you cannot see them clearly. Other blessings are for the present. The very process of waiting for Me is beneficial. It keeps your soul on tiptoe, as you look up to Me in hope. You acknowledge that I am in control, and you rest in My goodness. Though you may not understand why you have to wait so long, I bless you as you choose to *trust Me with all your heart*.

Yet the Lord longs to be gracious to you; he rises to show you compassion. For the Lord is a God of justice. Blessed are all who wait for him!—Isaiah 30:18

Cause me to hear Your lovingkindness in the morning, for in You do I trust; cause me to know the way in which I should walk, for I lift up my soul to You.—Psalm 143:8 nkjv

Trust in the Lord with all your heart, and do not lean on your own understanding.—Proverbs 3:5 esv

March 5

I AM TAKING CARE OF YOU. Sometimes you feel alone and vulnerable—exposed to the "elements" of a fallen world. When you are feeling this way, stop and remind yourself, "Jesus is taking care of me." This reminder can comfort you and help you relax. It draws you back from obsessing about the future, trying to figure out and orchestrate what will happen.

When circumstances are confusing and you don't know which way to proceed, remember that you are in My watchcare. I know everything about you and your situation. I also know the future. A child in a good family with adequate resources doesn't need to know how his parents will provide for him tomorrow, next week, next year. *You* are in the best Family imaginable, and My resources are absolutely unlimited! So bring Me all your needs and concerns. Entrust them to Me and live confidently—as a child of the *King of kings*! Relax and rejoice, for I am taking good care of you.

> *Cast all your anxiety on him because he cares for you.*—1 PETER 5:7

> *The LORD will guide you always; he will satisfy your needs in a sun-scorched land and will strengthen your frame. You will be like a well-watered garden, like a spring whose waters never fail.*—ISAIAH 58:11

> *And He has on His robe and on His thigh a name written:*
> KING OF KINGS AND LORD OF LORDS.—REVELATION 19:16 NKJV

March 6

DO NOT DREAD *walking through the valley of the shadow of death.* My radiant Presence shines brightly in that *deep, sunless valley*—strengthening, encouraging, and comforting you. Since *I never sleep*, I am able to watch over you constantly. Moreover, no valley is so deep, no pit so dark, that I cannot see all the way to the bottom of it.

Even if you wander from Me at times and fall into a *slimy pit*, you can count on Me to rescue you. When you cry out to Me, I *lift you out of the mud and mire* and *set your feet on a rock*—giving you *a firm place to stand*. Find comfort in My commitment to help you, even when you slip up.

Whenever you start to feel afraid, remember that *I am with you.* I've promised *I will never leave you; I Myself go before you.* While you are walking through the valley of adversity, keep these words of comfort flowing through your mind: *I will fear no evil, for You are with me.*

> *Yes, though I walk through the [deep, sunless] valley of the shadow of death, I will fear or dread no evil, for You are with me; Your rod [to protect] and Your staff [to guide], they comfort me.*—PSALM 23:4 AMP

> *My help comes from the LORD, who made heaven and earth. He will not let you be defeated. He who guards you never sleeps.*—PSALM 121:2–3 NCV

> *I waited patiently for the LORD; he turned to me and heard my cry. He lifted me out of the slimy pit, out of the mud and mire; he set my feet on a rock and gave me a firm place to stand.*—PSALM 40:1–2

> *The LORD himself goes before you and will be with you; he will never leave you nor forsake you. Do not be afraid; do not be discouraged.*—DEUTERONOMY 31:8

March 7

Blessed are those who rejoice in My Name all day long and exult in My righteousness. This Name represents *Me* in all of My glorious attributes. Used properly, it draws you closer to My loving Presence. Many people abuse My Name by using it as a swear word. Hearing this verbal abuse is exceedingly offensive to Me. However, My followers can lovingly utter the word "Jesus" *all day long*—to rejoice in Me and ask for help. *I am God your Savior, and I will help you for the Glory of My Name.*

I invite you to exult in My righteousness. To "exult" is to be delighted, elated, joyful, jubilant—especially because of triumph or success. Just before I died on the cross, I said, *"It is finished!"* I was announcing the accomplishment of the greatest triumph imaginable: victory over sin and death for everyone who believes in Me. Through this crowning achievement, My righteousness has been credited to you forever, beloved. *I have covered you with the robe of righteousness.* Wear My glorious *garments of salvation* with delight, elation, and joyful jubilation!

> They rejoice in your name all day long;
> they exult in your righteousness.—Psalm 89:16

> Help us, O God our Savior, for the glory of your name; deliver us and forgive our sins for your name's sake.—Psalm 79:9

> So when Jesus had received the sour wine, He said, "It is finished!" And bowing His head, He gave up His spirit.—John 19:30 nkjv

> I will greatly rejoice in the Lord; my soul shall exult in my God, for he has clothed me with the garments of salvation; he has covered me with the robe of righteousness, as a bridegroom decks himself like a priest with a beautiful headdress, and as a bride adorns herself with her jewels.—Isaiah 61:10 esv

March 8

I ENABLE YOU TO STAND on the heights. This term "the heights" can refer to a number of things. Taken literally, it means that something is physically very high up. This is appropriate language for describing mountaintops or the uppermost floors of skyscrapers. Taken figuratively, the term can refer to euphoric pleasure *or* to something quite different: weighty experiences of responsibility. If you aspire to reach the heights—especially the high places of achievement and recognition—be prepared to shoulder the responsibilities that accompany success. But don't forget to enjoy the satisfaction of accomplishing good things with Me, through Me, and for Me.

Because you are Mine, you can *stand firm, with the belt of truth buckled around your waist* and *the breastplate of righteousness in place.* All of My teaching is absolutely true, for *I am the Truth.* This provides a firm foundation for you—solid rock on which to stand. My perfect righteousness has been credited to your account forever. No matter how much trouble you encounter, *this righteousness* can keep you standing!

He makes my feet like the feet of a deer; he enables me to stand on the heights.—2 SAMUEL 22:34

Stand firm then, with the belt of truth buckled around your waist, with the breastplate of righteousness in place.—EPHESIANS 6:14

Jesus said to him, "I am the way, the truth, and the life. No one comes to the Father except through Me."—JOHN 14:6 NKJV

This righteousness from God comes through faith in Jesus Christ to all who believe.—ROMANS 3:22

March 9

My ways are mysterious and unpredictable, but they are good. When you look at world events—with so much rampant evil—it's easy to feel fearful and discouraged. You cannot comprehend why I allow such cruelty and suffering. The difficulty lies in the fact that I am infinite and you are not. Many things are simply beyond your comprehension. But do not despair. When you reach the limits of your understanding, trusting Me will carry you onward. Affirm your *trust in Me* through silent and spoken prayers. Stay in communication with Me!

Don't get trapped in a posture of demanding to know "Why?" That is the wrong question to ask Me. The right questions are: "How do You want me to view this situation?" and "What do You want me to do right now?" You cannot change the past, so start with the present moment and seek to find My way forward. Trust Me one day, one moment, at a time. *Do not fear, for I am with you. I will strengthen you and help you.*

Trust in the Lord with all your heart, and do not lean on your own understanding.—Proverbs 3:5 esv

I realized that no one can discover everything God is doing under the sun. Not even the wisest people discover everything, no matter what they claim.—Ecclesiastes 8:17 nlt

The wicked plot against the righteous and gnash their teeth at them; but the Lord laughs at the wicked, for he knows their day is coming.—Psalm 37:12–13

"So do not fear, for I am with you; do not be dismayed, for I am your God. I will strengthen you and help you; I will uphold you with my righteous right hand."—Isaiah 41:10

March 10

From the fullness of My grace, you have received one blessing after another. Stop for a moment, beloved, and ponder the astonishing gift of salvation—*by grace through faith* in Me. Because it's entirely a gift—*not as a result of works*—this salvation is secure. Your part is just to receive what I accomplished for you on the cross, believing with the faith that was given you. This undeserved Love and favor is yours forever. My grace has infinite value!

Multiple blessings flow out of grace because of its extraordinary fullness. Guilt feelings melt away in the warm Light of My forgiveness. Your identity as a *child of God* gives your life meaning and purpose. Relationships with other people improve as you relate to them with love and forgiveness.

The best response to My bountiful grace is a heart overflowing with gratitude. Take time each day to think about and thank Me for blessings in your life. This protects your heart from weeds of ingratitude that spring up so easily. *Be thankful*!

From the fullness of his grace we have all received one blessing after another.—John 1:16

For by grace you have been saved through faith. And this is not your own doing; it is the gift of God, not a result of works, so that no one may boast.—Ephesians 2:8–9 esv

Yet to all who received him, to those who believed in his name, he gave the right to become children of God.—John 1:12

Let the peace of Christ rule in your hearts, to which indeed you were called in one body; and be thankful.—Colossians 3:15 nasb

March 11

SEEK TO LIVE IN THE PRESENT—with *Me*! Your life is a gift from Me, consisting of millions upon millions of moments. These countless, tiny gifts can easily slip away unnoticed and unused. The best remedy to such wastefulness is to fill your moments with My Presence. You can begin your day connecting with Me by praying: "Thank You, Jesus, for this precious day of life. Help me stay aware of Your Presence with me."

Thankfulness keeps you linked to Me and anchored in the present. Worry, on the other hand, pulls you into the future, where you wander in barren places of uncertainty. However, you can always return to Me by whispering, "Lord, help me."

To live consistently in the present, seek to become more grateful. Look around you, searching for the many gifts I shower upon you. As you thank Me for these blessings, go into detail—express yourself enthusiastically! This will increase your gratitude and enhance your ability to grasp how blessed you really are.

This is the day the LORD *has made; let us rejoice and be glad in it.*—PSALM 118:24

So then, just as you received Christ Jesus as Lord, continue to live in him, rooted and built up in him, strengthened in the faith as you were taught, and overflowing with thankfulness.—COLOSSIANS 2:6–7

But I trust in your unfailing love; my heart rejoices in your salvation.—PSALM 13:5

Thanks be to God for His indescribable gift!—2 CORINTHIANS 9:15 NKJV

March 12

The Joy you have in Me is independent of your circumstances. *In My Presence is fullness of Joy*, and you are never separated from Me. *Search for Me* as you go along your pathway today. I delight in disclosing Myself to you. Sometimes I communicate with you in grand, unmistakable ways—"coincidences" that are clearly the work of My hands. At other times I display My unseen Presence in subtle ways. These are often so personal to you that others wouldn't even notice them. Yet these subtle signs can be a source of deep, intimate Joy.

The more attentive you are, the more you can find Me in the details of your day. So try to stay alert—be on the lookout for Me!

Fill your mind and heart with Scripture, where I reveal Myself most clearly. Let My promises permeate your thinking and keep you close to Me. *Listen to My voice. I know you, and you follow Me. I give you eternal Life; no one can snatch you out of My hand.* Rejoice!

> *You will show me the path of life; in Your presence is fullness of joy; at Your right hand are pleasures forevermore.*—Psalm 16:11 nkjv

> *"And you will seek Me and find Me, when you search for Me with all your heart."*—Jeremiah 29:13 nkjv

> *"My sheep listen to my voice; I know them, and they follow me. I give them eternal life, and they shall never perish; no one can snatch them out of my hand."*—John 10:27–28

March 13

D O NOT DWELL ON THE PAST, beloved. You can learn from the past, but don't let it become your focus. You cannot undo things that have already occurred, no matter how much you may yearn to do so. Instead of wishing for the impossible, come to Me and *pour out your heart*. Remember that I am *your Refuge*; *trust in Me at all times*.

Reinforce your confidence in Me by saying frequently: "I trust You, Jesus." Uttering those four words can brighten your day immediately. Dark clouds of worry are blown away by simple, childlike trust.

I am doing a new thing! Be on the lookout for all that I am accomplishing in your life. Ask Me to open the eyes of your mind and heart so you can see the many opportunities I've placed along your path. Don't fall into such a routine that you see only the same old things—and miss the newness. Remember that I can make a way where there appears to be no way. *With Me all things are possible*!

> "Forget the former things; do not dwell on the past. See, I am doing a new thing! Now it springs up; do you not perceive it? I am making a way in the desert and streams in the wasteland."—ISAIAH 43:18–19

> Trust in him at all times, O people; pour out your hearts to him, for God is our refuge.—PSALM 62:8

> Jesus looked at them and said, "With man this is impossible, but with God all things are possible."—MATTHEW 19:26

March 14

I REJOICE OVER YOU WITH SINGING. Open wide your heart, mind, and spirit to receive My richest blessings. Because you are My blood-bought child, My Love for you flows continuously from *the throne of grace*. Look up and receive all that I have for you. Listen and hear Me singing songs of Joy because of My *great delight in you*. You can approach Me boldly—with confidence—trusting that you are indeed *the one I love*.

The world teaches you that love is conditional: based on performance, appearance, and status. Even though you don't believe this lie, the constant onslaught of this message in the media can penetrate your thinking. That's why it is so important to spend time focusing on Me—soaking in My Presence, absorbing My Word.

Setting aside time to be alone with Me is countercultural, so this practice requires discipline and determination. However, it is well worth the effort. Living close to Me brightens your life immeasurably. *With Me is the fountain of Life; in My Light you see Light.*

> "The LORD your God is with you, he is mighty to save. He will take great delight in you, he will quiet you with his love, he will rejoice over you with singing."—ZEPHANIAH 3:17

> Let us then approach the throne of grace with confidence, so that we may receive mercy and find grace to help us in our time of need.—HEBREWS 4:16

> About Benjamin he said: "Let the beloved of the LORD rest secure in him, for he shields him all day long, and the one the LORD loves rests between his shoulders."—DEUTERONOMY 33:12

> For with you is the fountain of life; in your light we see light.—PSALM 36:9

March 15

I UPHOLD ALL THOSE WHO FALL and lift up all who are bowed down. Sometimes you and I are the only ones who know you have fallen. It's tempting at such times to gloss over what you have done (or failed to do). You may not be overwhelmed by feelings of shame, but you feel restless and unsettled—mildly guilty. Even at times like this, I continue to love you perfectly. Sometimes I display My Love for you in unexpected ways—humbling and delighting you simultaneously. This deepens your awareness of your sin, intensifying your desire to confess and draw near Me. As you settle into your rightful position, My redeemed one, your restlessness yields to calmness. This is how I lift you up when you've stumbled.

Remember that I can make *all things*—including your failures—*work together for good* because *you love Me and are called according to My purpose*. Realizing how much I cherish you even when you're not living well deepens your relationship with Me. It also helps you relax and rejoice in *My steadfast Love*.

The Lord upholds all those who fall and lifts up all who are bowed down.—Psalm 145:14

And we know that God causes all things to work together for good to those who love God, to those who are called according to His purpose.—Romans 8:28 NASB

The steadfast love of the Lord never ceases, his mercies never come to an end; they are new every morning; great is thy faithfulness.—Lamentations 3:22–23 RSV

March 16

I AM THE ANTIDOTE TO LONELINESS. *For I am the Lord, your God, who takes hold of your right hand and says to you, "Do not fear; I will help you."* Close your right hand, as if you are grasping onto *My* hand. This symbolic gesture helps you feel connected to Me—to My living Presence. Whenever you start to feel lonely or afraid, you need to reconnect with Me.

Tell Me about your feelings and the struggles you face. I already know about them, but it does you good to bring them to Me. Spend time basking in the Light of My Presence, realizing how safe and secure you are in Me. *I am with you* every nanosecond of your life. You are never alone!

Seek My Face and My perspective on your life. Sometimes it's beneficial to write out your concerns. This clarifies your thinking and provides a record of your prayers. It also helps you release your problems to Me. *I am watching over you* continually.

> "For I am the LORD, your God, who takes hold of your right hand and says to you, Do not fear; I will help you."—ISAIAH 41:13

> ". . . Teaching them to observe all things that I have commanded you; and lo, I am with you always, even to the end of the age." Amen.—MATTHEW 28:20 NKJV

> One thing I have desired of the LORD, that will I seek: that I may dwell in the house of the LORD all the days of my life, to behold the beauty of the LORD, and to inquire in His temple.—PSALM 27:4 NKJV

> "I am with you and will watch over you wherever you go, and I will bring you back to this land."—GENESIS 28:15

March 17

Nothing in all creation can separate you from My Love. Pause and ponder what an astonishing promise this is! You live in a world where separations abound: wives from husbands, children from parents, friends from friends, childhood dreams from adult realities. But there is one terrible separation you will never have to face: isolation from My loving Presence.

I want you to cling to Me with tenacious confidence. This gives you strength to cope with the uncertainties of living in such a broken, unstable world. Anxious thoughts can assault your mind and fill you with fear if you forget that My Love will never fail you. When you find yourself feeling afraid, grasp My hand in childlike trust. Rest in the protection of My Presence, and remember that *perfect Love drives out fear.*

The greatest wealth on earth is minuscule compared with the riches of My boundless Love. Yet this is My free gift to all who follow Me. *How priceless is My unfailing Love!*

> For I am convinced that neither death nor life, neither angels nor demons, neither the present nor the future, nor any powers, neither height nor depth, nor anything else in all creation, will be able to separate us from the love of God that is in Christ Jesus our Lord.—Romans 8:38–39

> For thus says the Lord God, the Holy One of Israel: "In returning and rest you shall be saved; in quietness and confidence shall be your strength." But you would not.—Isaiah 30:15 nkjv

> There is no fear in love. But perfect love drives out fear, because fear has to do with punishment. The one who fears is not made perfect in love.—1 John 4:18

> How priceless is your unfailing love! Both high and low among men find refuge in the shadow of your wings.—Psalm 36:7

March 18

STRIVE TO LIVE MORE FULLY in the present, refusing to *worry about tomorrow.* Striving involves devoting serious effort and energy to something; it usually includes struggle. You must exert continual effort if you want to live present-tense in My Presence. I urge you to make *Me* the major pursuit of your everyday life.

It's essential to resist the temptation to worry. You live in a fallen world, full of sin and struggles—you will never run short of things that can provoke anxiety. However, remember that *each day has enough trouble of its own.* I carefully calibrate the amount of difficulty you will encounter on a given day. I know exactly how much you can handle with My help. And I'm always near—ready to strengthen, encourage, and comfort you.

Pursuing a close walk with Me is the best way to live in the present. Keep bringing your thoughts back to Me whenever they wander. Return to Me joyfully, beloved. *I will take great delight in you* and *rejoice over you with singing.*

> "Therefore do not worry about tomorrow, for tomorrow will worry about itself. Each day has enough trouble of its own."—MATTHEW 6:34

> "Fear not, for I am with you; be not dismayed, for I am your God. I will strengthen you, yes, I will help you, I will uphold you with My righteous right hand."—ISAIAH 41:10 NKJV

> "The LORD your God is with you, he is mighty to save. He will take great delight in you, he will quiet you with his love, he will rejoice over you with singing."—ZEPHANIAH 3:17

March 19

You are ready for anything and equal to anything through your living relationship with Me. Rest in My Presence while *I infuse inner strength into you.* Because you are a child of the King of kings, you are capable of so much more than you realize. To benefit fully from your privileged position, however, you need to spend ample time with Me. As you relax in My Presence—delighting in Me and opening your heart to Me—I fill you with inner strength. This time spent together is not only pleasurable, it is empowering.

When there is much to do, it's tempting to rush through your time with Me and dive into the activities of the day. But just as eating a healthy breakfast helps you function at your best, so does feeding your soul a healthy diet of *Me.* Bask in My Word, asking My Spirit to make it come alive to you. Savor these words of Life! Your living relationship with Me helps you approach each new day with confidence—ready for anything that comes your way.

I have strength for all things in Christ Who empowers me [I am ready for anything and equal to anything through Him Who infuses inner strength into me; I am self-sufficient in Christ's sufficiency].—Philippians 4:13 AMP

Delight yourself in the Lord and he will give you the desires of your heart.—Psalm 37:4

In the morning, O Lord, you hear my voice; in the morning I lay my requests before you and wait in expectation.—Psalm 5:3

March 20

Stop your incessant worry-planning! Draw your mind back from the future to the present moment, where My Presence lovingly awaits you. *Seek My Face* with a smile in your heart, knowing that I take delight in you. Talk with Me about all that concerns you and the tasks that are weighing on you. Call out to Me for help as you set priorities according to My will. Then keep returning your focus to Me and to the work at hand. Inviting Me into your activities increases your Joy and helps you to be more effective.

When you need to take a break, remember that I am your resting place. My *everlasting arms* are always available to support you and hold you close. When you relax in My company—waiting with Me for a time—this demonstrates genuine trust in Me. As you prepare to return to your tasks, make the effort to include *Me* in your plans. This protects you from worrying; it also helps you stay close to Me, enjoying My Presence.

> *"Who of you by worrying can add a single hour to his life? Since you cannot do this very little thing, why do you worry about the rest?"*—Luke 12:25–26

> *Find rest, O my soul, in God alone; my hope comes from him. He alone is my rock and my salvation; he is my fortress, I will not be shaken.*—Psalm 62:5–6

> *The eternal God is your refuge, and underneath are the everlasting arms. He will drive out your enemy before you, saying, "Destroy him!"*—Deuteronomy 33:27

March 21

I AM TRAINING YOU not only to endure your difficulties but to transform them into Glory. This is a supernatural feat, and it requires the help of My supernatural Spirit. When problems are weighing heavily on you, your natural tendency is to speed up your pace of living, frantically searching for answers. But what you need at such times is to *slow down* and seek My Face. Invite the Spirit to help you as you discuss your difficulties with Me. Then *lay your requests before Me and wait in expectation.*

Even though you wait expectantly, I may not answer your prayers quickly. I am always doing something important in your life—far beyond simply solving your problems. Your struggles are part of a much larger battle, and the way you handle them can contribute to outcomes with eternal significance. When you respond to your troubles by trusting Me and *praying with thanksgiving,* you glorify Me. Moreover, your practice of praying persistently will eventually make a vast difference in *you*—My loved one *crowned with Glory.*

In the morning, O LORD, you hear my voice; in the morning I lay my requests before you and wait in expectation.—PSALM 5:3

Be anxious for nothing, but in everything by prayer and supplication, with thanksgiving, let your requests be made known to God.—PHILIPPIANS 4:6 NKJV

You made him a little lower than the heavenly beings and crowned him with glory and honor.—PSALM 8:5

March 22

Rejoice, beloved, because My sacrifice on the cross absorbed all your guilt: past, present, and future. *There is no condemnation for those who are in Me.* Your guilt-free status as My follower is good reason to be joyful each day of your life. Ever since the Fall in the Garden of Eden, mankind's worst problem has been sin. My sacrificial death provided the solution to this terrible problem. The gospel really *is* the best news imaginable: I took your sin—*I became sin for you*—and I gave you My perfect righteousness. This is an amazing, eternal transaction!

I want you to learn to enjoy more fully your guilt-free standing in My kingdom. *Through Me, the law of the Spirit of life set you free*! This is *not* an invitation to dive into a sinful lifestyle. Instead, I'm inviting you to live jubilantly, reveling in the glorious privilege of belonging to Me forever! This is your true identity, and it makes every moment of your life meaningful. Rejoice in knowing who you really are—a beloved *child of God.*

> *Therefore, there is now no condemnation for those who are in Christ Jesus, because through Christ Jesus the law of the Spirit of life set me free from the law of sin and death.*—Romans 8:1–2

> *When the woman saw that the fruit of the tree was good for food and pleasing to the eye, and also desirable for gaining wisdom, she took some and ate it. She also gave some to her husband, who was with her, and he ate it. Then the eyes of both of them were opened, and they realized they were naked.*—Genesis 3:6–7

> *For He made Him who knew no sin to be sin for us, that we might become the righteousness of God in Him.*—2 Corinthians 5:21 nkjv

> *He came to his own, and his own people did not receive him. But to all who did receive him, who believed in his name, he gave the right to become children of God.*—John 1:11–12 esv

March 23

I AM THE RISEN ONE—your *living God*. Celebrate the Joy of serving a Savior who is exuberantly alive! Rejoice also in My promise to be with you continually—throughout time and eternity. These truths can sustain you through the greatest trials or disappointments you will ever encounter. So walk boldly along the path of Life with Me, trusting confidently in the One who never lets go of your hand.

Consider what I offer you: Myself, forgiveness of *all* your sins, forever-pleasures in heaven. This is all so extravagant and lavish that you cannot comprehend it fully. That is why worshiping Me is so important: It's a powerful way of connecting with Me that transcends your understanding. It also proclaims My Presence. There are numerous ways of worshiping Me: singing hymns and praise songs, studying and memorizing My Word, praying individually and with others, glorying in the wonders of My creation. Serving and loving others with My Love can also be worship. *Whatever you do, do it all for the Glory of God*—My Glory!

> *Do not be afraid, for I know that you are looking for Jesus, who was crucified. He is not here; he has risen, just as he said.* —MATTHEW 28:5–6

> *My soul thirsts for God, for the living God.* —PSALM 42:2

> *This is what I have asked of God for you: that you will be encouraged and knit together by strong ties of love, and that you will have the rich experience of knowing Christ with real certainty and clear understanding. For God's secret plan, now at last made known, is Christ himself. In him lie hidden all the mighty, untapped treasures of wisdom and knowledge.* —COLOSSIANS 2:2–3 TLB

> *So whether you eat or drink or whatever you do, do it all for the glory of God.* —1 CORINTHIANS 10:31

March 24

No matter how inadequate you may feel, you can always look to Me for help. You don't need to go to a special place or assume a certain posture to *seek My Face*. Nor do you need to use elegant language or work to win My favor. I always look favorably on you because I see you clothed in My righteousness. I am alive in you, and I understand your thoughts perfectly. So a simple glance at Me—made in faith—is enough to connect you to My help.

You tend to waste energy trying to determine whether your resources are adequate for the day. You keep checking your "power gauge" instead of looking to Me for My provision. How much better to simply acknowledge your insufficiency when you awaken! This frees you to rely on My boundless sufficiency. If you stay in touch with Me, I will place enough Power at your disposal to meet your needs as they arise. Keep turning toward Me, your *ever-present Help*, and your strength will be equal to the demands of your day.

> Look to the Lord and his strength; seek his face always.—Psalm 105:4

> I will greatly rejoice in the Lord, my soul shall be joyful in my God; for He has clothed me with the garments of salvation, He has covered me with the robe of righteousness, as a bridegroom decks himself with ornaments, and as a bride adorns herself with her jewels.—Isaiah 61:10 nkjv

> God is our refuge and strength, an ever-present help in trouble.—Psalm 46:1

> The bolts of your gates will be iron and bronze, and your strength will equal your days.—Deuteronomy 33:25

March 25

I am the Resurrection and the Life. He who believes in Me will live, even though he dies. I spoke this truth to Martha when her brother Lazarus had died, and she believed Me. Shortly thereafter, I commanded Lazarus to come out of his tomb, and he did. Even though he eventually died again—as all people do—he knew he would rise again to Life, as all believers will.

Shortly before My crucifixion, I taught My disciples: *"I am the Way, the Truth, and the Life."* I am everything you could possibly need—for this life and the next. I am the Treasure that encompasses all treasures. This truth can simplify your life immensely! I am the answer to all your struggles, the Joy that pervades all time and circumstances. I can make hard times bearable and good times utterly delightful. So *come to Me* just as you are, beloved; share more and more of your life with Me. Rejoice as you journey with Me—the Way who guides you always and the Resurrection who gives you eternal Life.

> *"I am the resurrection and the life. He who believes in me will live, even though he dies." . . . Jesus called in a loud voice, "Lazarus, come out!" The dead man came out, his hands and feet wrapped with strips of linen, and a cloth around his face. Jesus said to them, "Take off the grave clothes and let him go."*—John 11:25, 43–44

> *Jesus said to him, "I am the way, the truth, and the life. No one comes to the Father except through Me."*—John 14:6 nkjv

> *My purpose is that they may be encouraged in heart and united in love, so that they may have the full riches of complete understanding, in order that they may know the mystery of God, namely, Christ, in whom are hidden all the treasures of wisdom and knowledge.*—Colossians 2:2–3

> *"Come to me, all you who are weary and burdened, and I will give you rest."*—Matthew 11:28

March 26

ASK ME TO INCREASE YOUR THANKFULNESS. This will brighten your day and open your heart to Me. Seek to "see" Me in the midst of your circumstances. Look for signs of My unseen Presence as you walk along *the path of Life*. Gratefulness opens not only your heart but also your eyes. When you know Me intimately, you can find Me in myriad tiny details as well as in the big picture of your life. Take time to notice all My blessings—small and large—and to thank Me for them. This practice will help you enjoy My many gifts.

Ask Me also to train you in trusting Me more consistently. Well-developed trust enables you to go across treacherous terrain without stumbling. The more challenging your journey, the more frequently you need to voice your confidence in Me. You can pray, "Lord, *I trust in Your unfailing Love*." This short prayer reminds you that I am with you, I am taking care of you, and I love you forever. Rejoice, beloved, for I am truly worthy of your thankfulness and trust.

Therefore as you have received Christ Jesus the Lord, so walk in Him, having been firmly rooted and now being built up in Him and established in your faith, just as you were instructed, and overflowing with gratitude.—COLOSSIANS 2:6–7 NASB

You will show me the path of life; in Your presence is fullness of joy; at Your right hand are pleasures forevermore.—PSALM 16:11 NKJV

But I am like an olive tree flourishing in the house of God; I trust in God's unfailing love for ever and ever.—PSALM 52:8

March 27

Through My resurrection from the dead, you have *new birth into a living hope*. My work in you is all about "newness." Because you belong to Me, you're *a new creation; the old has gone, the new has come!* Your adoption into My royal family occurred instantaneously, at the moment you first trusted Me as Savior. At that instant, your spiritual status changed from death to life—eternal Life. You have *an inheritance that can never perish, spoil, or fade—kept in heaven for you.*

You are indeed a new creation, with the Holy Spirit living in you. But your becoming a Christian was only the *beginning* of the work I'm doing in you. You need *to be made new in the attitude of your mind and to put on the new self*—becoming increasingly godly, righteous, and holy. This is a lifelong endeavor, and it is preparing you for heaven's Glory. So receive this assignment with courage and gratitude. Be alert, and look for all the wonderful things I am doing in your life.

Praise be to the God and Father of our Lord Jesus Christ! In his great mercy he has given us new birth into a living hope through the resurrection of Jesus Christ from the dead, and into an inheritance that can never perish, spoil or fade—kept in heaven for you.—1 Peter 1:3–4

Therefore, if anyone is in Christ, he is a new creation; the old has gone, the new has come!—2 Corinthians 5:17

You were taught, with regard to your former way of life, to put off your old self, which is being corrupted by its deceitful desires; to be made new in the attitude of your minds; and to put on the new self, created to be like God in true righteousness and holiness.—Ephesians 4:22–24

Therefore we were buried with Him through baptism into death, that just as Christ was raised from the dead by the glory of the Father, even so we also should walk in newness of life.—Romans 6:4 nkjv

March 28

As you come to know Me more intimately, you grow increasingly aware of your sins. This presents you with a choice: to focus on your flaws and failures or to rejoice in My glorious gift of salvation. When you keep your focus on my sacrifice for your sins, you live in the joyful awareness that you are wonderfully loved. There is *no greater Love than Mine*, and it is yours forever! The best response to such a fathomless gift is to *love Me with all your heart*.

Tragically, many people think they have little—or even nothing—for Me to forgive. They've been deceived by the prevailing lie that there is no absolute truth. They believe good and evil are relative terms, so they see no need for a Savior. These deluded ones do not seek My forgiveness, and their sins remain unpardoned. The evil one's deceptions have darkened their minds. But *I am the Light of the world*, and My Light can shine through you into their lives. Because you are My follower, *you never walk in darkness—you have the Light of Life*!

But I trust in your unfailing love; my heart rejoices in your salvation. I will sing to the Lord, for he has been good to me.—Psalm 13:5–6

"Greater love has no one than this, than to lay down one's life for his friends."—John 15:13 nkjv

Jesus replied, "'Love the Lord your God with all your heart and with all your soul and with all your mind.' This is the first and greatest commandment. And the second is like it: 'Love your neighbor as yourself.'"—Matthew 22:37–39

When Jesus spoke again to the people, he said, "I am the light of the world. Whoever follows me will never walk in darkness, but will have the light of life."—John 8:12

March 29

IF YOU WALK IN THE LIGHT—living close to Me—*My blood continually cleanses you from all sin.* When you become aware of sins, I want you to confess them and seek My help in making needed changes. Nonetheless, your status with Me is not based on confessing your sins quickly enough or thoroughly enough. The only thing that keeps you right with Me is *My* perfect righteousness, which I gave you freely and permanently when you joined My eternal family. Since you are Mine—gloriously attired *in a robe of righteousness*—I invite you to come confidently into My bright Presence.

Walking in the Light of My Presence blesses you in many ways. Good things are better and bad things are more bearable when you share them with Me. As you delight in My Love-Light, you can love other believers more fully and *have fellowship* with them. You are less likely to stumble or fall, because sins are glaringly obvious in My holy Light. *Rejoice in My Name all day long,* enjoying My Presence and *exulting in My righteousness.*

But if we walk in the light as He is in the light, we have fellowship with one another, and the blood of Jesus Christ His Son cleanses us from all sin.—1 JOHN 1:7 NKJV

I delight greatly in the LORD; my soul rejoices in my God. For he has clothed me with garments of salvation and arrayed me in a robe of righteousness, as a bridegroom adorns his head like a priest, and as a bride adorns herself with her jewels.—ISAIAH 61:10

Blessed are those who have learned to acclaim you, who walk in the light of your presence, O LORD. They rejoice in your name all day long; they exult in your righteousness.—PSALM 89:15–16

March 30

I AM THE *LIGHT FROM ON HIGH* that dawns upon you, to give light to those who sit in darkness. Sometimes your circumstances are so difficult and confusing that you feel as if you're surrounded by darkness. Your mind offers up various solutions to your problems, but you've already tried them—without success. So you fret and wonder what to do next, feeling helpless and frustrated. At times like this, you need to look up and see My Light shining down upon you. Gaze at Me in childlike trust, resting in My Presence. Let go of problem-solving efforts for a while. *Cease striving, and know that I am God.*

As you relax in My Presence, remember that I am the *Prince of Peace*. The more of Me you absorb, the more peaceful you will be. Breathe Me in with each breath. After resting with Me for a while, tell Me about your troubles—trusting Me to help you with them. Stay close to Me, My child, and I will *guide your feet into the way of Peace.*

> *Because of and through the heart of tender mercy and loving-kindness of our God, a Light from on high will dawn upon us and visit [us] to shine upon and give light to those who sit in darkness and in the shadow of death, to direct and guide our feet in a straight line into the way of peace.* —LUKE 1:78–79 AMP

> *"Cease striving and know that I am God; I will be exalted among the nations, I will be exalted in the earth."* —PSALM 46:10 NASB

> *For to us a child is born, to us a son is given, and the government will be on his shoulders. And he will be called Wonderful Counselor, Mighty God, Everlasting Father, Prince of Peace.* —ISAIAH 9:6

March 31

REJOICE THAT YOUR NAME IS WRITTEN *in heaven*—in the book of Life. Because you are Mine, you have Joy that is independent of circumstances. You have received eternal Life that will *never* be taken away from you. *Those who are justified* (through faith in Me as their risen Savior) *are also glorified.* There is a very real sense in which you are already *seated with Me in the heavenly realms.*

Joy is the birthright of all who belong to Me. It can coexist with the most difficult, heartrending circumstances. So come to Me each morning with open hands and an open heart, saying, "Jesus, I receive your Joy." Then wait with Me while the Light of My Presence shines upon you—soaking into the depths of your inner being. Thus I strengthen you, preparing you for the day that stretches out before you.

As you journey through this day, return to Me for fresh Joy as often as you need. I am a God of unlimited abundance, so I always have more than enough for you.

> "However, do not rejoice that the spirits submit to you, but rejoice that your names are written in heaven."—LUKE 10:20

> *And those he predestined, he also called; those he called, he also justified; those he justified, he also glorified.*—ROMANS 8:30

> *And God raised us up with Christ and seated us with him in the heavenly realms in Christ Jesus.*—EPHESIANS 2:6

April

"The LORD bless you
and keep you;
the LORD make his face shine upon you
and be gracious to you."

NUMBERS 6:24–25

April 1

I DELIGHT IN BRIGHTENING your perspective. That's why I ventured into your world, knowing full well the terrible price I would pay. I came *to open eyes that are blind, to free captives from prison, and to release from the dungeon those who sit in darkness.* When you find yourself imprisoned by ingratitude, ask Me to open your eyes and release you from that dark place.

You live in an age of entitlement, so you need to counteract the messages proclaiming that you deserve more. One way is to jot down some things you're thankful for each day. This changes your focus from things you wish you had to blessings you already have.

Saturating your mind with Scripture can help you see from My infinitely wise perspective. My Word is *sharper than any double-edged sword*; I use it to perform spiritual surgery on *the thoughts and attitudes of your heart.* As Scripture lights up your point of view, I set you free from the dungeon of ingratitude, releasing you to enjoy the pleasures of a thankful heart.

> "To open eyes that are blind, to free captives from prison and to release from the dungeon those who sit in darkness."—ISAIAH 42:7

> *Your word is a lamp to my feet and a light for my path.*—PSALM 119:105

> *For the word of God is living and active. Sharper than any double-edged sword, it penetrates even to dividing soul and spirit, joints and marrow; it judges the thoughts and attitudes of the heart.*—HEBREWS 4:12

April 2

Believing in Me has many beneficial effects—including *Joy that is inexpressible and filled with Glory*! If something is inexpressible, it is too great and wondrous to be described. But it *can* be experienced. So come into My Presence expectantly; open wide your heart to Me. The Joy you can have in Me is triumphant and filled with heaven's Glory. I triumphed over sin and death once for all time! This opens up the way to heaven for all who believe in Me.

No matter how many difficulties you face, the *outcome of your faith—the salvation of your soul*—is secure. This is true for all who really trust Me as Savior-God. As you rejoice in your glorious heavenly future, *let your light shine before other people*. My Spirit, the Spirit of truth, will help you speak truth into others' lives. Align yourself with Me, for *I came into the world to testify to the truth*. Join Me in this quest so that *people living in darkness* can find Me and walk in My *great Light*.

Though you have not seen him, you love him. Though you do not now see him, you believe in him and rejoice with joy that is inexpressible and filled with glory, obtaining the outcome of your faith, the salvation of your souls.—1 Peter 1:8–9 esv

"Let your light so shine before men, that they may see your good works and glorify your Father in heaven."—Matthew 5:16 nkjv

"You are a king, then!" said Pilate. Jesus answered, "You are right in saying I am a king. In fact, for this reason I was born, and for this I came into the world, to testify to the truth. Everyone on the side of truth listens to me."—John 18:37

The people walking in darkness have seen a great light; on those living in the land of the shadow of death a light has dawned.—Isaiah 9:2

April 3

Look up to Me, beloved, for *My Face is shining upon you.* Be awed by the Glory of My holiness, and let the Light of My Love soak into your inner being. Remember that *I dwell in your heart through faith.* I am simultaneously Master of the universe—which I created and I control—and the Savior who lives inside you. My majestic greatness and My gentle humility combine to give you everything you need. You are rich beyond your wildest imagination!

Because you live in a terribly broken world, it can be hard to remember that you are royalty: adopted into the family of the *King of kings.* Your journey through this world may take you along paths of pain and problems, deserts of deprivation and distress. Do not be surprised by these fiery trials; rather, take them in stride, trusting in the One who never leaves your side. In due time I will take you into the realm of My Glory-Light where *there will be no more night.*

"The Lord bless you and keep you; the Lord make his face shine upon you and be gracious to you."—Numbers 6:24–25

I pray that out of his glorious riches he may strengthen you with power through his Spirit in your inner being, so that Christ may dwell in your hearts through faith. And I pray that you, being rooted and established in love . . . —Ephesians 3:16–17

And He has on His robe and on His thigh a name written: KING OF KINGS AND LORD OF LORDS.—Revelation 19:16 nkjv

On no day will its gates ever be shut, for there will be no night there.—Revelation 21:25

APRIL 4

YOUR TIMES ARE IN MY HANDS. My holy hands are absolutely capable of caring for you and meeting your needs. I want you to relax in My sovereign watchcare, trusting Me to do what is best. Because I am totally trustworthy, it's safe to commit both the "whats" and the "whens" of your life into My care.

As long as you remain on this side of heaven, you will have to submit to the reality of time. Consider the following examples: A bride whose wedding date has been set may yearn to fast-forward to that magical day. But her longing does not change the passage of time; she must wait. Someone who is suffering may yearn for relief—and want it instantly—but he also must wait. I, however, live above the tyranny of time; I am its Master. If you're struggling with having to wait for something, turn to Me in trusting acceptance. Don't fight against what you cannot change. Instead, rejoice in the knowledge that the Master of time understands your struggles and loves you *with an everlasting Love*.

> *But I trust in you, O LORD; I say, "You are my God." My times are in your hands; deliver me from the hands of my enemies and from those who pursue me.*—PSALM 31:14–15

> *Trust in Him at all times, you people; pour out your heart before Him; God is a refuge for us.*—PSALM 62:8 NKJV

> *The LORD has appeared of old to me, saying: "Yes, I have loved you with an everlasting love; therefore with lovingkindness I have drawn you."*—JEREMIAH 31:3 NKJV

April 5

I WANT YOU TO DRAW WATER *from the wells of salvation with Joy*! Knowing that I have saved you forever from your sins can be a wellspring of Joy in your daily life. Because you know Me as your Savior, you have inside you *a spring of water welling up to eternal life*. Ponder the enormity of this amazing gift, and rejoice! Try to begin and end each day thanking Me for all I have provided.

My gift of salvation is designed to bless not only you but the people around you. As you trust in Me, *streams of living water will flow from within you*. Ask My Spirit, who dwells inside of you, to bless others through you—flowing into their lives. One way to make this request is to pray: "Holy Spirit, think through me; live through me; love through me." While His streams of living water are passing through you into the hearts of other people, I fill both them *and* you with Joy!

With joy you will draw water from the wells of salvation. —ISAIAH 12:3

Jesus answered, "Everyone who drinks this water will be thirsty again, but whoever drinks the water I give him will never thirst. Indeed, the water I give him will become in him a spring of water welling up to eternal life." —JOHN 4:13–14

"Whoever believes in me, as the Scripture has said, streams of living water will flow from within him." —JOHN 7:38

April 6

Even though your journey often feels haphazard, *your steps are directed by Me.* When the path that lies before you is veiled in uncertainty, the best thing you can do is cling to Me. Picture a young child walking along busy city streets with a trustworthy adult. The child may feel overwhelmed by all the sensory stimulation—fearful of getting separated and losing her way. However, if she keeps holding onto the adult's hand, she will come safely to her destination. Similarly, as you clasp My hand for help and guidance, you are ultimately safe.

Though you may not know the way you should go, you *do* know the One who is *the Way.* Because I am sovereign over your life, I *direct your steps and make them sure* even when they seem random to you. Talk with Me about your uncertainty, your fear of making wrong decisions. The most important choice you make moment by moment is to stay in communication with Me. *This* is how you cling to Me. This is how you trust My guiding Presence to keep you safe.

A man's steps are directed by the Lord. *How then can anyone understand his own way?*—Proverbs 20:24

Jesus said to him, "I am the way, the truth, and the life. No one comes to the Father except through Me."—John 14:6 nkjv

A man's mind plans his way, but the Lord directs his steps and makes them sure.—Proverbs 16:9 amp

For we walk by faith, not by sight.—2 Corinthians 5:7 nkjv

April 7

I give eternal Life to you, and you will never perish; no one will snatch you out of My hand. This is astonishingly good news for all who know Me as Savior. Your promised inheritance is far more glorious than anything you can imagine! The gift of eternal Life provides a Light that shines on even in your darkest days. So let this brightness beckon you onward, protecting you from discouragement. Refuse to let hard circumstances or the wickedness of this world drag you down. Instead, look ahead to the Glory that awaits you. See it sparkling in the distance, just beyond the horizon.

You may have to go through some deep waters on your journey, but remember: *I will be with you when you pass through the waters. They will not sweep over you.* Keep holding onto My hand in trusting dependence—confident that I love you and *nothing will be able to separate you from Me.* Rather than dreading the challenging times ahead of you, seek to enjoy the adventure of journeying with Me through your life.

> "My sheep hear My voice, and I know them, and they follow Me; and I give eternal life to them, and they will never perish."—John 10:27–28 nasb

> Praise be to the God and Father of our Lord Jesus Christ! In his great mercy he has given us new birth into a living hope through the resurrection of Jesus Christ from the dead, and into an inheritance that can never perish, spoil or fade.—1 Peter 1:3–4

> "When you pass through the waters, I will be with you; and when you pass through the rivers, they will not sweep over you."—Isaiah 43:2

> For I am convinced that neither death nor life, neither angels nor demons, neither the present nor the future, nor any powers, neither height nor depth, nor anything else in all creation, will be able to separate us from the love of God that is in Christ Jesus our Lord.—Romans 8:38–39

April 8

ALWAYS BE PREPARED to give an answer to everyone who asks you the reason for the hope you have. It is easier to obey this command when you're well rested and your life is flowing smoothly. It's quite another matter when you're feeling exhausted and frazzled. Yet *this* may be the time when your hopeful answer will make the greatest impact. So make it your goal to be prepared *always*. You also need to be ready to answer *everyone* who asks you the reason for your hopefulness. It is tempting to judge some people as poor candidates for learning about Me and what I mean to you. But only *I* know their hearts and the plans I have for them.

Essential preparation for giving a good answer is living in awareness of My Presence—trusting Me fully as your Hope. This will steady you as you deal with the frequent ups and downs of your life. Whenever you're struggling, encourage yourself by pondering truths of the gospel and by gazing at Me, your glorious Hope.

But in your hearts set apart Christ as Lord. Always be prepared to give an answer to everyone who asks you to give the reason for the hope that you have. But do this with gentleness and respect.—1 PETER 3:15

And hope does not disappoint, because the love of God has been poured out within our hearts through the Holy Spirit who was given to us.—ROMANS 5:5 NASB

One thing I ask of the LORD, this is what I seek: that I may dwell in the house of the LORD all the days of my life, to gaze upon the beauty of the LORD and to seek him in his temple.—PSALM 27:4

April 9

Be willing to follow My lead, beloved. Open yourself more fully to Me and My way for you. Don't get so focused on what you want that you miss the things I've prepared for you. Relax with Me while *I transform you by the renewal of your mind*—working My newness into your innermost being. Trust Me enough to let go of your expectations and demands. *Be still, and know that I am God.*

Sometimes you obstruct the very things you desire by trying too hard to make things go according to your will and timing. I know the desires of your heart, and I also know the best way to reach those goals. Instead of striving to be in control so you can get what you want, *seek My Face*. Talk with Me openly, and rest for a while in My Presence. When you are feeling more refreshed, invite Me to show you the way forward. *I will guide you along the best pathway for your life. I will advise you and watch over you.*

> *Do not conform any longer to the pattern of this world, but be transformed by the renewing of your mind. Then you will be able to test and approve what God's will is—his good, pleasing and perfect will.* —Romans 12:2

> *"Be still, and know that I am God; I will be exalted among the nations, I will be exalted in the earth!"* —Psalm 46:10 nkjv

> *Seek the Lord and His strength; seek His face continually.* —1 Chronicles 16:11 nasb

> *The Lord says, "I will guide you along the best pathway for your life. I will advise you and watch over you."* —Psalm 32:8 nlt

April 10

Great is My Love, *reaching to the heavens; My faithfulness reaches to the skies*. You can feel wonderfully secure in Love that has no boundaries or limits. My faithfulness also has no bounds.

Respond to these wondrous gifts with worship. The more you praise Me, the more you can *reflect My Glory* to other people. This is the work of the Holy Spirit, who is *transforming you into My likeness with ever-increasing Glory*. As you draw near Me through worship, I change you profoundly, equipping you to make Me known to others.

My Love not only reaches to the heavens but descends upon you from heavenly realms. Keep looking up to Me, beloved. See Me smiling on you in radiant approval. My limitless Love falls continually upon you, like heavenly snowflakes that melt into your upturned face. No matter how distressing your circumstances, this Love is sufficient to sustain you. Someday you will even ascend to heaven on it. I eagerly anticipate the time when *I will take you into Glory*—to be with Me forever!

> *I will praise you, O Lord. . . . For great is your love, reaching to the heavens; your faithfulness reaches to the skies.*—Psalm 57:9–10

> *And we, who with unveiled faces all reflect the Lord's glory, are being transformed into his likeness with ever-increasing glory, which comes from the Lord, who is the Spirit.*—2 Corinthians 3:18

> *"The Lord make His face to shine upon and enlighten you and be gracious (kind, merciful, and giving favor) to you; the Lord lift up His [approving] countenance upon you and give you peace."*—Numbers 6:25–26 AMP

> *Yet I am always with you; you hold me by my right hand. You guide me with your counsel, and afterward you will take me into glory.*—Psalm 73:23–24

April 11

SEEK TO THINK MY THOUGHTS more and more. Enlist My Spirit's help in this endeavor, *for the mind controlled by the Spirit is Life and Peace.*

When the worries of this world are pressing in on you, take time to think things out in My Presence. Rest in Me, beloved. Let My *everlasting arms* enfold you in Peace. Take a break from your concerns, and *fix your thoughts on Me.* Intersperse quietness with reading Scripture and speaking or singing praises to Me. You can also use Bible verses in your prayers to Me. When your thoughts and prayers are permeated with Scripture, you're able to have more confidence in them.

I want you to *be transformed by the renewal of your mind.* The world exerts massive amounts of pressure on you through ever-present electronic communications. Instead of letting the world and its gadgets shape you, invite Me to transform the way you think. As I renew your mind, your ideals and attitudes will reflect *Me* more and more.

The mind of sinful man is death, but the mind controlled by the Spirit is life and peace.—ROMANS 8:6

The eternal God is your refuge, and underneath are the everlasting arms; He will thrust out the enemy from before you, and will say, "Destroy!"—DEUTERONOMY 33:27 NKJV

Therefore, holy brothers, who share in the heavenly calling, fix your thoughts on Jesus, the apostle and high priest whom we confess.—HEBREWS 3:1

Do not be conformed to this world, but be transformed by the renewal of your mind, that by testing you may discern what is the will of God, what is good and acceptable and perfect.—ROMANS 12:2 ESV

April 12

YOUR RELATIONSHIP WITH ME TRANSCENDS all your circumstances. This is why you can praise Me and enjoy My Presence in the midst of the darkest difficulties. To find Me in such times, you have to really exert your faith; but I am always near.

As a Christian, you live on two planes simultaneously: the natural world, where adverse situations abound; and the supernatural world, where I reign supreme. Your trust-muscles empower you to experience My Presence even in your hardest times. In fact, trials can both strengthen your faith and help you discern how much you actually trust Me.

I want you to work on strengthening your trust-muscles. One way is to fill your mind and heart with Scripture. Another is to *seek My Face continually*. Instead of getting stuck in introspection, turn your thoughts toward Me. Make it a practice to affirm your faith in Me frequently, whether you're feeling confident or inadequate. Remember that your adequacy rests in your relationship with Me. I make you *ready for anything and equal to anything* by *infusing inner strength into you*!

Consider it pure joy, my brothers, whenever you face trials of many kinds, because you know that the testing of your faith develops perseverance. —JAMES 1:2–3

Seek the LORD and His strength; seek His face continually. —PSALM 105:4 NASB

I have strength for all things in Christ Who empowers me [I am ready for anything and equal to anything through Him Who infuses inner strength into me; I am self-sufficient in Christ's sufficiency]. —PHILIPPIANS 4:13 AMP

April 13

Seek to include Me in more of your moments by living in joyful dependence on Me. *I am with you, watching over you* continually. Nothing you do is beyond My sight. No task or opportunity is too small to ask for My help. Actually, your very existence—including each breath you breathe—depends on My sustaining Power.

When a difficult task lies before you, you usually remember to pray about it, both before you begin and throughout the challenging endeavor. You punctuate your work with brief prayers such as: "Help me, Lord" and "Thank You, Jesus." These communications increase both your reliance on Me and your gratitude for My continual Presence. When you're involved in less challenging activities, however, you often forget about Me and plunge ahead on your own. You may experience some degree of success, but you miss a far greater blessing that was available had you sought My help. Or you may fail miserably, whereas depending on Me would have brought success. So rely on Me in *all* you do; I have blessings waiting for you.

"I am with you and will watch over you wherever you go, and I will bring you back to this land. I will not leave you until I have done what I have promised you."—Genesis 28:15

The Son is the radiance of God's glory and the exact representation of his being, sustaining all things by his powerful word. After he had provided purification for sins, he sat down at the right hand of the Majesty in heaven.—Hebrews 1:3

In all your ways acknowledge Him, and He will make your paths straight.—Proverbs 3:6 nasb

April 14

You are not your own, for you were bought with a price. And that price was exorbitant—My very Life! I went through excruciating pain and humiliation as I sacrificed Myself for your sins. This was a gift of infinite value—an act of indescribable Love. However, only those who recognize their sinfulness, their need for a Savior, can receive this astonishing gift of Love. Hear My invitation calling out: *"Come to Me, all you who are weary and burdened, and I will give you rest."* Sin is a terrible, crushing burden, but I have paid the price *in full* to remove it from you forever.

When you awaken each morning, say to yourself: "I am not my own. I belong to Jesus." Then keep in mind Whose you are as you make your way through the day, especially as you make plans and decisions. Knowing that you belong to Me helps you keep your feet on *the path of Peace*. This knowledge meets deep-seated needs. You can find spiritual and emotional security by remembering that you are *Mine*—My beloved.

Or do you not know that your body is a temple of the Holy Spirit within you, whom you have from God? You are not your own, for you were bought with a price. So glorify God in your body.—1 Corinthians 6:19–20 esv

"Come to me, all you who are weary and burdened, and I will give you rest."—Matthew 11:28

And you, my child, will be called a prophet of the Most High; for you will go on before the Lord to prepare the way for him, to give his people the knowledge of salvation through the forgiveness of their sins, because of the tender mercy of our God, by which the rising sun will come to us from heaven to shine on those living in darkness and in the shadow of death, to guide our feet into the path of peace.—Luke 1:76–79

April 15

You can trust the One who died for you. In this world of spin and scams, people often find it hard to believe anyone. They talk about requiring others to "earn" their trust by proving themselves. *I am the quintessential Person who has earned the right to be trusted.* For your sake, I left the glorious perfection of heaven and began life in your world as a helpless, stable-born infant. I resisted all temptations for thirty-three years so that My sacrifice for sinners would be sufficient. I lived a perfect life and freely gave My body to be tortured and executed—to pay the full penalty for sin. As a result of My death and resurrection, *whoever believes in Me has eternal Life!*

I want you to rely confidently on Me—not only as your Savior but also as the God-Friend who is taking care of you. I have already proved how trustworthy I am. Now I invite you to relax in My loving Presence and confide in Me. Tell Me your hopes and fears. *Cast all your anxiety on Me because I care for you.*

For you know the grace of our Lord Jesus Christ, that though He was rich, yet for your sakes He became poor, that you through His poverty might become rich. —2 Corinthians 8:9 nkjv

Whoever believes in the Son has eternal life, but whoever rejects the Son will not see life, for God's wrath remains on him. —John 3:36

Cast all your anxiety on him because he cares for you. —1 Peter 5:7

April 16

This is the day that I have made. I invite you to rejoice in this day as you share it with Me. The more of Me you have in your life, the more joyful you will be.

Invite Me into your moments by talking with Me about everything that concerns you, whatever is on your mind. Your conversations with Me will radically change the way you think. If you've been preoccupied with something trivial, bringing Me into your thoughts helps you recognize how silly they are. If you're stuck in the past—yearning to change what has happened—My Presence lovingly draws you back into the present. Whatever you're facing, I can help you handle it better.

Seek to find Joy in this day I have made for you. I've hidden small pleasures along your pathway. Search for them, and thank Me for each one you find. Many of the little things that delight your heart are unique to you. I know you so intimately that I can provide just what you need to make you glad. *Rejoice*, beloved!

> *This is the day the Lord has made; we will rejoice and be glad in it.*—Psalm 118:24 NKJV

> *Be joyful always; pray continually; give thanks in all circumstances, for this is God's will for you in Christ Jesus.*—1 Thessalonians 5:16–18

O Lord, You have searched me and known me. You know when I sit down and when I rise up; You understand my thought from afar. You scrutinize my path and my lying down, and are intimately acquainted with all my ways.—Psalm 139:1–3 NASB

April 17

LOOK TO ME AS YOUR JOYFUL FOCUS. You were *made* for Joy, and I am the boundless, overflowing Source of delight in your life.

I never run out of anything because I am infinite. If you draw too much from other pleasures, they will eventually let you down. The nature of addiction is that you need more and more of a substance to get the same effect as before. This is a self-destructive trap. However, the more you make *Me* your Focus, the less dependent you are on other things. You can still enjoy the good gifts I provide, but you don't need to grasp onto them, trying to milk every possible bit of pleasure from them.

Learn to fix your gaze on Me even as the world parades before you. Whisper My Name in remembrance that I am near, and tell Me about what troubles you. Thank Me for the things you enjoy—loved ones, shelter, food, sunlight, starlight, and *especially* My glorious Presence. *Seek My Face* and My will; *look to Me and My strength.*

Looking to Jesus, the founder and perfecter of our faith, who for the joy that was set before him endured the cross, despising the shame, and is seated at the right hand of the throne of God. —HEBREWS 12:2 ESV

"I have told you this so that my joy may be in you and that your joy may be complete." —JOHN 15:11

Now to the King eternal, immortal, invisible, to God who alone is wise, be honor and glory forever and ever. Amen. —1 TIMOTHY 1:17 NKJV

Look to the LORD and his strength; seek his face always. —PSALM 105:4

April 18

Thank Me for the glorious gift of forgiveness. I am your Savior-God, and I alone can give you this blessing. I went to exorbitant expense to procure this gift for you. You receive forgiveness and become My child by receiving *Me* and *believing in My Name*. This Name, Jesus, means *the Lord saves*. To receive this gift of salvation, you need to trust Me as your only Hope—the One who delivers you from all your sins.

There is no condemnation for those who are in Me. I want you to enjoy the wonder of walking through your life as My follower—totally forgiven! The best response to this wondrous gift is to live in gratitude, seeking to please Me above all else. You don't need to do good things to secure My Love, because it's already yours. Just let your desire to please Me flow readily out of your grateful heart. Thanking Me frequently will help you stay close to Me, ready to follow wherever I lead. Rejoice, beloved, for *through Me the law of the Spirit of Life has set you free*!

> Yet to all who received him, to those who believed in his name,
> he gave the right to become children of God.—John 1:12

> And there is salvation in no one else; for there is no other name under heaven
> that has been given among men by which we must be saved.—Acts 4:12 NASB

> Therefore, there is now no condemnation for those who are in Christ
> Jesus, because through Christ Jesus the law of the Spirit of life set
> me free from the law of sin and death.—Romans 8:1–2

April 19

You love Me because I first loved you. I had My eye on you long before you were interested in Me. I noticed everything about you and followed you everywhere. I orchestrated circumstances and events in your life to help you see your need of Me. I provided people and teaching that told you the truth about Me in ways you could understand. My Spirit worked within you to make you spiritually alive—enabling you to *receive Me and believe in My Name.* All of this flowed out of My deep, powerful affection for you. *I have loved you with an everlasting Love!*

The more you realize the immensity of My ardor for you, the more fully you can love *Me*. This enables you to grow, little by little, into the person I designed you to be. As you spend time in My tender Presence, it becomes easier for you to delight in Me and to show kindness to other people. When you are with others, ask Me to help you love them—with *My* Love.

We love Him because He first loved us. —1 John 4:19 NKJV

Yet to all who received him, to those who believed in his name, he gave the right to become children of God. —John 1:12

The Lord appeared to us in the past, saying: "I have loved you with an everlasting love; I have drawn you with loving-kindness." —Jeremiah 31:3

April 20

THIS DAY OF LIFE IS A PRECIOUS GIFT from Me. Treat it as the treasure it is by prayerfully prioritizing. As you look into the day that stretches out before you, *seek My Face* to help you discern what is most important. Set priorities according to My will, and use them to guide you as you go along your pathway. This practice will help you make good choices about the use of your time and energy. When you reach the end of the day, you can feel at peace about the things you have done—and also the things you have *not* done.

I encourage you to invite Me into everything you do. The briefest prayer, "Help me, Lord," is sufficient to involve Me in your activities. I delight in your acknowledgment that you need Me continually. And I want *you* to delight in your neediness, for it is a strong link to My radiant Presence. Although living in a dependent mode is countercultural, it is a blessed way to live—rejoicing in the Glory of My Presence.

*This is the day the L*ORD *has made; we will*
rejoice and be glad in it.—P SALM 118:24 NKJV

*Glory in his holy name; let the hearts of those who seek the L*ORD *rejoice. Look*
*to the L*ORD *and his strength; seek his face always.*—1 CHRONICLES 16:10–11

"I am the vine; you are the branches. If a man remains in me and I in him,
he will bear much fruit; apart from me you can do nothing."—JOHN 15:5

To him who is able to keep you from falling and to present you before his
glorious presence without fault and with great joy . . . —JUDE V. 24

April 21

The prospect of the righteous is Joy. This means that your prospects are excellent, beloved. I lived a perfectly righteous life for you and died in your place, enduring the full punishment for your sins. This made it possible to clothe you in My own *robe of righteousness*. I invite you to wear the *garments of salvation* with overflowing gratitude and Joy.

A thankful, joyful attitude will help you live well, according to My will. Beginning your day in this positive frame of mind sets your feet on the right path. Thankfulness increases your Joy, which in turn augments your gratitude. There is delightful synergy between these two attitudes. When your ability to be joyful seems to be flagging, energize it with a hearty dose of thanksgiving! Reading psalms can help you with this, and so can singing hymns or praise songs. Making a list—mentally or on paper—of blessings in your life is another effective way to give thanks. I want you to remember the *great things I have done for you*; this will *fill you with Joy*.

> The prospect of the righteous is joy, but the hopes of the wicked come to nothing.—Proverbs 10:28

> I delight greatly in the Lord; my soul rejoices in my God. For he has clothed me with garments of salvation and arrayed me in a robe of righteousness, as a bridegroom adorns his head like a priest, and as a bride adorns herself with her jewels.—Isaiah 61:10

> I will sing to the Lord, for he has been good to me.—Psalm 13:6

> The Lord has done great things for us, and we are filled with joy.—Psalm 126:3

April 22

Do not worry about tomorrow! This is a most gracious command. I understand human frailty; I know that *you are dust*. This command is not meant to burden you or condemn you. It is meant to set you free from worldly cares.

Just before I gave this directive to My followers, I spoke about how to enjoy such freedom. Remember that *your heavenly Father knows what you need*. As you *seek first His kingdom and His righteousness*, your perspective changes. Worldly pursuits become secondary to matters of unseen, eternal reality—the advancement of My kingdom. So put more time and energy into developing your relationship with Me, seeking not only My Presence but also My will. Be ready to follow wherever I lead. I will guide you along adventurous paths that can fill your life with meaning.

I created you to enjoy My Presence in the present—entrusting your future into My care and keeping. As you *delight yourself in Me, I give you the desires of your heart.*

> "For the pagans run after all these things, and your heavenly Father knows that you need them. But seek first his kingdom and his righteousness, and all these things will be given to you as well. Therefore do not worry about tomorrow, for tomorrow will worry about itself. Each day has enough trouble of its own."—Matthew 6:32–34

> For He knows our frame; He remembers that we are dust.—Psalm 103:14 NKJV

> Delight yourself in the Lord and he will give you the desires of your heart.—Psalm 37:4

April 23

I AM THE ONE AND ONLY *who came from the Father, full of grace and truth.* I came from Him and I returned to Him because I am God—the second Person of the Trinity.

I entered your world to provide a way for you to have a living, eternal relationship with your Father-God. People who do not know Me have often stated that there are many ways to God. But that claim is absolutely untrue. *I am the Way, the Truth, and the Life. No one comes to the Father except through Me.*

I come to *you*, beloved, *full of grace.* Because you have trusted Me to save you from your sins through My sacrificial death on the cross, you have nothing to fear. You don't need to dread failure or performing below expectations. Since I am your Savior—and you cannot save yourself—your security rests in My grace. Rejoice that I am both faithful and sufficient. In spite of all the trouble in this world, *in Me you may have Peace. I have overcome the world*!

> *The Word became flesh and made his dwelling among us. We have seen his glory, the glory of the One and Only, who came from the Father, full of grace and truth.*—JOHN 1:14

> *Jesus said to him, "I am the way, the truth, and the life. No one comes to the Father except through Me."*—JOHN 14:6 NKJV

> *"I have told you these things, so that in me you may have peace. In this world you will have trouble. But take heart! I have overcome the world."*—JOHN 16:33

April 24

I AM A SHIELD for all who take refuge in Me. On some days you feel your need of My shielding Presence more than on other days. At times you're not even aware that you need protection, but I am continually close by—watching over you. I delight in being your Protector, so you can always find shelter in Me.

One of the best ways to make Me *your Refuge* is to spend focused time with Me and *pour out your heart to Me*. Tell Me about the things that have wounded you: the unfair things done to you or said about you. Trust that I care about you and want to heal your hurts. Also, I know the truth about everything; My view of you is untainted by innuendos and half-truths.

Knowing that I understand you completely is vital to your healing. It is also crucial for forgiving those who have wounded you. Forgiveness is usually a process, so keep at it till you are free. Rejoice in Me, beloved, for I came to *make you free*.

> *As for God, his way is perfect; the word of the LORD is flawless. He is a shield for all who take refuge in him.*—PSALM 18:30

> *Trust in him at all times, O people; pour out your hearts to him, for God is our refuge.*—PSALM 62:8

> *"And you shall know the truth, and the truth shall make you free."*—JOHN 8:32 NKJV

April 25

I AM THE TRUTH—unchanging, transcendent Truth! Many, many people believe that truth is relative—to the situation, the person, the day. But only absolute truth can provide a firm foundation for your life. Everything else is shifting sand.

Because I am inerrant Truth, *all the treasures of wisdom and knowledge* are hidden in Me. You can find everything you need in your relationship with Me. I provide the foundation on which to build your life, and I Myself *am* Life. So the closer you live to Me, the more alive you will feel!

Many people struggle with issues of identity, wondering who they really are and what they're supposed to be doing with their lives. But the more fully you know Me—*the Truth*—the better you can understand yourself and the meaning of your life. So make every effort to know Me as I truly am. Also, *be prepared* to tell others about the Savior-God who has redeemed you and *set you free*.

> *Jesus said to him, "I am the way, the truth, and the life. No one comes to the Father except through Me."*—JOHN 14:6 NKJV

> *My purpose is that they may be encouraged in heart and united in love, so that they may have the full riches of complete understanding, in order that they may know the mystery of God, namely, Christ, in whom are hidden all the treasures of wisdom and knowledge.*—COLOSSIANS 2:2–3

> *But in your hearts set apart Christ as Lord. Always be prepared to give an answer to everyone who asks you to give the reason for the hope that you have. But do this with gentleness and respect.*—1 PETER 3:15

> *"Then you will know the truth, and the truth will set you free."*—JOHN 8:32

April 26

There will be no night in heaven, *for the Glory of God gives it Light.* You will not need nighttime for sleeping, because your glorified body will always be full of energy. Tiredness is one of the main things people have to contend with in this world, especially as they grow old or sickly. But there will be no fatigue in heaven and therefore no need for sleep.

The Glory-Light of heaven is perfect and brilliant, without a speck of darkness in it. There will be no sin there—nothing to hide. You will see everything through glorified eyes, as you've never seen before. Colors will be more vivid; faces will be more vibrant. You will be able to look fully into *My* Face. Your experience will be far better than that of Moses, who had to hide in the cleft of a rock while My Glory passed by. He was allowed to see only My back, but you will have no such limitations. In heaven *you will see Me face to Face*—in all My Glory!

> *The city does not need the sun or the moon to shine on it, for the glory of God gives it light, and the Lamb is its lamp. . . . On no day will its gates ever be shut, for there will be no night there.*—Revelation 21:23, 25

> *This is the message we have heard from him and declare to you: God is light; in him there is no darkness at all.*—1 John 1:5

> *"When my glory passes by, I will put you in a cleft in the rock and cover you with my hand until I have passed by. Then I will remove my hand and you will see my back; but my face must not be seen."*—Exodus 33:22–23

> *For now we see in a mirror, dimly, but then face to face. Now I know in part, but then I shall know just as I also am known.*—1 Corinthians 13:12 NKJV

April 27

You are troubled by fear of failure, but My Love for you will never fail. Let Me describe what I see as I gaze at you, beloved. You look regal, for I have clothed you in My righteousness and *crowned you with glory and honor.* You *are radiant*, especially when you are looking at Me. You are beautiful as you *reflect My Glory* back to Me. In fact, you delight Me so much that *I rejoice over you with shouts of Joy*! This is how you appear through My grace-filled vision.

Because I am infinite, I can see you as you are now and as you will be in heaven—simultaneously. Viewing you in the present, I work with you on things you need to change. Seeing you from the heavenly perspective, I love you as if you were already perfect.

I want you to learn to look at yourself—and others—through the lens of My unfailing Love. As you persevere in this, you will gradually find it easier to love yourself *and* others.

You made him a little lower than the angels; you crowned him with glory and honor.—Hebrews 2:7

Those who look to him are radiant, and their faces shall never be ashamed.—Psalm 34:5 esv

And we, who with unveiled faces all reflect the Lord's glory, are being transformed into his likeness with ever-increasing glory, which comes from the Lord, who is the Spirit.—2 Corinthians 3:18

"The Lord your God is in your midst, a victorious warrior. He will exult over you with joy, He will be quiet in His love, He will rejoice over you with shouts of joy."—Zephaniah 3:17 nasb

April 28

Trust in Me at all times. Pour out your heart to Me, for I am your refuge. The more you rely on Me, the more effectively I can help you. Trusting Me is appropriate for all circumstances: joyful and sorrowful, peaceful and stressful. In fact, things that cause you stress can serve as reminders to *seek My Face*. I want you to remember that I am with you, taking care of you, even when life hurts. Talk with Me about your troubles and leave them with Me. Then rest in My Presence while I go to work on your behalf.

Tell yourself the truth about Me. Use words of Scripture to describe Me: "You are *my refuge and my fortress, my God, in whom I trust.*" I am indeed a refuge—a safe place to find shelter in the storms of life. Speaking or singing such truths is an effective way to draw near Me. Your mind usually has several thoughts or thought-fragments passing through it at once. Instead of just thinking about Me, speak out loud; this gives focus to your thoughts—and to your trust in Me.

Trust in him at all times, O people; pour out your hearts to him, for God is our refuge.—Psalm 62:8

Seek the Lord and His strength; seek His face evermore!—1 Chronicles 16:11 nkjv

Cast all your anxiety on him because he cares for you.—1 Peter 5:7

I will say of the Lord, "He is my refuge and my fortress, my God, in whom I trust."—Psalm 91:2

April 29

I AM WORTHY of all your confidence, all your trust. So refuse to let world events spook you. Instead, pour your energy into trusting Me and looking for evidence of My Presence in the world. Whisper My Name to reconnect your heart and mind to Me quickly. *I am near to all who call upon Me.* Let Me wrap you up in My abiding Presence and comfort you with My Peace.

Remember that I am both loving and faithful. *My Love reaches to the heavens, My faithfulness to the skies*! This means you can never come to the end of My Love. It is limitless and everlasting. Moreover, you can stand on the Rock of My faithfulness, no matter what circumstances you may be facing.

People routinely put their confidence in their abilities, education, wealth, or appearance. But I urge you to place your confidence fully in Me—the Savior whose sacrificial death and miraculous resurrection opened the way for you into *eternal Glory*!

> *The Lord is near to all who call upon Him, to all who call upon Him in truth.* —Psalm 145:18 nkjv

> *Your love, O Lord, reaches to the heavens, your faithfulness to the skies.* —Psalm 36:5

> *For our light and momentary troubles are achieving for us an eternal glory that far outweighs them all.* —2 Corinthians 4:17

April 30

Let Me satisfy you in the morning with My unfailing Love, that you may sing for Joy and be glad all your days. People seek satisfaction in a vast variety of hurtful ways, many of which are addicting. Even good things can fail to satisfy you if you elevate them above Me. So come to Me each morning with your emptiness and longings. Sit quietly in My Presence, communing with Me. Invite Me to fill you up to the full with My limitless Love. Ponder *how wide and long and high and deep* is this vast ocean of blessing.

Finding your satisfaction in Me above all else provides a firm foundation for your life. Building on this solid foundation enables you to be joyful and glad as you go through your days. You will still encounter hardships because you live in such a broken world. However, I will lovingly guide you along your way as you cling to Me in trust. Then your life will be meaningful and satisfying while you're traveling toward your ultimate goal: the gates of Glory!

> *Satisfy us in the morning with your unfailing love, that we may sing for joy and be glad all our days.*—Psalm 90:14

> *And I pray that you, being rooted and established in love, may have power, together with all the saints, to grasp how wide and long and high and deep is the love of Christ, and to know this love that surpasses knowledge—that you may be filled to the measure of all the fullness of God.*—Ephesians 3:17–19

> *You will guide me with Your counsel, and afterward receive me to glory.*—Psalm 73:24 nkjv

May

"I came that they may have and enjoy life, and have it in abundance (to the full, till it overflows)."

JOHN 10:10 AMP

May 1

THE PRESENT MOMENT is the point at which time intersects eternity. It is also the place where you can encounter *Me*—your eternal Savior. So keep your thoughts focused on the present as much as you can, enjoying My Presence here and now.

Invite Me into whatever you are engaged in. Ask Me to help you *do your work heartily.* Working collaboratively with Me lightens your load and enables you to be more effective. Share with Me not only your work but also your leisure—thanking Me for both. When something upsets you, don't let fearful or obsessive thoughts take over your mind. Instead, talk with Me about whatever is troubling you. Then *cast all your anxiety on Me,* knowing that *I care for you.*

If you ask, I will open your eyes and awaken your heart so you can see more fully all that the present contains. I delight in meeting with you in your wide-awake heart! *I came into the world so that you may have life in abundance—till it overflows.*

> *Whatever you do, do your work heartily, as for the Lord rather than for men.*—COLOSSIANS 3:23 NASB

> *Cast all your anxiety on him because he cares for you.*—1 PETER 5:7

> *"The thief comes only in order to steal and kill and destroy. I came that they may have and enjoy life, and have it in abundance (to the full, till it overflows)."*—JOHN 10:10 AMP

May 2

TRUSTING ME is the alternative to falling into despair or escaping into unreality. When you're in the midst of adversity, it can be hard to think clearly. Yet this is when it's vitally important to make wise decisions. Sometimes it's as if choices are swirling around you, waiting for you to grab onto the right one. However, there is *one* choice that is always appropriate and always effective: the decision to *trust Me with all your heart and mind*.

If you're on the verge of sliding into the depths of despair, stop and declare your trust in Me. Whisper it, speak it, shout it! Spend some time thinking about all the reasons you have for *being confident in Me*. Remember and rejoice in My endless, *unfailing Love* for you.

If you've been numbing your pain through denial of reality, expressing your trust can bring you into contact with *ultimate* Reality—Me! Confide in Me, beloved, for I am infinitely knowing. I understand everything about your circumstances, and *I will help you*.

Lean on, trust in, and be confident in the Lord with all your heart and mind and do not rely on your own insight or understanding.—PROVERBS 3:5 AMP

But I am like an olive tree flourishing in the house of God; I trust in God's unfailing love for ever and ever.—PSALM 52:8

"For I am the LORD, your God, who takes hold of your right hand and says to you, Do not fear; I will help you."—ISAIAH 41:13

May 3

It is only as *I work* that anything really works well. When what you are doing is pleasing to Me, I come alongside you—helping in your endeavor. Sometimes you're aware of My empowering Presence, and at other times you are not. But the more you turn to Me for guidance and help, the more blessings I shower on you. Some of the blessings are work-oriented; others are matters of the heart. Awareness of My Presence increases your sense of security and fills you with Joy.

I am training you to look for Me wherever you are, in all situations. There will be times when you have to look *through* your circumstances to find signs of My radiant Presence. Imagine gazing through a dirty window into a gorgeous, sun-drenched garden. If you focus on the dirt that's on the glass, you'll miss the exquisite beauty of the garden. Just as you can train your eyes to see the splendor beyond the window, you can learn to look through your circumstances and "see" *My Face shining upon you.* Seek to find Me everywhere.

To this end I labor, struggling with all his energy, which so powerfully works in me. —Colossians 1:29

You have made known to me the paths of life; you will fill me with joy in your presence. —Acts 2:28

"The Lord bless you and keep you; the Lord make His face shine upon you, and be gracious to you." —Numbers 6:24–25 nkjv

May 4

I KNOW ABOUT EVERY ONE of your troubles. *I have collected all your tears and preserved them in My bottle.* So don't be afraid of tears—or of the hardships that cause them. Your problems are not random or meaningless. I'm calling you to trust not only in Me but also in My sovereignty. I know what I am doing!

Because My perspective is infinite—unlimited by time or space—My ways of working in the world are often beyond your comprehension. If it were possible for you to see things from My God-perspective, you would understand the perfection of My will—and revel in My Glory. But now you see *only a poor reflection*, so you must learn to live with mystery.

I have collected your tears in My bottle because you are exceedingly precious to Me. And someday *I will wipe every tear from your eyes. There will be no more death or mourning or crying or pain.* Rejoice in this glorious, heavenly future awaiting you!

> *You have seen me tossing and turning through the night.*
> *You have collected all my tears and preserved them in your bottle!*
> *You have recorded every one in your book.*—PSALM 56:8 TLB

> *Now we see but a poor reflection as in a mirror; then we shall*
> *see face to face. Now I know in part; then I shall know fully,*
> *even as I am fully known.*—1 CORINTHIANS 13:12

> *"He will wipe every tear from their eyes. There will be*
> *no more death or mourning or crying or pain, for the old*
> *order of things has passed away."*—REVELATION 21:4

May 5

I want you to linger in gratitude. This is a most delightful place—where the Joy of My Presence shines warmly upon you.

You often pray fervently for something until you receive the answer you desire. When I grant your request, you respond joyfully and thankfully. But your tendency is to move on rather quickly to the next matter. I want you to remain for a while in an attitude of grateful Joy. Instead of experiencing only a short-lived burst of gratitude, let this pleasure flow freely into the future by training yourself to recall what I have done. One way is to tell others about it. This blesses both them and you, and it pleases Me. Another way is to write down the prayer-answer someplace where you will see it again and again.

Keep bringing your gratitude to Me. This thankfulness will bless you doubly—with happy memories of answered prayer and with the delight of sharing Joy with Me.

Let us come before His presence with thanksgiving; let us shout joyfully to Him with psalms. —Psalm 95:2 nkjv

But thanks be to God! He gives us the victory through our Lord Jesus Christ. —1 Corinthians 15:57

Remember His marvelous works which He has done, His wonders, and the judgments of His mouth. —1 Chronicles 16:12 nkjv

May 6

THIS IS WHAT I SAY—*I who made you, who formed you in the womb, and who will help you: Do not be afraid.* I have always been involved in your life, even before you were born. Because you are Mine, purchased with My own blood, you can count on My promise to help you as you journey through this world. This is how you gain victory over fear: through trusting in My *ever-present help.*

The problem arises when you gaze too long into the future, trying to visualize and take control of those not-yet events. A future-focus can easily deteriorate into a problem-focus. Weeds of worry and fear spring up quickly in this sort of "soil." When you realize this has happened, turn away from your worries and back to the One who is lovingly present with you. Rejoice that I will *still* be with you when you arrive at each coming stage of your journey. Lean hard on My Presence, trusting Me to help you today—and *all the days of your life.*

"This is what the LORD says—he who made you, who formed you in the womb, and who will help you: Do not be afraid, O Jacob, my servant, Jeshurun, whom I have chosen."—ISAIAH 44:2

God is our refuge and strength, an ever-present help in trouble.—PSALM 46:1

Surely or only goodness, mercy, and unfailing love shall follow me all the days of my life, and through the length of my days the house of the Lord [and His presence] shall be my dwelling place.—PSALM 23:6 AMP

May 7

YOU ARE A CHILD OF GOD. Someday you will *see Me as I am*—you will be face to Face with Me in Glory. Until then, I am training you *to be made new in the attitude of your mind, to put on the new self.* Although your new self is being conformed to My image, this process doesn't erase the essence of who you are. Instead, the more you become *like Me*, the more you develop into the unique person I designed you to be.

You have been a member of My royal family since you first trusted Me as Savior. Thus you're a *fellow heir with Me—sharing My inheritance.* However, *you must share My suffering if you are to share My Glory.* When you encounter hard times, search for Me in the midst of your struggles. Ask Me to help you suffer well, in a manner worthy of the King's household. Everything you endure can help you become more like Me. Remember the ultimate goal: *You will see My Face in righteousness—and be satisfied!*

> *Beloved, now we are children of God; and it has not yet been revealed what we shall be, but we know that when He is revealed, we shall be like Him, for we shall see Him as He is.*—1 JOHN 3:2 NKJV

> *You were taught, with regard to your former way of life, to put off your old self, which is being corrupted by its deceitful desires; to be made new in the attitude of your minds; and to put on the new self, created to be like God in true righteousness and holiness.*—EPHESIANS 4:22–24

> *If we are [His] children, then we are [His] heirs also: heirs of God and fellow heirs with Christ [sharing His inheritance with Him]; only we must share His suffering if we are to share His glory.*—ROMANS 8:17 AMP

> *As for me, I will see Your face in righteousness; I shall be satisfied when I awake in Your likeness.*—PSALM 17:15 NKJV

May 8

I REDEEM YOU FROM HELL—crowning you with Love and mercy; I wrap you in goodness and renew your youth.

I give you these magnificent gifts because *I take pleasure in you.* Let My delight in you soak into the depths of your being—satisfying your soul. Although I see your sins and flaws, my perfect Love never wavers. I look on you first and foremost as My redeemed one, wearing *a paradise crown and wrapped in beauty eternal.*

I want your identity as My beloved to be front and center in your mind. However, your thoughts often get stuck on trivial matters, especially when your mind is in neutral. This is why I urge you to *be alert and always keep on praying.* Invite Me to enter into your circumstances—including your thoughts, feelings, and decisions. Communicating with Me will help you focus less on trivial matters and more on glorious realities. While you wait in My Presence, I will *renew your strength.* Regardless of how old you are, *you're always young in My Presence!*

> *He redeems you from hell—saves your life! He crowns you with love and mercy—a paradise crown. He wraps you in goodness—beauty eternal. He renews your youth—you're always young in his presence.*—PSALM 103:4–5 MSG

> *For the LORD takes pleasure in His people; He will beautify the humble with salvation.*—PSALM 149:4 NKJV

> *Pray in the Spirit on all occasions with all kinds of prayers and requests. With this in mind, be alert and always keep on praying for all the saints.*—EPHESIANS 6:18

> *But those who hope in the LORD will renew their strength. They will soar on wings like eagles; they will run and not grow weary, they will walk and not be faint.*—ISAIAH 40:31

May 9

I MEET YOU in the place of your deepest need. So come to Me just as you are, leaving pretense and performance behind. You are totally transparent to Me: I know everything about you. Yet because you are My own—redeemed by My blood—I have unlimited, unfailing Love for you.

Ask My Spirit to help you be honest and open with Me. Don't be ashamed of your neediness; instead, use it to connect with Me in humble dependence. Invite Me to have My way in your life. Remember that *I am the Potter, and you are the clay.* The weakness you bring Me is malleable in My hands, and I use it to mold you according to My will.

Your deepest need is to *lean on, trust in, and be confident in Me.* Accepting your lack of strength helps you lean on Me in unashamed dependence. I am training you to trust Me *with all your heart and mind*—a lifelong endeavor. And the best way to *not be afraid* is to have confidence in Me, *your Strength.*

> *For you know that it was not with perishable things such as silver or gold that you were redeemed from the empty way of life handed down to you from your forefathers, but with the precious blood of Christ, a lamb without blemish or defect.*—1 PETER 1:18–19

> *Yet, O LORD, you are our Father. We are the clay, you are the potter; we are all the work of your hand.*—ISAIAH 64:8

> *Lean on, trust in, and be confident in the Lord with all your heart and mind and do not rely on your own insight or understanding.*—PROVERBS 3:5 AMP

> *Behold, God is my salvation, I will trust and not be afraid; for the LORD GOD is my strength and song, and He has become my salvation.*—ISAIAH 12:2 NASB

May 10

Your choices matter, beloved. They are a vital part of My transforming work in you. You make most of your choices alone—in the solitude of your heart and mind. But remember: I am *Christ in you*! I know every thought before you think it, every decision before you make it. Your realization that I'm aware of everything going on within you can protect you from careless, selfish living. Let your desire to *please Me*, the One who knows you so intimately, change the way you think and live.

You may have assumed that your choices are mostly insignificant, but this is not true. A good decision you make today, however small, may set you on a path to accomplish something very important. A bad decision, seemingly minor, can lead to serious failure or loss in the future. Though your choices do indeed matter, remember that *there is no condemnation for those who belong to Me*. I am able to see all your flaws and failures, yet simultaneously love you with glorious, *unfailing Love*.

> *To them God has chosen to make known among the Gentiles the glorious riches of this mystery, which is Christ in you, the hope of glory.* —Colossians 1:27

> *Finally, dear brothers and sisters, we urge you in the name of the Lord Jesus to live in a way that pleases God, as we have taught you. You live this way already, and we encourage you to do so even more.* —1 Thessalonians 4:1 NLT

> *There is therefore now no condemnation for those who are in Christ Jesus. For the law of the Spirit of life has set you free in Christ Jesus from the law of sin and death.* —Romans 8:1–2 ESV

> *But I trust in your unfailing love; my heart rejoices in your salvation.* —Psalm 13:5

May 11

I am your Brother and your Friend. I'm *the Firstborn among many brothers*; you are *being conformed to My likeness.* This is an astonishing privilege and blessing! Some children are blessed to have a strong, loving older brother who helps and protects them. *You* have an all-powerful Big Brother who is constantly looking out for your interests. Even the most committed family member or friend cannot be with you always, but I never leave your side. I am the *Friend who sticks closer than a brother.*

My continual Presence with you should never be taken for granted. Remember that your faithful Friend is also *King of kings.* If you could glimpse Me in all My Glory, you would understand why *John fell at My feet as though dead* when he saw Me. *I am the First and the Last—the Living One who was dead and is alive forever and ever!* I want you to relate to Me with reverence because I am your Savior-God. Remind yourself that the glorious gift of salvation is yours forever—and honor Me with gratitude.

> *For those God foreknew he also predestined to be conformed to the likeness of his Son, that he might be the firstborn among many brothers.*—Romans 8:29

> *There is a friend who sticks closer than a brother.*—Proverbs 18:24 esv

> *These will make war with the Lamb, and the Lamb will overcome them, for He is Lord of lords and King of kings; and those who are with Him are called, chosen, and faithful.*—Revelation 17:14 nkjv

> *When I saw him, I fell at his feet as though dead. Then he placed his right hand on me and said: "Do not be afraid. I am the First and the Last. I am the Living One; I was dead, and behold I am alive for ever and ever! And I hold the keys of death and Hades."*—Revelation 1:17–18

May 12

Praise Me for the help of My Presence. At all times and in all circumstances, it's appropriate to pray: "Thank You, Jesus, for being *with me* here and now." You may not sense My Presence with you, but I have promised—and that is enough!

An important part of your assignment as a Christian is to trust that *I am with you always.* In faith, talk to Me about your thoughts and feelings, your struggles and pleasures. Believe that I care for you deeply and I hear all your prayers. Seek My help with confident anticipation. Be on the lookout for all the ways I am at work: in you and through you. Rejoice that you and I together can *do immeasurably more than all you ask or imagine. My Power is at work within you*—especially as it connects with your weakness offered up to Me for My purposes.

Remember that *nothing is impossible with Me,* and refuse to be intimidated by daunting circumstances. Praise Me for the help of My Presence!

Why are you in despair, O my soul? And why have you become disturbed within me? Hope in God, for I shall again praise Him for the help of His presence.—Psalm 42:5 NASB

"Teach these new disciples to obey all the commands I have given you. And be sure of this: I am with you always, even to the end of the age."—Matthew 28:20 NLT

Now to him who is able to do immeasurably more than all we ask or imagine, according to his power that is at work within us . . .—Ephesians 3:20

For nothing will be impossible with God.—Luke 1:37 ESV

May 13

Stop judging by mere appearances, and make a right judgment. I made this statement at the temple in Jerusalem, teaching that judging can be either good or bad. I was speaking to people who had assessed Me on the basis of appearances: focusing on the letter of the Law rather than the spirit of the Law. What they were doing was wrong, but that doesn't mean *all* judgments are wrong. I forbid superficial, self-righteous, and hypocritical evaluations. But I do want My followers to make *righteous* assessments about moral and theological issues—based on biblical truth.

In this age of "tolerance," there is immense pressure on people to refrain from making statements that differentiate right from wrong. The fear of being labeled "intolerant" has silenced many people who know how to make right judgments. I want you to have the courage to *speak the truth in love* as I lead you to do so. The best preparation is to search the Scriptures and your heart. Then ask My Spirit to speak through you even as He loves others through you.

"Stop judging by mere appearances, and make a right judgment."—JOHN 7:24

"Do not judge and criticize and condemn others, so that you may not be judged and criticized and condemned yourselves."—MATTHEW 7:1 AMP

Speaking the truth in love, we will in all things grow up into him who is the Head, that is, Christ.—EPHESIANS 4:15

May 14

I AM ABLE to keep you from stumbling. I know how weak you are, how easily you would lose your footing if I were not holding onto you. You are *growing in grace*, but complete freedom from sin will not be possible as long as you live in this fallen world. So you need My help continually.

I am able to *present you faultless*—blameless, perfect, unblemished—*before the Presence of My Glory* because *I have clothed you with garments of salvation and arrayed you in a robe of righteousness*. I want you to wear these royal raiments with confidence. You are absolutely secure because it is *My* righteousness that saves you, not yours.

Exceeding Joy is for you and for Me. I delight in you now, but this Joy will be immeasurably magnified when you join Me in Glory. The jubilation you will experience in heaven is indescribable—far beyond any pleasure you could know in this world. Nothing can rob you of this glorious *inheritance that can never perish, spoil, or fade*!

Now to Him who is able to keep you from stumbling, and to present you faultless before the presence of His glory with exceeding joy, to God our Savior, who alone is wise, be glory and majesty, dominion and power, both now and forever. Amen.—Jude vv. 24–25 NKJV

But grow in the grace and knowledge of our Lord and Savior Jesus Christ. To him be glory both now and forever! Amen.—2 Peter 3:18

I delight greatly in the Lord; my soul rejoices in my God. For he has clothed me with garments of salvation and arrayed me in a robe of righteousness, as a bridegroom adorns his head like a priest, and as a bride adorns herself with her jewels.—Isaiah 61:10

Praise be to the God and Father of our Lord Jesus Christ! In his great mercy he has given us new birth into a living hope through the resurrection of Jesus Christ from the dead, and into an inheritance that can never perish, spoil or fade—kept in heaven for you.—1 Peter 1:3–4

May 15

As you seek Me, I encourage you to *rejoice and be glad in Me*. Take time to praise Me in psalms and song. Think about who I am: I dwell in *splendor, majesty, and beauty*. Then remember how I left the Glory of heaven and came into the world—so I could bring you into My kingdom of everlasting Life and Light. All of this helps you to *be joyful in Me, your Savior*. This Joy ushers you further into My holy Presence, helping you draw nearer to Me. And this nearness gives you even more reason to rejoice!

Being joyful blesses not only you but other people. Your family and friends will benefit from your gladness, which can rub off on them. You can also influence many beyond your inner circle. When My followers are joyful, unbelievers are more likely to be drawn to Me. Joy shines in stark contrast to your ever-darkening world, and some people will ask you about it. *Always be prepared to give an answer to everyone who asks you the reason for your hope.*

> *But may all who seek you rejoice and be glad in you; may those who love your salvation always say, "Let God be exalted!"*—Psalm 70:4

> *Splendor and majesty are before him; strength and beauty are in his sanctuary.*—Psalm 96:6 esv

> *Yet I will rejoice in the Lord, I will be joyful in God my Savior.*—Habakkuk 3:18

> *But in your hearts set apart Christ as Lord. Always be prepared to give an answer to everyone who asks you to give the reason for the hope that you have. But do this with gentleness and respect.*—1 Peter 3:15

May 16

When you begin a day—or a task—feeling inadequate, remember this: *My grace is sufficient for you.* The present tense of the verb "is" highlights the continual availability of My wondrous grace. So don't waste energy regretting how weak you feel. Instead, embrace your insufficiency—rejoicing that it helps you realize how much you need Me. Come to Me for help, and delight in My infinite sufficiency! *My Power is made perfect in weakness.*

As you go about a task in joyful dependence on Me, you will be surprised by how much you can accomplish. Moreover, the quality of your work will be greatly enhanced by your collaboration with Me. Ponder the astonishing privilege of living and working alongside Me, the *King of kings and Lord of lords*. Seek to align yourself with My will, making yourself a *living sacrifice*. This is a form of worship, and it pleases Me. It also makes your life meaningful and joyful. This is a tiny foretaste of the immense, indescribably glorious Joy that awaits you in heaven!

> *But he said to me, "My grace is sufficient for you, for my power is made perfect in weakness." Therefore I will boast all the more gladly about my weaknesses, so that Christ's power may rest on me.*—2 Corinthians 12:9

> *And He has on His robe and on His thigh a name written:*
> KING OF KINGS AND LORD OF LORDS.—Revelation 19:16 NKJV

> *Therefore, I urge you, brothers, in view of God's mercy, to offer your bodies as living sacrifices, holy and pleasing to God— this is your spiritual act of worship.*—Romans 12:1

> *Now to Him who is able to keep you from stumbling, and to present you faultless before the presence of His glory with exceeding joy . . .* —Jude v. 24 NKJV

May 17

Cast your cares on Me, and I will sustain you. Carrying your own burdens is wearing you out. Your shoulders were not designed for carrying heavy loads, so I want you to learn to cast your burdens on *Me*. The first step is to recognize that something is weighing you down. Next, examine the difficulty to determine whether it is yours or someone else's. If it isn't yours, simply let go of it and leave it behind. If it *is* your problem, talk with Me about it. I will help you see from My perspective, and I'll show you the way forward.

Be prepared to take action as needed, but don't let problems weigh you down by becoming your focus. Make a concerted effort to cast your cares on Me, for I have very strong shoulders! Then simply do the next thing—in joyful dependence on Me.

Be encouraged by My promise to sustain you—to hold you up and provide what you need. *I will supply all your needs according to My riches in Glory.*

> *Cast your cares on the Lord and he will sustain you; he will never let the righteous fall.* —Psalm 55:22

> *For unto us a Child is born, unto us a Son is given; and the government will be upon His shoulder. And His name will be called Wonderful, Counselor, Mighty God, Everlasting Father, Prince of Peace.* —Isaiah 9:6 nkjv

> *And my God will supply all your needs according to His riches in glory in Christ Jesus.* —Philippians 4:19 nasb

May 18

To increase your awareness of My Presence, you need to learn the art of self-forgetfulness. You were not designed to stay focused on yourself. However, Adam and Eve's disobedience in the Garden of Eden made selfishness the natural bent of mankind. This inclination is a deadly trap, but I have equipped you to live *supernaturally*. Since the moment you asked Me to be your Savior, you have had My Spirit living in you. Ask this Holy Helper to free you from self-centeredness. You may pray as often as you like: "Help me, Holy Spirit."

One thing that traps you in self-absorption is being overly concerned about how you look—in the mirror or in the eyes of others. Instead of making yourself the object of your thoughts, gaze at *Me* and be attentive to the people around you. Ask My Spirit to help you look beyond yourself with eyes that really see. You are safe in My *everlasting arms* and complete in My loving Presence. So turn your attention to trusting and loving Me.

> *When the woman saw that the fruit of the tree was good for food and pleasing to the eye, and also desirable for gaining wisdom, she took some and ate it. She also gave some to her husband, who was with her, and he ate it. Then the eyes of both of them were opened, and they realized they were naked; so they sewed fig leaves together and made coverings for themselves.*—Genesis 3:6–7

> *You, however, are controlled not by the sinful nature but by the Spirit, if the Spirit of God lives in you. And if anyone does not have the Spirit of Christ, he does not belong to Christ.*—Romans 8:9

> *"But when the Helper comes, whom I shall send to you from the Father, the Spirit of truth who proceeds from the Father, He will testify of Me."*—John 15:26 nkjv

> *The eternal God is your refuge, and underneath are the everlasting arms. He will drive out your enemy before you, saying, "Destroy him!"*—Deuteronomy 33:27

May 19

Look for Me in the hard places of your life. It's easy to find Me in answered prayer, in beauty and heartfelt Joy. But I am also tenderly present in difficulties. In fact, your problems are fertile soil for growing in grace and encountering My loving Presence in greater depth and breadth. So search for Me in dark times—both past and present. If you're plagued by painful memories and hurtful past experiences, look for *Me* in them. I know all about them, and I am ready to meet you there. Invite Me into those broken places, and cooperate with Me in putting the fragments back together in *new* ways.

If you are walking through tough times in the present, remember to cling to My hand. Against the dark backdrop of adversity, the Light of My Presence shines in transcendent radiance. This Light blesses you abundantly—providing both comfort and guidance. I will show you the way forward step by step. As you walk close to Me, I will draw you into deeper, richer intimacy with Me.

> *If I say, "Surely the darkness will overwhelm me, and the light around me will be night," even the darkness is not dark to You, and the night is as bright as the day. Darkness and light are alike to You.*—Psalm 139:11–12 nasb

> *And the Light shines on in the darkness, for the darkness has never overpowered it [put it out or absorbed it or appropriated it, and is unreceptive to it].*—John 1:5 amp

> *Yet I am always with you; you hold me by my right hand. You guide me with your counsel, and afterward you will take me into glory.*—Psalm 73:23–24

May 20

I AM THE GATE; whoever enters through Me will be saved. I am not a locked barrier but an open door for you—for all My chosen followers. I came into the world so that you might *have Life and have it to the full.*

A full life means different things for different people. So in your quest to live abundantly, don't compare your circumstances with those of others. You don't need as much money or as many luxuries as your neighbor in order to live well.

Godliness with contentment is great gain. I want you to be satisfied with My provision for you. *If you have food and clothing*—the basic necessities of life—seek to *be content with that.* If I give you more, respond with Joy and thankfulness. But don't cling to what you have or covet things you do not have. The only thing you can cling to without harming your soul is *Me.* No matter what you possess in this world, remember: Little (or much) + Me = everything!

> "I am the gate; whoever enters through me will be saved. He will come in and go out, and find pasture. The thief comes only to steal and kill and destroy; I have come that they may have life, and have it to the full."—JOHN 10:9–10

> *But godliness with contentment is great gain. For we brought nothing into the world, and we can take nothing out of it. But if we have food and clothing, we will be content with that.*—1 TIMOTHY 6:6–8

> *My soul clings to you; your right hand upholds me.*—PSALM 63:8

> "For God so loved the world, that he gave his only Son, that whoever believes in him should not perish but have eternal life."—JOHN 3:16 ESV

May 21

TREASURE ME ABOVE ALL ELSE. This will infuse Joy into your heart and mind. It will also glorify Me! To treasure something is to hold or keep it, esteeming it as precious. I am training you to hold securely onto *Me*, your Savior-God and constant Companion. Knowing that I never leave your side can increase your Joy and Peace immeasurably. Also, esteeming Me as your precious Savior strengthens your desire to keep Me "in your sights" and live according to My will.

When you prize Me above all else, other things lose their grip on you. One way to discern what you hold dearest is to examine your thoughts when your mind is at rest. If you don't like what you find, do not despair—you can teach yourself to think about Me more consistently. It's helpful to memorize Scripture, especially verses that draw you closer to Me. Try putting reminders of My loving Presence throughout your home and workplace. And remember to enlist My Spirit to help you; He delights in pointing you back to Me.

"The kingdom of heaven is like treasure hidden in a field. When a man found it, he hid it again, and then in his joy went and sold all he had and bought that field."—MATTHEW 13:44

I consider everything a loss compared to the surpassing greatness of knowing Christ Jesus my Lord, for whose sake I have lost all things. I consider them rubbish, that I may gain Christ and be found in him, not having a righteousness of my own that comes from the law, but that which is through faith in Christ.—PHILIPPIANS 3:8–9

"But the Helper, the Holy Spirit, whom the Father will send in My name, He will teach you all things."—JOHN 14:26 NKJV

"He will glorify Me, for He will take of what is Mine and declare it to you."—JOHN 16:14 NKJV

May 22

I WANT YOU TO KNOW the depth and breadth of *My Love that surpasses knowledge.* There is an enormous difference between knowing Me and knowing *about* Me. Similarly, experiencing My loving Presence is vastly different from knowing facts about My character. To experience My Presence, you need the empowering work of My Spirit. Ask Him to *strengthen you with Power in your inner being* so that you can *know My Love* in full measure.

Since the moment of your salvation, I have been alive in your heart. The more room you make for Me there, the more I can fill you with My Love. There are several ways to expand this space in your heart. It's crucial to take time with Me—enjoying My Presence and studying My Word. It is also vital to stay in communication with Me. As the apostle Paul wrote, *pray continually.* This joyful practice will keep you close to Me. Finally, let My Love flow through you to others—in both your words and your actions. This *makes My Love in you complete.*

I pray that out of his glorious riches he may strengthen you with power through his Spirit in your inner being, so that Christ may dwell in your hearts through faith. And I pray that you, being rooted and established in love, may . . . grasp how wide and long and high and deep is the love of Christ, and to know this love that surpasses knowledge— that you may be filled to the measure of all the fullness of God.—EPHESIANS 3:16–19

And there is salvation in no one else; for there is no other name under heaven that has been given among men by which we must be saved.—ACTS 4:12 NASB

Pray continually.—1 THESSALONIANS 5:17

Dear friends, since God so loved us, we also ought to love one another. No one has ever seen God; but if we love one another, God lives in us and his love is made complete in us.—1 JOHN 4:11–12

May 23

When the way just ahead of you seems too difficult, turn to Me and say: "I can't, but *we* (You and I together) *can*." Acknowledging your inability to handle things on your own is a healthy dose of reality. However, this is only one part of the equation, because a sense of inadequacy by itself can be immobilizing. The most important part of the equation is recognizing My abiding Presence with you and My desire to help you.

Pour out your heart to Me. Ask Me to carry your burdens and show you the way forward. Don't waste energy worrying about things that are beyond your control. Instead, use that energy to connect with Me. *Seek My Face continually.* Be ready to follow wherever I lead, trusting Me to open up the way before you as you go.

Dare to see your inadequacy as a door to My Presence. View your journey as an adventure that you share with Me. Remain in close communication with Me, enjoying My company as we journey together.

I can do all things through Christ who strengthens me.—Philippians 4:13 nkjv

Trust in him at all times, O people; pour out your hearts to him, for God is our refuge.—Psalm 62:8

Seek the Lord and His strength; seek His face continually.—Psalm 105:4 nasb

May 24

THERE IS PEACE AND FULLNESS OF JOY in My loving Presence. Look for Me as you go through this day—I am eager to be found by you. I never lose sight of you; I watch over you continually. However, there are many ways you can lose sight of Me. Most of these are just temporary distractions, which abound in the world. The remedy is simple: Remind yourself that I am with you.

A much more serious problem is *forsaking your First Love*. If you realize this has happened, repent and run back to Me. Confess the idols that have drawn you away from Me. Take time to receive My forgiveness with thanksgiving. Collaborate with Me in rearranging your priorities—making Me first in your life. As you spend time in My Presence, think about who I Am: King of the universe, *Light of the world*. Bask in this *Light of Life* so that you can reflect Me to others. While you are delighting in Me, I fill you up with *Love, Joy, and Peace*.

The LORD keeps watch over you as you come and go, both now and forever.—PSALM 121:8 NLT

"Yet I hold this against you: You have forsaken your first love."—REVELATION 2:4

When Jesus spoke again to the people, he said, "I am the light of the world. Whoever follows me will never walk in darkness, but will have the light of life."—JOHN 8:12

But the fruit of the Spirit is love, joy, peace, patience, kindness, goodness, faithfulness, gentleness and self-control. Against such things there is no law.—GALATIANS 5:22–23

May 25

THANK ME FOR ALL THE CHALLENGES in your life. They are gifts from Me—opportunities to grow stronger and more dependent on Me. Most people think that the stronger they get, the less dependent they will be. But in *My* kingdom, strength and dependence go hand in hand. This is because you were designed to walk close to Me as you journey through your life. Challenging circumstances highlight your neediness and help you rely on My infinite sufficiency.

When circumstances are tough and you rise to the occasion, trusting in Me, you are blessed. It's exhilarating to get through challenges that you thought were too much for you. When you do so in reliance on Me, our relationship grows stronger.

Your success in handling difficulties also increases your sense of security. You gain confidence that you and I *together* can cope with whatever hard times the future may bring. *You are ready for anything and equal to anything through the One who infuses inner strength into you.* Rejoice in My sufficiency!

Consider it a sheer gift, friends, when tests and challenges come at you from all sides.—JAMES 1:2 MSG

But I trust in you, O LORD; I say, "You are my God." My times are in your hands; deliver me from my enemies and from those who pursue me. Let your face shine on your servant; save me in your unfailing love.—PSALM 31:14–16

I have strength for all things in Christ Who empowers me [I am ready for anything and equal to anything through Him Who infuses inner strength into me; I am self-sufficient in Christ's sufficiency].—PHILIPPIANS 4:13 AMP

May 26

I AM GOD, YOUR JOY *and your delight.* I want you to find pleasure in Me and in My Word. I am the ever-living Word: *in the beginning* and forevermore. So you can find Me richly present in My written Word, the Bible. As more and more Scripture soaks into your inner being, you will experience the delight of My Presence more consistently. Make time to meditate on Bible passages—and to memorize some of them. They will help you get through sleepless nights and encounters with adversity.

Knowing that I am *your Joy* can protect you from bemoaning your circumstances or envying others whose situations seem better than yours. Because I am always with you, you have an ever-present source of Joy in your life. You can find pleasure in Me by *rejoicing in My Name all day long.* Simply uttering "Jesus" as a prayer can lift your spirits. An excellent way to *delight greatly in Me* is to *exult in My righteousness,* which I have lovingly bestowed on you. This *robe of righteousness* covers you perfectly—forever!

Then will I go to the altar of God, to God, my joy and my delight. I will praise you with the harp, O God, my God.—PSALM 43:4

In the beginning was the Word, and the Word was with God, and the Word was God.—JOHN 1:1 NKJV

They rejoice in your name all day long; they exult in your righteousness.—PSALM 89:16

I delight greatly in the LORD; my soul rejoices in my God. For he has clothed me with garments of salvation and arrayed me in a robe of righteousness, as a bridegroom adorns his head like a priest, and as a bride adorns herself with her jewels.—ISAIAH 61:10

May 27

My kingdom is not of this world; it is indestructible and eternal. When you see shocking evil and mismanagement all around you, do not despair. As I was being arrested, I told My disciples that *I could call on My Father and He would send more than twelve legions of angels* to rescue Me. However, this was not the plan We had chosen. It was necessary for Me to be crucified—to save *everyone who calls on My Name.*

Remember that you are part of My kingdom of everlasting Life and Light. The darker your planet becomes, the more you need to cling to the hope you have in Me. Despite the way things look, I am in control, and I'm accomplishing My purposes in ways you cannot understand. Though this world is deeply fallen, it's possible to live in it with Joy and Peace in your heart. As I told My disciples, so I say to you now: *Be of good cheer; I have overcome the world.* Because you belong to My kingdom, *in Me you may have Peace.*

> Jesus said, "My kingdom is not of this world. If it were, my servants would fight to prevent my arrest by the Jews. But now my kingdom is from another place."—John 18:36

> "Do you think I cannot call on my Father, and he will at once put at my disposal more than twelve legions of angels?"—Matthew 26:53

> And everyone who calls on the name of the Lord will be saved.—Acts 2:21

> "These things I have spoken to you, that in Me you may have peace. In the world you will have tribulation; but be of good cheer, I have overcome the world."—John 16:33 NKJV

May 28

I AM THE VINE; you are one of the branches. Whoever lives in Me and I in him bears abundant fruit. Apart from Me—cut off from vital union with Me—you can do nothing.

Ponder this glorious truth: I am alive within you! Just as sap flows from a vine through its branches, so My Life flows through you. I am infinite and perfect, yet I choose to live inside you. This intimacy you have with Me is wondrously rich. I read your every thought. I'm aware of all your feelings. I know how weak you are, and I stand ready to infuse you with My strength.

When you cooperate with My indwelling Presence, asking Me to be in control, you can produce abundant fruit. If you try to do things in your own strength, ignoring your vital union with Me, you're likely to fall flat on your face. Anything you *do* produce apart from Me will have no value in My kingdom. So nourish well your intimacy with Me, beloved. Delight in My Life-giving Presence!

> *"I am the Vine; you are the branches. Whoever lives in Me and I in him bears much (abundant) fruit. However, apart from Me [cut off from vital union with Me] you can do nothing."*—JOHN 15:5 AMP

> *To them God has chosen to make known among the Gentiles the glorious riches of this mystery, which is Christ in you, the hope of glory.*—COLOSSIANS 1:27

> *And He said to me, "My grace is sufficient for you, for My strength is made perfect in weakness." Therefore most gladly I will rather boast in my infirmities, that the power of Christ may rest upon me.*—2 CORINTHIANS 12:9 NKJV

> *About Benjamin he said: "Let the beloved of the LORD rest secure in him, for he shields him all day long, and the one the LORD loves rests between his shoulders."*—DEUTERONOMY 33:12

May 29

Thank Me joyfully for forgiving *all* your sins—past, present, and future; known and unknown. Forgiveness is your greatest need, and I have met that need perfectly—forever! I am *the eternal Life that was with the Father and has appeared to you.* Because you believe in Me as your Savior-God, you have *everlasting Life.* Let this amazing promise fill you with Joy and drive out fear of the future. Your future is glorious and secure: *an inheritance that can never perish, spoil, or fade—kept in heaven for you.* The best response to this priceless, infinite gift is gratitude!

The more frequently you thank Me, the more joyful your life will be. So be on the lookout for things that fuel your gratitude. The very act of thanking Me—in spoken or written word, in silent prayers, whispers, shouts, or songs of praise—increases your Joy and lifts you above your circumstances. A delightful way to express your adoration is reading psalms out loud. Rejoice in Me, My redeemed one, for *nothing can separate you from My Love.*

> *The life appeared; we have seen it and testify to it, and we proclaim to you the eternal life, which was with the Father and has appeared to us.* —1 John 1:2

> *"For God so loved the world that He gave His only begotten Son, that whoever believes in Him should not perish but have everlasting life."* —John 3:16 NKJV

> *Praise be to the God and Father of our Lord Jesus Christ! In his great mercy he has given us new birth into a living hope through the resurrection of Jesus Christ from the dead, and into an inheritance that can never perish, spoil or fade—kept in heaven for you.* —1 Peter 1:3–4

> *For I am convinced that neither death nor life, neither angels nor demons, neither the present nor the future, nor any powers, neither height nor depth, nor anything else in all creation, will be able to separate us from the love of God that is in Christ Jesus our Lord.* —Romans 8:38–39

May 30

I AM GOD, AND YOU ARE *NOT*. This may sound harsh, but it's actually a blessed dose of reality. In the Garden of Eden, Satan tempted Eve with the very same desire that had caused him to fall from heaven: to *be like God*, usurping My divine position. Eve succumbed to this temptation, as did Adam. Since that time, the sin-nature in people prompts them to act as if they are God—trying to control everything, judging Me when circumstances don't go as they'd like.

Remembering you are *not* God helps you live in freedom. You don't take responsibility for matters that are beyond your control—which includes *most* matters. If you let go of everything that is not your responsibility, you are freed from carrying unnecessary burdens. And you can be more effective in areas where you *do* have some control. Moreover, you can pray about all your concerns, trusting in My sovereignty. Bring Me your *prayers with thanksgiving; present your requests to Me.* Living this way will shield you from anxiety and bless you with *Peace that transcends all understanding.*

> And He said to them, "I saw Satan fall like
> lightning from heaven."—LUKE 10:18 NKJV

> For God knows that in the day you eat of it your eyes will be opened,
> and you will be like God, knowing good and evil.—GENESIS 3:5 NKJV

> Do not be anxious about anything, but in everything, by prayer and
> petition, with thanksgiving, present your requests to God. And the
> peace of God, which transcends all understanding, will guard your
> hearts and your minds in Christ Jesus.—PHILIPPIANS 4:6–7

May 31

Continue to live in Me, rooted and built up in Me—and overflowing with thankfulness. The relationship you have with Me is unlike any other. You live in Me, and I live in you. You never go anywhere without Me! This amazing degree of connectedness with Me provides a rock-solid foundation for your life. I want you to continue building on this foundation—living in joyful awareness of My Presence.

Thankfulness provides some of the most important building blocks for your life. The more of these blocks you use as you build, the better your life-experience will be. Thankfulness enlarges the capacity of your heart for abundant Joy. It also helps you endure suffering without falling into despair or self-pity. No matter what is happening, you can always thank Me for your eternal salvation and *My unfailing Love*. These are constant, unchangeable blessings. Other blessings—such as your relationships, your finances, your health—may change quite frequently. I encourage you to count *both* types of blessings until you overflow with thankfulness!

> *So then, just as you received Christ Jesus as Lord, continue to live in him, rooted and built up in him, strengthened in the faith as you were taught, and overflowing with thankfulness.*—Colossians 2:6–7

> *To them God willed to make known what are the riches of the glory of this mystery among the Gentiles: which is Christ in you, the hope of glory.*—Colossians 1:27 nkjv

> *But I trust in your unfailing love; my heart rejoices in your salvation. I will sing to the Lord, for he has been good to me.*—Psalm 13:5–6

June

*He will cover you with his feathers,
and under his wings you will find refuge;
his faithfulness will be your shield and rampart.*

Psalm 91:4

June 1

I APPROVE OF YOU, MY CHILD. Because you are Mine—adopted into My royal family—I see you through eyes of grace. *I chose you before the creation of the world to be holy and blameless in My sight.* I know you fall short of this perfect standard in your daily living. But I *view* you as holy and blameless because this is your permanent position in My kingdom. Of course, I don't endorse everything you do (or fail to do). Still, I approve of *you*—your true self, the one I created you to be.

I know how much you long for My affirmation—and how hard it is for you to accept it. I want you to learn to see yourself and others through grace-vision. Looking through eyes of grace, you can focus more on what is good and right than on what is bad and wrong. You learn to cooperate with Me and embrace what I'm doing in your life: *transforming you into My likeness with ever-increasing Glory.* I not only *approve* of you, I *delight* in you!

> For he chose us in him before the creation of the world to be holy and blameless in his sight.—EPHESIANS 1:4

> Brothers and sisters, think about the things that are good and worthy of praise. Think about the things that are true and honorable and right and pure and beautiful and respected.—PHILIPPIANS 4:8 NCV

> And we, who with unveiled faces all reflect the Lord's glory, are being transformed into his likeness with ever-increasing glory, which comes from the Lord, who is the Spirit.—2 CORINTHIANS 3:18

> For the LORD delights in his people; he crowns the humble with victory.—PSALM 149:4 NLT

June 2

Fix your eyes not on what is seen but on what is unseen. You spend too much time and mental energy thinking about trivial things—surface matters that have no value in My kingdom. The sense of sight is a wondrous gift from Me, but it can become a source of bondage if misused. You have such easy access to mirrors shining your reflection back to you in glaring accuracy. This, in conjunction with media images of people who look perfect, makes it tempting to be overly focused on your appearance. The same can be true of your home or family. This focus on appearances distracts you from the soul-satisfying pleasures of knowing Me.

When you seek *Me*, you enjoy the company of the only perfect Person who ever existed. However, My perfection was not in My appearance but in My divine, sinless character. I am the One who can love you with *unfailing Love* and give you *perfect Peace*. So don't waste time thinking about trivialities. Instead, *fix your thoughts on Me* and receive My Peace.

> *So we fix our eyes not on what is seen, but on what is unseen. For what is seen is temporary, but what is unseen is eternal.* —2 Corinthians 4:18

> *How priceless is your unfailing love! Both high and low among men find refuge in the shadow of your wings.* —Psalm 36:7

> *You will keep in perfect peace all who trust in you, all whose thoughts are fixed on you!* —Isaiah 26:3 nlt

June 3

I INVITE YOU TO GAZE UPON *My beauty and to seek Me* more and more. This is a most delightful invitation! You can get glimpses of My loveliness in the wonders of nature, but these are only tiny, weak reflections of My massive Glory. The best is indeed yet to come—when you will see Me face to Face in heaven. For now, gazing upon My beauty requires focusing on My unseen Presence through prayer and meditating on My Word.

Foundational to your search for Me is remembering that I am continually with you. I am always attuned to you, and I am training you to be increasingly aware of Me. Place reminders of My Presence in your home, car, and office. Whisper My Name to remind you of My nearness. Sing praises to Me. Read or recite Scripture passages out loud. Find others who desire to know Me more fully, and share this glorious quest with them. *Seek Me, and require Me as a vital necessity; search for Me with all your heart.*

> *One thing I ask of the LORD, this is what I seek: that I may dwell in the house of the LORD all the days of my life, to gaze upon the beauty of the LORD and to seek him in his temple.* —PSALM 27:4

> *Now we see but a poor reflection as in a mirror; then we shall see face to face. Now I know in part; then I shall know fully, even as I am fully known.* —1 CORINTHIANS 13:12

> *"Then you will seek Me, inquire for, and require Me [as a vital necessity] and find Me when you search for Me with all your heart."* —JEREMIAH 29:13 AMP

June 4

I AM YOUR JOY! Let these words reverberate in your mind and sink into your innermost being. I—your Companion who *will never leave you*—am a boundless source of Joy. If you really believe this, you can rest in the truth that every day of your life is a good day. So refuse to use the label "a bad day," even when you're struggling deeply. Your circumstances may indeed be very hard, but I am nonetheless with you, *holding you by your right hand.* There is good to be found in this day—and every day—because of My constant Presence and steadfast Love.

You may not be rich by worldly standards, but *My unfailing Love is priceless!* This Love guarantees that you can *find refuge in the shadow of My wings* no matter what is happening. Also, it gives you access to *My river of delights.* When your world feels anything but delightful, turn to Me and drink deeply from this ravishing river: My loving Presence. *I* am your Joy!

> *The LORD himself goes before you and will be with you; he will never leave you nor forsake you. Do not be afraid; do not be discouraged.* —DEUTERONOMY 31:8

> *Nevertheless I am continually with You; You hold me by my right hand.* —PSALM 73:23 NKJV

> *How priceless is your unfailing love! Both high and low among men find refuge in the shadow of your wings. They feast on the abundance of your house; you give them drink from your river of delights.* —PSALM 36:7–8

June 5

Do what you can, and leave the rest to Me. When you're embroiled in a difficult situation, *pour out your heart to Me,* knowing that I listen and I care. Rely on Me, your *ever-present Help in trouble.* Refuse to let your problem become your main focus, no matter how anxious you are to solve it. When you've done all you can for the time being, the best thing is simply to wait—finding refreshment in My Presence. Don't fall for the lie that you can't enjoy life until the problem has been resolved. *In the world you have trouble,* but *in Me you may have Peace*—even in the midst of the mess!

Your relationship with Me is collaborative: you and I working together. Look to Me for help and guidance, doing whatever you can and trusting Me to do what you cannot do. Instead of trying to force things to a premature conclusion, relax and ask Me to *show you the way you should go*—in *My* timing. Hold My hand in confident trust, beloved, and enjoy the journey in My Presence.

> Trust in him at all times, O people; pour out your hearts to him, for God is our refuge.—Psalm 62:8

> God is our refuge and strength, an ever-present help in trouble.—Psalm 46:1

> "I have told you these things so that in me you may have peace. In the world you have trouble and suffering, but take courage—I have conquered the world."—John 16:33 net

> Let the morning bring me word of your unfailing love, for I have put my trust in you. Show me the way I should go, for to you I lift up my soul.—Psalm 143:8

June 6

Nurture well your thankfulness, for it is the royal road to Joy! In fact, no pleasure is really complete without expressing gratitude for it. It's good to thank the people through whom you receive blessings, but remember that I am *God from whom all blessings flow*. So praise and thank *Me* frequently each day. This nurtures your soul and completes your Joy. It also enhances your relationship with Me, providing an easy way for you to draw near Me.

As My cherished follower, you have received the glorious gift of grace—unearned, undeserved favor. No one and no set of circumstances can strip you of this lavish gift. You belong to Me forever! *Nothing in all creation will be able to separate you from My Love.*

When you awaken each morning, say, "Thank You, Jesus, for the gift of this new day." As you journey through the day, be on the lookout for blessings and pleasures I scatter along your path. The greatest treasure is My Presence with you, for I am the *indescribable Gift!*

Let us come before His presence with thanksgiving; let us make a joyful noise to Him with songs of praise!—Psalm 95:2 amp

For it is by grace you have been saved, through faith—and this not from yourselves, it is the gift of God—not by works, so that no one can boast.—Ephesians 2:8–9

For I am convinced that neither death nor life, neither angels nor demons, neither the present nor the future, nor any powers, neither height nor depth, nor anything else in all creation, will be able to separate us from the love of God that is in Christ Jesus our Lord.—Romans 8:38–39

Thanks be to God for His indescribable gift!—2 Corinthians 9:15 nkjv

June 7

IF YOU HAVE ME—your Savior, Lord, and Friend—you have everything that really matters. You may not have riches, fame, or success, but don't let that discourage you. As I said to My disciples, *"What do you benefit if you gain the whole world but lose your own soul?"* Nothing can be compared with the priceless treasure of eternal Life! Consider *a jewel merchant on the hunt for excellent pearls. When he found one that was flawless, he sold everything and bought it.* My kingdom is like that: of inestimable worth! So learn to be content with having *Me*, beloved, regardless of what you may lack in this world.

The source of much discontentment is comparing oneself with others. I want you to make every effort to avoid this deadly trap. Remember that you are My unique creation—redeemed by My blood and exquisitely precious to Me. Stay in joyful communication with Me, the Savior who loves you immeasurably more than you can imagine. I will transform you more and more into the *masterpiece* I designed you to be.

> *"And what do you benefit if you gain the whole world but lose your own soul? Is anything worth more than your soul?"*—MATTHEW 16:26 NLT

> *"God's kingdom is like a jewel merchant on the hunt for excellent pearls. Finding one that is flawless, he immediately sells everything and buys it."*—MATTHEW 13:45–46 MSG

> But godliness with contentment is great gain.—1 TIMOTHY 6:6

> For we are God's masterpiece. He has created us anew in Christ Jesus, so we can do the good things he planned for us long ago.—EPHESIANS 2:10 NLT

June 8

My Love has conquered you and *set you free*! The Power of My Love is so great that it has enslaved you to Me. *You are not your own. You were bought at a price*—My holy blood. The more you love Me, the more you will want to serve Me with every fiber of your being. This service can fill you with heavenly Joy as you yield yourself to Me more fully.

Because I am perfect in all My ways, you can give yourself wholeheartedly to Me without fear that I might take advantage of you. On the contrary, being conquered by Me is what makes you truly free. I have invaded the innermost core of your being, and My Spirit within you is taking over more and more territory. *Where the Spirit of the Lord is, there is freedom.* I want you *to reflect My Glory* to others, for I am *transforming you into My likeness with ever-increasing Glory*. Rejoice in the freedom you have found in Me, and surrender gladly to My victorious Love!

And having been set free from sin, you became slaves of righteousness.—Romans 6:18 nkjv

Do you not know that your body is a temple of the Holy Spirit, who is in you, whom you have received from God? You are not your own; you were bought at a price. Therefore honor God with your body.—1 Corinthians 6:19–20

Now the Lord is the Spirit, and where the Spirit of the Lord is, there is freedom. And we, who with unveiled faces all reflect the Lord's glory, are being transformed into his likeness with ever-increasing glory, which comes from the Lord, who is the Spirit.—2 Corinthians 3:17–18

June 9

Apart from Me you can do nothing. On days when the tasks before you seem overwhelming, remember this: I am with you, ready to help. Take a moment to rest in My loving Presence. Whisper: *"Surely the Lord is in this place."* Relax, knowing that you're not meant to be self-sufficient. I designed you to need Me and depend on Me. So *come to Me* just as you are—without shame or pretense. Talk with Me about the challenges you face and the inadequacy you feel. Entreat Me to show you the way forward. Instead of rushing ahead, take small steps of trust, staying in communication with Me.

I am the Vine; you are one of My branches. As you stay connected to Me, My Life flows through you, enabling you to *bear much fruit.* Don't worry about being successful in the eyes of the world. Bearing fruit in My kingdom means *doing the good things planned for you long ago.* So live close to Me—ready to do My will—and I will open up the way before you.

> "I am the vine, you are the branches; he who abides in Me and I in him, he bears much fruit, for apart from Me you can do nothing."—John 15:5 NASB

> When Jacob awoke from his sleep, he thought, "Surely the Lord is in this place, and I was not aware of it."—Genesis 28:16

> "Come to me, all you who are weary and burdened, and I will give you rest. Take my yoke upon you and learn from me, for I am gentle and humble in heart, and you will find rest for your souls."—Matthew 11:28–29

> For we are God's masterpiece. He has created us anew in Christ Jesus, so we can do the good things he planned for us long ago.—Ephesians 2:10 NLT

June 10

RECEIVE MY GLORY-STRENGTH. When ongoing problems require you to *stick it out over the long haul,* beware of responding by grimly *gritting your teeth*—just passing time in a gloomy frame of mind. This passive, negative attitude is *not* the way I want you to approach difficulties.

I am sovereign over the circumstances of your life, so there are always opportunities to be found in them. Don't be like the man who *hid his master's talent in the ground* because he was disgruntled with his circumstances. He gave up and took the easy way out, blaming his hard situation rather than making the most of his opportunity. Actually, the more difficult your circumstance, the more you can gain through it.

I gladly give you Glory-strength. It is exceedingly potent because the Spirit Himself empowers you—*strengthening you in your inner being.* Moreover, My limitless Glory-strength enables you to keep on *enduring the unendurable.* Since this Power is so vast, there is more than enough of it to *spill over into Joy!*

> *We pray that you'll have the strength to stick it out over the long haul—not the grim strength of gritting your teeth but the glory-strength God gives. It is strength that endures the unendurable and spills over into joy.*—COLOSSIANS 1:11 MSG

> *See, the Sovereign LORD comes with power, and his arm rules for him. See, his reward is with him, and his recompense accompanies him.*—ISAIAH 40:10

> *"I was afraid, and went and hid your talent in the ground. Look, there you have what is yours."*—MATTHEW 25:25 NKJV

> *I pray that out of his glorious riches he may strengthen you with power through his Spirit in your inner being.*—EPHESIANS 3:16

June 11

My Presence will go with you, and I will give you rest. Wherever you are, wherever you go, I am with you! This is an astonishing statement, yet it is true. My unseen Presence is more *real* than the flesh-and-blood people around you. But you must "see" Me with the eyes of your heart and communicate with Me through prayer, trusting that I really do hear and care.

I assure you that your prayers make a difference, though not always in ways you can see or in the timeframe you desire. I factor the prayers of believers into My sovereign governing of your world—in ways far too complex for finite minds to grasp. Remember: *As the heavens are higher than the earth, so are My ways and thoughts higher than yours.*

Since My methods of working in the world are often mysterious, it's important to take time to *be still and know that I am God.* Sit quietly in My Presence, breathing in My Peace, and I will give you rest.

> The Lord replied, "My Presence will go with you, and I will give you rest."—Exodus 33:14

> "For My thoughts are not your thoughts, nor are your ways My ways," says the Lord. "For as the heavens are higher than the earth, so are My ways higher than your ways, and My thoughts than your thoughts."—Isaiah 55:8–9 NKJV

> "Be still, and know that I am God; I will be exalted among the nations, I will be exalted in the earth!"—Psalm 46:10 NKJV

> The Lord gives strength to his people; the Lord blesses his people with peace.—Psalm 29:11

June 12

If I am for you, who can be against you? Beloved, I most assuredly *am* for you since you are My follower. Of course, this doesn't mean that no one will ever oppose you. It means that having Me on your side is the most important fact of your existence. Regardless of what happens in your life, you are on the winning side! I already won the victory through My death and resurrection. I am the eternal Victor, and you share in My triumph—no matter how much adversity you encounter on your journey to heaven. Ultimately, nothing and no one can prevail against you because you belong to Me forever.

Knowing that your future is utterly secure can change your perspective dramatically. Instead of living in defensive mode—trying desperately to protect yourself from suffering—you learn to follow Me boldly, wherever I lead. I am training you not only to *seek My Face* and follow My lead but to enjoy this adventure of abandoning yourself to Me. Remember: I am your *ever-present Help in trouble.*

> *What, then, shall we say in response to this? If God is for us, who can be against us?*—Romans 8:31

> *When You said, "Seek My face," my heart said to You, "Your face, Lord, I will seek."*—Psalm 27:8 nkjv

> *God is our refuge and strength, an ever-present help in trouble.*—Psalm 46:1

June 13

Let My Peace protect your mind and heart. Remember that *I am near*, and *rejoice* in My abiding Presence. Spend ample time with Me, *presenting your requests to Me with thanksgiving*. This is the way to receive *My Peace that transcends understanding*. This is how I *guard your heart and your mind*. It's a collaborative, you-and-I-together effort. You never face anything alone!

For Christians, aloneness is an illusion—a dangerous one that can lead to depression or self-pity. The devil and his underlings work hard to cloud your awareness of My Presence. It's crucial for you to recognize and resist their attacks. Fight back with My powerful Word, which is *living and active*. Read it; ponder it; memorize it; speak it.

Even if you're feeling alone, you can talk freely with Me—trusting that *I am with you always*. The longer you communicate with Me, the more convinced you'll become of My nearness. *Resist the devil, and he will flee from you. Come close to Me, and I will come close to you.*

Rejoice in the Lord always. I will say it again: Rejoice! Let your gentleness be evident to all. The Lord is near. Do not be anxious about anything, but in everything, by prayer and petition, with thanksgiving, present your requests to God. And the peace of God, which transcends all understanding, will guard your hearts and your minds in Christ Jesus. —Philippians 4:4–7

For the word of God is living and active and sharper than any two-edged sword, and piercing as far as the division of soul and spirit, of both joints and marrow, and able to judge the thoughts and intentions of the heart. —Hebrews 4:12 nasb

"Surely I am with you always, to the very end of the age." —Matthew 28:20

So humble yourselves before God. Resist the devil, and he will flee from you. Come close to God, and God will come close to you. —James 4:7–8 nlt

June 14

Love is patient. Notice that the very first adjective the apostle Paul uses to describe love is "patient." I treasure this quality in My followers, even though it is not highly visible in most twenty-first-century depictions of love.

Patient people can stay calm while enduring lengthy waits or dealing with difficult people and problems. I encourage you to examine your own life: to see how you respond to waiting and difficulties. This will give you a good measure of how patient—how loving—you are.

"Patience" is listed fourth in *the fruit of the Spirit.* My Spirit will help you grow in this important character trait, especially as you ask Him. Some Christians are afraid to pray for patience. They fear that I'll answer their prayer by subjecting them to severe suffering and trials. However, suffering serves an important purpose in My kingdom, and trials are not optional. They *come so that your faith may be proved genuine and may result in praise, glory, and honor* to Me!

> *Love is patient, love is kind. It does not envy, it does not boast, it is not proud.* —1 Corinthians 13:4

> *But the fruit of the Spirit is love, joy, peace, patience, kindness, goodness, faithfulness, gentleness, self-control; against such things there is no law.* —Galatians 5:22–23 nasb

In this you greatly rejoice, though now for a little while you may have had to suffer grief in all kinds of trials. These have come so that your faith—of greater worth than gold, which perishes even though refined by fire—may be proved genuine and may result in praise, glory and honor when Jesus Christ is revealed. —1 Peter 1:6–7

June 15

COME TO ME, BELOVED. I continually invite you to draw near Me. Be still in My Presence, and *fix your thoughts on Me*. Relax and listen to My Love whispering in your heart: *"I have loved you with an everlasting Love."* Meditate on the glorious truth that *I am with you always*. You can build your life on this rock-solid reality!

The world you inhabit is constantly in flux—you will find no solid ground there. So I challenge you to remain aware of *Me* as you go about your day. You won't be able to do this perfectly, but I'll help you when you ask. You can pray: "Jesus, keep me aware of Your Presence." Let these words echo through your heart and mind frequently. Though your thoughts will sometimes go elsewhere, this simple prayer can draw you back to Me.

The more of Me you have in your life—through staying close to Me—the more joyful you will be and the more I can bless others through you.

> *Therefore, holy brothers, who share in the heavenly calling, fix your thoughts on Jesus, the apostle and high priest whom we confess.* —HEBREWS 3:1

> *The LORD has appeared of old to me, saying: "Yes, I have loved you with an everlasting love; therefore with lovingkindness I have drawn you."* —JEREMIAH 31:3 NKJV

> *"Therefore go and make disciples of all nations, baptizing them in the name of the Father and of the Son and of the Holy Spirit, and teaching them to obey everything I have commanded you. And surely I am with you always, to the very end of the age."* —MATTHEW 28:19–20

June 16

I HAVE GOOD INTENTIONS FOR YOU. They may be radically different from what you hoped or expected, but they are nonetheless good. *I am Light; in Me there is no darkness at all.* So look for My Light in all your circumstances. I am abundantly present in your moments. Your assignment is to be open to Me and My ways with you. Sometimes this requires relinquishing things you had planned or dreamed. You need to remember and wholeheartedly believe that *My way is perfect*, no matter how hard it is.

I am a shield for all who take refuge in Me. When you're feeling afflicted or afraid, come to Me and say: "Lord, I take refuge in *You*." I don't shield you from things I intend for you to deal with, for you have an important part to play in this world. However, I protect you from more dangers and troubles than you can imagine. So make every effort to *live the life I have assigned to you*. Do this in joyful dependence on Me, and *your soul will be richly satisfied.*

> *This is the message we have heard from Him and announce to you, that God is Light, and in Him there is no darkness at all.* —1 JOHN 1:5 NASB

> *As for God, his way is perfect; the word of the LORD is flawless. He is a shield for all who take refuge in him.* —PSALM 18:30

> *Only let each person lead the life that the Lord has assigned to him, and to which God has called him.* —1 CORINTHIANS 7:17 ESV

> *My soul will be satisfied as with the richest of foods; with singing lips my mouth will praise you.* —PSALM 63:5

June 17

SEEK TO BECOME increasingly receptive and responsive to Me. I am always actively involved in your life. Instead of trying to force Me to do what you want, *when* you want it, relax and look for what I'm already doing. Live in a receptive mode—waiting for Me, trusting in My timing. *I am good to those who wait hopefully and expectantly for Me.* Ask Me to open your eyes to see all that I have for you. Such awareness helps you live responsively, ready to do My will.

My followers often fail to see the many blessings I shower on them. They're so busy looking for other things that they miss what is before them—*or* is on the way. They forget I am sovereign God and the timing of events is My prerogative.

I want you to trust Me enough to let Me lead. When a couple is dancing, one of them leads and the other follows. Otherwise, there is confusion and awkwardness. Dance with *Me*, beloved. Follow My lead as I guide you gracefully through your life.

> *The Lord is good to those who wait hopefully and expectantly for Him, to those who seek Him [inquire of and for Him and require Him by right of necessity and on the authority of God's word].*—LAMENTATIONS 3:25 AMP

> *Therefore do not be unwise, but understand what the will of the Lord is.*—EPHESIANS 5:17 NKJV

> *From birth I have relied on you; you brought me forth from my mother's womb. I will ever praise you.*—PSALM 71:6

> *The LORD is my strength and my shield; my heart trusts in him, and I am helped. My heart leaps for joy and I will give thanks to him in song.*—PSALM 28:7

June 18

Stillness is increasingly hard to come by in this restless, agitated world. You must fight to carve out time for Me. Distractions come at you from all sides when you try to sit quietly with Me. But our intimate connection is worth fighting for, so don't give up! Set aside uninterrupted time to spend with Me. Focus on a favorite scripture, and breathe deeply to help yourself unwind. Remember that I am *Immanuel—God with you*. Relax in My peaceful Presence, letting your concerns slip away. *Be still,* My loved one, *and know that I am God.*

The longer you gaze at Me, the more you can rejoice in My majestic splendors—and trust in My sovereign control. *Though the earth give way and the mountains fall into the heart of the sea,* I am *your Refuge.* There is transcendent stability in My Presence. As you ponder the vastness of My Power and Glory, your perspective will change, and your problems will look smaller. *In this world you will have trouble. But take heart! I have overcome the world.*

> "Behold, the virgin shall be with child, and bear a Son, and they shall call His name Immanuel," which is translated, "God with us." —Matthew 1:23 NKJV

> "Be still, and know that I am God; I will be exalted among the nations, I will be exalted in the earth!" —Psalm 46:10 NKJV

> God is our refuge and strength, an ever-present help in trouble. Therefore we will not fear, though the earth give way and the mountains fall into the heart of the sea. —Psalm 46:1–2

> "I have told you these things, so that in me you may have peace. In this world you will have trouble. But take heart! I have overcome the world." —John 16:33

June 19

I GUIDE YOU IN THE WAY OF WISDOM and lead you along straight paths. Wisdom can be defined as "the ability to make good decisions based on knowledge and experience." So it's important to learn what is true and apply that knowledge to your life—especially your decisions. Since *I am the Way, the Truth, and the Life,* I'm the best Guide imaginable. I am also *the Word* who *was with God and is God.* The way of wisdom found in the written Word guides you very effectively. So study My Word and stay near Me as you journey through this world.

Look for and follow the *straight paths* I have for you. I don't promise that these paths will always be easy. But if you walk close to Me, your journey will be much less circuitous. When you look ahead, you perceive confusing bends and turns. Yet when you look back at the ground you've already covered, you can see that I have been with you each step of the way—shielding you from dangers, removing obstacles, straightening out your path.

I guide you in the way of wisdom and lead you along straight paths. —PROVERBS 4:11

Jesus said to him, "I am the way, the truth, and the life. No one comes to the Father except through Me." —JOHN 14:6 NKJV

In the beginning was the Word, and the Word was with God, and the Word was God. —JOHN 1:1

June 20

Don't worry about evil people *who prosper; don't fret about their wicked schemes.* In this day of instant communication, you have access to so much information and news that it's easy to feel overwhelmed. Not only do you *hear* about evil people and their wicked schemes, you also *see* the graphic details. This visual imagery has a powerful impact on your brain chemistry. A steady diet of such carnage can make you anxious and fearful.

I want you to pray about world events and pursue peace as you are able. However, it's crucial to recognize what you can change and what you cannot. Fretting about things that are beyond your control will drain your energy and discourage you. Instead of this hurtful focus, endeavor to *fix your thoughts on Me.* I am with you and for you. *Delight yourself in Me*!

Remember that I am a God of justice and I know everything. Eventually I will right all wrongs. So *be still in My Presence—trusting in Me* with a steadfast heart while *waiting for Me to act.*

Be still in the presence of the Lord, and wait patiently for him to act. Don't worry about evil people who prosper or fret about their wicked schemes. —Psalm 37:7 nlt

Therefore, holy brothers, who share in the heavenly calling, fix your thoughts on Jesus, the apostle and high priest whom we confess. —Hebrews 3:1

Trust in the Lord and do good; dwell in the land and enjoy safe pasture. Delight yourself in the Lord and he will give you the desires of your heart. —Psalm 37:3–4

June 21

I live in you! I am everything you could possibly need in a Savior-God, and I am alive within you. I fill you with radiant Life and Love. I want My Life in you to overflow and impact other people. As you interact with them, ask Me to live through you and love through you. When you collaborate with Me in this way, My Light will reflect from your face, and My Love will grace your words.

You are complete in Me. All that you need for your salvation and your spiritual growth is found in Me. Through *My divine Power* you have everything necessary to persevere in the eternal Life I have given you. I also give you intimate *knowledge of Me.* I invite you to open up and share with Me at the deepest levels—both your struggles and your delights.

Find rest in My finished work on the cross, and rejoice that you are eternally secure in Me. Enjoy rich soul-satisfaction through knowing *Me,* your loving Savior and forever-Friend.

> *My old self has been crucified with Christ. It is no longer I who live, but Christ lives in me.*—Galatians 2:20 NLT

> *And we, who with unveiled faces all reflect the Lord's glory, are being transformed into his likeness with ever-increasing glory, which comes from the Lord, who is the Spirit.*—2 Corinthians 3:18

> *For in Him dwells all the fullness of the Godhead bodily; and you are complete in Him, who is the head of all principality and power.*—Colossians 2:9–10 NKJV

> *His divine power has given us everything we need for life and godliness through our knowledge of him who called us by his own glory and goodness.*—2 Peter 1:3

June 22

Whenever you are feeling sad, I want you to anticipate feeling joyful again. This takes the sting out of your sorrow because you know it is only temporary. Sadness tends to duplicate itself along the timeline—convincing you that you'll always be unhappy. But this is a lie! The truth is, *all* My followers have infinite Joy ahead of them, guaranteed throughout eternity! *No one can take this away from you.*

Your path through this world has many ups and downs. Your down times are difficult, but they serve an important purpose. Pain and struggle help you change and grow stronger when you trust Me in the midst of adversity. Your troubles are comparable to a woman enduring labor pains. Her suffering is very real, and she may wonder how much longer she can bear the pain. However, this arduous struggle produces a wonderful result—a newborn baby. While *you* labor through your earthly struggles, keep your eyes on the promised reward: boundless Joy in heaven! Even now you can grow in awareness of My Presence, where there is *fullness of Joy.*

> "Therefore you now have sorrow; but I will see you again and your heart will rejoice, and your joy no one will take from you."—John 16:22 nkjv

> "A woman giving birth to a child has pain because her time has come; but when her baby is born she forgets the anguish because of her joy that a child is born into the world."—John 16:21

> *You will show me the path of life; in Your presence is fullness of joy; at Your right hand are pleasures forevermore.*—Psalm 16:11 nkjv

June 23

Your citizenship is in heaven. Someday *I will transform your lowly body so that it will be like My glorious body.* You will have an eternity to enjoy your perfect, glorified body. So don't be overly concerned about your physical condition now. Many of My followers cling desperately to their earthly lives when they are at the very portals of paradise. Yet once they let go and pass through that thin veil into heaven, they experience ecstatic Joy surpassing anything they've ever imagined!

Your times are in My hands. I have planned out all your days, and I know exactly how many you have left. Since *your body is a temple of the Holy Spirit,* I expect you to take care of it, but I don't want you to be too focused on its condition. This can make you anxious and distract you from My Presence. Instead, receive each day as a precious gift from Me. Look for both the pleasures and the responsibilities I've placed before you on your path. Hold My hand in joyful trust; I am always by your side.

But our citizenship is in heaven. And we eagerly await a Savior from there, the Lord Jesus Christ.—Philippians 3:20

However, as it is written: "No eye has seen, no ear has heard, no mind has conceived what God has prepared for those who love him."—1 Corinthians 2:9

My times are in your hands.—Psalm 31:15

Do you not know that your body is a temple of the Holy Spirit, who is in you, whom you have received from God? You are not your own; you were bought at a price. Therefore honor God with your body.—1 Corinthians 6:19–20

June 24

I AM MAKING YOU NEW *in the attitude of your mind.* Living close to Me is all about newness and change. I am transforming you *by the entire renewal of your mind.* This is a massive undertaking; you will be under construction till the day you die. However, unlike the inanimate materials that builders use to construct houses, *you* are living, breathing "material." I have given you the amazing ability to think things out and make important choices. I want you to use this godlike ability to cooperate with Me as I transform you. This involves *putting off your old self*—your old way of thinking and doing things—and *putting on the new self.*

To make good, godly choices, you need to know Me as I truly am. Search for Me in My Word; ask My Spirit to illuminate it—shining His Light so that Scripture comes alive to you. The more you choose to live according to My will, the more you will become *like Me*, and the more you can enjoy *walking in the Light of My Presence.*

> *You were taught, with regard to your former way of life, to put off your old self, which is being corrupted by its deceitful desires; to be made new in the attitude of your minds; and to put on the new self, created to be like God in true righteousness and holiness.*—EPHESIANS 4:22–24

> *Therefore, if anyone is in Christ, he is a new creation; the old has gone, the new has come!*—2 CORINTHIANS 5:17

> *Do not be conformed to this world (this age), [fashioned after and adapted to its external, superficial customs], but be transformed (changed) by the [entire] renewal of your mind [by its new ideals and its new attitude], so that you may prove [for yourselves] what is the good and acceptable and perfect will of God.*—ROMANS 12:2 AMP

> *Blessed are those who have learned to acclaim you, who walk in the light of your presence, O LORD.*—PSALM 89:15

June 25

REFUSE TO WORRY, MY CHERISHED ONE. Displace those worry-thoughts with trusting and thankful thoughts. Affirm your faith in Me while praising Me for all that I am and all I have done. This combination of praise and trust is potent. It drives away anxiety and powers of darkness. Also, it strengthens your relationship with Me. You may still have legitimate concerns to deal with, but I will help you with them. As you become more peaceful, you can look at your problems in the Light of My Presence and seek My counsel. Let Scripture inform your thinking so that I can communicate with you more clearly.

Take time to thank Me for the many good things in your life. I want you to express gratefulness in your prayers, in your conversations with others, and in your private thoughts. I read your thoughts continually, and I rejoice when they contain gratitude. You can thank Me even for things you wish were different. This act of faith helps you break free from negative thinking. *In everything give thanks; this is My will for you.*

But I trust in you, O LORD; I say, "You are my God."—PSALM 31:14

I will instruct you and teach you in the way you should go; I will counsel you and watch over you.—PSALM 32:8

In everything give thanks; for this is the will of God in Christ Jesus for you.—1 THESSALONIANS 5:18 NKJV

June 26

If I am for you, who can be against you? It is essential for you to grasp that I truly *am* for you. This is a promise for all of My followers. When things are not going your way and people you trusted turn against you, it's easy to feel as if I've abandoned you. At such times it's vital to tell yourself the truth: I am not only *with* you always, I am also *for* you all the time. This is true on days when you perform well and on days when you don't, when people treat you well and when they don't.

If you really understand and fully believe that I am *for you*, then fear will diminish and you can face adversity more calmly. Knowing that I will never turn against you gives you confidence to persevere in tough times. I approve of you, beloved, because you are Mine! It is *My* opinion of you that prevails—and will continue to prevail throughout eternity. No person and no thing *will be able to separate you from My loving Presence*!

What, then, shall we say in response to this? If God is for us, who can be against us?—Romans 8:31

"The Lord lift up His [approving] countenance upon you and give you peace (tranquility of heart and life continually)."—Numbers 6:26 AMP

Neither height nor depth, nor anything else in all creation, will be able to separate us from the love of God that is in Christ Jesus our Lord.—Romans 8:39

June 27

I AM RICHLY PRESENT in the world around you, in the Word, and in your heart through My Spirit. Ask Me to open the eyes of your heart so that you can "see" Me—for I am lovingly present in all your moments. It's vital to set aside blocks of time for *seeking My Face*. This requires sustained mental discipline: pulling your thoughts back from the idols that entice you and choosing to think about Me. I am the living Word, so you will find Me vibrantly present when you search for Me in the Scriptures.

I created breathtaking beauty in the world, to point you to the One who made everything. *Without Me, nothing was made that has been made.* Whenever you are enjoying something beautiful, thank Me. This pleases Me, and it also increases your pleasure. When you encounter difficult, ugly things in this broken world, trust Me then too. Keep looking for Me in the midst of your good times *and* your hard times. Find hope and comfort through knowing that *all your times are in My hands*.

Look to the LORD and his strength; seek his face always.—1 CHRONICLES 16:11

Through him all things were made; without him nothing was made that has been made.—JOHN 1:3

But as for me, I trust in You, O LORD; I say, "You are my God." My times are in Your hand.—PSALM 31:14–15 NKJV

June 28

Everything you have is a gift from Me, including each breath you breathe. I shower so many blessings on you that it's easy to take some of My precious gifts for granted. Most people don't recognize the wonder of inhaling My Life continually. Yet it was only when I breathed *the breath of Life* into Adam that he *became a living being*.

As you sit quietly in My Presence, try thanking Me silently each time you inhale. As you exhale, affirm your trust in Me. The longer you do this, the more relaxed you will become. While you are taking time with Me, I help you appreciate and thank Me for blessings you often overlook: skies and trees, light and colors, loved ones and daily comforts. The list is endless! The more you look for good things in your life, the clearer your vision becomes.

Of course, your greatest gratitude should be for *eternal Life*, which is yours because you *believe in Me*. This is a priceless forever-gift that will fill you with ever-increasing *Joy in My Presence*!

And the Lord God formed man of the dust of the ground, and breathed into his nostrils the breath of life; and man became a living being. —Genesis 2:7 nkjv

"For God so loved the world that he gave his one and only Son, that whoever believes in him shall not perish but have eternal life." —John 3:16

You have made known to me the path of life; you will fill me with joy in your presence, with eternal pleasures at your right hand. —Psalm 16:11

June 29

Those who sow in tears will reap with songs of Joy. So do not despise your tears, My child; they are precious to Me. Someday *I will wipe every tear from your eyes,* but for now you inhabit a vale of tears. Just as water is necessary for seeds to grow into plants, your tears help you grow into a stronger, more joyful Christian. Your willingness to share in the sorrow of this deeply fallen world gives you depth and compassion. It also enlarges your capacity for Joy—your ability to enjoy Me in good times and tough times.

Songs of Joy have been your birthright ever since you became My follower. Do not neglect this delightful way of worshiping Me and lifting your spirits. Even though it is counterintuitive to sing praises when you're feeling sad, this is a powerful way to lift your heart to Me. As your Joy in Me encounters My delight in you, you can frolic in the Light of My Presence. This is *the Joy of the Lord*!

> Those who sow in tears will reap with songs of joy. He who goes out weeping, carrying seed to sow, will return with songs of joy, carrying sheaves with him.—Psalm 126:5–6

> "He will wipe every tear from their eyes. There will be no more death or mourning or crying or pain, for the old order of things has passed away."—Revelation 21:4

> You shall no longer be termed Forsaken, nor shall your land any more be termed Desolate; but you shall be called Hephzibah, and your land Beulah; for the Lord delights in you, and your land shall be married.—Isaiah 62:4 nkjv

> Nehemiah said, "Go and enjoy choice food and sweet drinks, and send some to those who have nothing prepared. This day is sacred to our Lord. Do not grieve, for the joy of the Lord is your strength."—Nehemiah 8:10

June 30

Trust Me and don't be afraid. Do not be frightened by world events or news reports. These reports are biased—presented as if I do not exist. News clips show tiny bits of world events from which the most important factor has been carefully removed: *My Presence in the world.* As journalists sift through massive amounts of information, they strain out everything about Me and what I'm accomplishing on the earth.

Whenever your world is feeling like a scary place, turn to Me and encourage yourself in My Presence. Follow the example of David, who *strengthened himself in the Lord* when his men were threatening to stone him. You also can find courage through remembering who I am. Ponder My awesome Glory and Power; delight in My unfailing Love. Rejoice that you are on an adventurous journey with Me and your ultimate destination is heaven. As you keep focusing on Me and enjoying the rich relationship I offer you, fear will subside and Joy will rise up within you. Trust in Me wholeheartedly, beloved, for *I am your Strength and your Song.*

> Surely God is my salvation; I will trust and not be afraid. The Lord, the Lord, is my strength and my song; he has become my salvation.—Isaiah 12:2

> The Lord replied, "My Presence will go with you, and I will give you rest."—Exodus 33:14

> Now David was greatly distressed, for the people spoke of stoning him, because the soul of all the people was grieved, every man for his sons and his daughters. But David strengthened himself in the Lord his God.—1 Samuel 30:6 NKJV

July

*"I will not forget you!
See, I have engraved you on the palms of my hands."*

Isaiah 49:15–16

July 1

I have engraved you on the palms of My hands, and this is an eternal commitment. Nothing could ever scrape off or corrode this inscription, for you are My treasured, blood-bought possession.

Engraving on precious metals is a practice that is meant to be permanent. However, the etching may wear off over the years, and sometimes these objects are lost or stolen or melted down. So, put first things first, beloved. Precious metals like gold and silver have *some* value in the world. But they are as worthless as *rubbish compared to the surpassing greatness of knowing Me* forever!

Since you are written on the palms of My hands, you can be assured that you are always visible to Me. People sometimes jot notes on their palms to remind themselves of something important. I have engraved you on *My* palms because you are eternally precious to Me. Rejoice in the wonder of knowing that I—the King of the universe—consider you a priceless treasure! Respond by treasuring *Me* above all else.

> *"Can a mother forget the baby at her breast and have no compassion on the child she has borne? Though she may forget, I will not forget you! See, I have engraved you on the palms of my hands; your walls are ever before me."*—Isaiah 49:15–16

> *What is more, I consider everything a loss compared to the surpassing greatness of knowing Christ Jesus my Lord, for whose sake I have lost all things. I consider them rubbish, that I may gain Christ and be found in him, not having a righteousness of my own that comes from the law, but that which is through faith in Christ— the righteousness that comes from God and is by faith.*—Philippians 3:8–9

> *Then will I go to the altar of God, to God, my joy and my delight. I will praise you with the harp, O God, my God.*—Psalm 43:4

July 2

When your spirit grows faint *within you, it is I who know your way.* This is one of the benefits of weakness. It highlights the fact that you cannot find your way without help from Me. If you are feeling weary or confused, you can choose to look away from those feelings and turn wholeheartedly toward Me. Pour out your heart freely, and then rest in the Presence of the One who *knows your way* perfectly—all the way to heaven.

Continue this practice of gazing at Me even during the times you're feeling strong and confident. In fact, this is when you are most at risk of going the wrong direction. Instead of assuming that you know the next step of your journey, train yourself to make your plans in My Presence—asking Me to guide you. Remember that *My ways and thoughts are higher than yours, as the heavens are higher than the earth.* Let this remembrance draw you into worshiping Me, *the High and Lofty One who inhabits eternity* and who reaches down to help you.

> *When my spirit grows faint within me, it is you who know my way. In the path where I walk men have hidden a snare for me.*—Psalm 142:3

> *"As the heavens are higher than the earth, so are my ways higher than your ways and my thoughts than your thoughts."*—Isaiah 55:9

> *For thus says the High and Lofty One who inhabits eternity, whose name is Holy: "I dwell in the high and holy place, with him who has a contrite and humble spirit, to revive the spirit of the humble, and to revive the heart of the contrite ones."*—Isaiah 57:15 NKJV

July 3

I AM THE LORD YOUR GOD, who takes hold of your right hand and says to you, Do not fear; I will help you. It is essential for you to recognize—and believe—that I am not only your Savior, I am also *your God*. Many people try to cast Me as a great human model, a martyr who sacrificed everything for others. But if I were only human, you would still be *dead in your sins*. The One who takes hold of your hand and calms your fears is the living God! Rejoice as you ponder this astonishing truth. Delight in the mysterious wonder of the Trinity—Father, Son, and Spirit—one God.

Take time to wait in My Presence. Tell Me your troubles; *pour out your heart before Me.* Hear Me saying, "Do not be afraid, beloved. I am here—ready to help you." I don't condemn you for your fears, but I do want you to displace them with hope and trust in Me. As you trustingly *put your hope in Me, My unfailing Love rests upon you.*

> "For I am the LORD, your God, who takes hold of your right hand and says to you, Do not fear; I will help you."—ISAIAH 41:13

> As for you, you were dead in your transgressions and sins.—EPHESIANS 2:1

> Trust in Him at all times, you people; pour out your heart before Him; God is a refuge for us.—PSALM 62:8 NKJV

> May your unfailing love rest upon us, O LORD, even as we put our hope in you.—PSALM 33:22

July 4

To everyone who is victorious, I will give fruit from the Tree of Life in paradise. Beloved, there is one sense in which you are already victorious. For *those I predestined, I also called; those I called, I also justified; those I justified, I also glorified.* I brought you out of darkness into My kingdom of Light; this means that you are on your way to Glory! The victory has been won—accomplished through My finished work on the cross.

There is another sense in which you must struggle throughout your lifetime to be victorious. In this world you will encounter fiery trials and temptations that highlight your sinfulness and weaknesses. This can lead to discouragement as you view your multiple failures. You may even feel as if you no longer belong to Me, but do not be deceived by feelings. Instead, cling tenaciously to My hand, trusting that the joyous wonders of paradise are indeed your promised inheritance. The Light in the heavenly city is dazzlingly bright, for *the Glory of God illumines it and the Lamb is its Light.*

> *"Let this message sink into the ears of anyone who listens to what the Spirit is saying to the churches: To everyone who is victorious, I will give fruit from the Tree of Life in the Paradise of God."*—Revelation 2:7 TLB

> *And those he predestined, he also called; those he called, he also justified; those he justified, he also glorified.*—Romans 8:30

> *The city had no need of the sun or of the moon to shine in it, for the glory of God illuminated it. The Lamb is its light.*—Revelation 21:23 NKJV

JULY 5

WALK IN THE LIGHT of My Presence. This delightful way to live involves *acclaiming Me, rejoicing in My Name,* and *exulting in My righteousness.* To acclaim Me is to praise Me in a very strong and enthusiastic way, sometimes with shouts and applause. When you rejoice in My Name, you find Joy in all that I am—your Savior and Shepherd, your Lord and God, your Sovereign King, your Friend who loves you with *unfailing Love.* You can exult in My righteousness because I have shared it with you. Though you will continue to sin in this life, My perfect righteousness is already credited to your account.

When you walk in My glorious Light, *My blood continually cleanses you from all sin.* As you seek to live near Me, acknowledging that you're a sinner in need of forgiveness, My holy illumination purifies you. This blessing is for all believers, making it possible for My followers to *have rich fellowship with one another.* So walk in the Light with Me, My friend. Spend time enjoying My bright, loving Presence.

> *Blessed are those who have learned to acclaim you, who walk in the light of your presence, O* LORD. *They rejoice in your name all day long; they exult in your righteousness.* —PSALM 89:15–16

Let your face shine on your servant; save me in your unfailing love. —PSALM 31:16

> *This righteousness from God comes through faith in Jesus Christ to all who believe.* —ROMANS 3:22

But if we walk in the light as He is in the light, we have fellowship with one another, and the blood of Jesus Christ His Son cleanses us from all sin. —1 JOHN 1:7 NKJV

July 6

I AM BEFORE ALL THINGS, and in Me all things hold together. I have always been and will always be. *All things were created by Me: things in heaven and on earth, visible and invisible.* I am Lord over creation, over the church, over everything! Worship Me as your vibrant Lord, *the living God.* I want My loved ones to thirst for Me—*as the deer pants for streams of water.*

Do not be satisfied with only thinking about Me or knowing Me intellectually. Thirst for experiential knowledge of Me, grounded in sound biblical truth. Seek to *know My Love that far surpasses mere knowledge.* You will need the help of My Spirit to accomplish this.

You must *be strengthened with mighty Power by the Holy Spirit, who indwells your innermost being and personality.* Invite Him to empower and guide you in this amorous adventure. But remember that *I* am the goal of your searching—make Me central in your quest. *You will seek Me and find Me when you search for Me with all your heart*!

> *For by him all things were created: things in heaven and on earth, visible and invisible . . . all things were created by him and for him. He is before all things, and in him all things hold together.*—COLOSSIANS 1:16–17

> *As the deer pants for streams of water, so my soul pants for you, O God. My soul thirsts for God, for the living God. When can I go and meet with God?*—PSALM 42:1–2

> *May He grant you out of the rich treasury of His glory to be strengthened and reinforced with mighty power in the inner man by the [Holy] Spirit. . . . May Christ through your faith [actually] dwell (settle down, abide, make His permanent home) in your hearts! May you be rooted deep in love and founded securely on love . . . [that you may really come] to know [practically, through experience for yourselves] the love of Christ, which far surpasses mere knowledge [without experience]; that you may be filled [through all your being] unto all the fullness of God!*—EPHESIANS 3:16–19 AMP

> *"And you will seek Me and find Me, when you search for Me with all your heart."*—JEREMIAH 29:13 NKJV

JULY 7

I AM THE GATE; whoever enters through Me will be saved. I am the only Entrance to *the path of Life*—to eternal Life. If you do not enter through Me, you will never find salvation from your sins.

Some people compare the spiritual journey to climbing a mountain: There are many paths that lead to the summit, and all the successful climbers will end up at the same place. People often use this analogy to claim that all paths to God are equally effective. Nothing could be further from the truth! You can enter salvation only through *Me*, the one true Gate.

Once you have come through this Gate, you can enjoy walking along the path of Life. I don't guarantee you an easy journey, but I *do* promise to be with you every moment. No matter what difficulties you may encounter along the way, *there is Joy to be found in My Presence.* Moreover, each step you take brings you closer to your goal—your heavenly home.

> "I am the gate; whoever enters through me will be saved. He will come in and go out, and find pasture."—JOHN 10:9

> *You will show me the path of life; in Your presence is fullness of joy; at Your right hand are pleasures forevermore.*—PSALM 16:11 NKJV

> *She will give birth to a son, and you are to give him the name Jesus, because he will save his people from their sins.*—MATTHEW 1:21

> *The Lord will certainly deliver and draw me to Himself from every assault of evil. He will preserve and bring me safe unto His heavenly kingdom. To Him be the glory forever and ever. Amen (so be it).*—2 TIMOTHY 4:18 AMP

July 8

I DRAW NEAR YOU in the present moment. Seek to enjoy My Presence in the present; trust and thankfulness are your best allies in this quest.

When you wallow in the past or worry about the future, your awareness of Me grows dim. But the more you trust Me, the more fully you can live in the present, where My Presence awaits you always. Speak to Me frequently: "I trust You, Jesus." *"I love You, O LORD, my strength."* These short prayers keep you close to Me—confident that I'm lovingly watching over you.

It's important for you to grow not only more trusting but more thankful. A grateful attitude is essential for living near Me. Ingratitude is offensive to Me, and it drags you down both spiritually and emotionally. Remember that *you are receiving a kingdom that cannot be shaken*—no matter what is happening in your life or in the world. This means that you have a constant, unshakable reason to *be thankful*. Stay anchored to Me and enjoy My Presence by *giving thanks in all circumstances*.

I love You, O LORD, my strength.—PSALM 18:1 NASB

Therefore, since we are receiving a kingdom that cannot be shaken, let us be thankful, and so worship God acceptably with reverence and awe, for our "God is a consuming fire."—HEBREWS 12:28–29

Give thanks in all circumstances; for this is the will of God in Christ Jesus for you.—1 THESSALONIANS 5:18 ESV

July 9

As you look to Me more and more, I become your joyful Focus. When you look at the world today, many disturbing things call out for your attention. If you concentrate too much on those things, you will become deeply discouraged. Meanwhile, the One who is *continually with you* calls out: "I am here! Look to Me, beloved, and find Joy in Me!"

My Presence can bless you always—even when it's only in the background of your mind. You can learn to stay conscious of Me while you are engaged in other matters. The magnificent brain I gave you can function on several tracks at once. When you're doing something that involves a lot of brainpower, your awareness of My Presence will be subtle. Nonetheless, it can be comforting and encouraging.

Making Me your joyous Focus is *not* escapism. On the contrary, your attentiveness to Me strengthens you and gives you courage to cope with the difficulties in your life. The more persistently you look to Me, the more effective and joyful you will be.

Look to the Lord and his strength; seek his face always.—Psalm 105:4

Nevertheless I am continually with You; You hold me by my right hand.—Psalm 73:23 nkjv

Be strong and courageous. Do not fear or be in dread of them, for it is the Lord your God who goes with you. He will not leave you or forsake you.—Deuteronomy 31:6 esv

July 10

You overwhelmingly conquer through Me, the King of Glory who loves you. No matter what is happening in this fractured, fallen world or in your own life, you are victorious. I won the Victory once for all time through My sacrificial death and miraculous resurrection. *My unfailing Love* has accomplished this wondrous conquest and made you much, much more than a conqueror. You're an heir of the kingdom of eternal Life and Light!

Nothing will be able to separate you from My Love! Ponder what it means to have *Me* as the Lover of your soul every moment, forever and ever. Your soul is the eternal part of you, the part that can never be separated from Me. It is not what you see in the mirror or what other people reflect back to you. It is the essence of who you are—the "real you" that is *being transformed from Glory to Glory*. Therefore, do not be discouraged by the defects you see in yourself. Instead, remember that you are continually being *transformed into My image*—and rejoice!

> *But in all these things we overwhelmingly conquer through Him who loved us. For I am convinced that neither death, nor life, nor angels, nor principalities, nor things present, nor things to come, nor powers, nor height, nor depth, nor any other created thing, will be able to separate us from the love of God, which is in Christ Jesus our Lord.*—Romans 8:37–39 NASB

> *But I trust in your unfailing love; my heart rejoices in your salvation. I will sing to the Lord, for he has been good to me.*—Psalm 13:5–6

> *But we all, with unveiled face, beholding as in a mirror the glory of the Lord, are being transformed into the same image from glory to glory, just as by the Spirit of the Lord.*—2 Corinthians 3:18 NKJV

July 11

Your competence comes from Me. This means there is no place for pride in your achievements. It also means you are capable of much more than you think possible. The combination of your natural abilities and My supernatural empowerment is very effective. I have called you to live in joyful dependence on Me, so don't hesitate to ask Me for help. Make every effort to discern My will for you—searching the Scriptures and *seeking My Face*. Also, seek wise counsel from other Christians. I will show you the way to go forward according to My wisdom and will.

Ask My Spirit to guide you along the pathway I have chosen for you. This Holy Helper will equip and empower you to achieve My purposes in your life. Thank Me for everything: the abilities I have given you, the opportunities before you, and My Spirit's enabling you to accomplish important things in My kingdom. Stay in communication with Me, enjoying My Company as you journey along *the path of Life. In My Presence is fullness of Joy*!

> *Not that we are competent in ourselves to claim anything for ourselves, but our competence comes from God.*—2 Corinthians 3:5

> *Glory in his holy name; let the hearts of those who seek the Lord rejoice. Look to the Lord and his strength; seek his face always.*—1 Chronicles 16:10–11

> *Rejoice always, pray without ceasing, in everything give thanks; for this is the will of God in Christ Jesus for you.*—1 Thessalonians 5:16–18 nkjv

> *You will show me the path of life; in Your presence is fullness of joy; at Your right hand are pleasures forevermore.*—Psalm 16:11 nkjv

July 12

I WANT YOU TO DRAW WATER *from the springs of salvation with Joy.* These wells are unfathomably deep, and they are filled to the brim with My blessings. The worth of your salvation is inestimable, far greater than all of earth's fortunes—past, present, and future. When your life in this world ends, you will live with Me *forever* in a perfect environment filled with dazzling Glory. You will worship Me with untold numbers of My followers, all of whom will relate to one another with wondrous Love—and respond to Me with even *greater* Love. Moreover, you will be able to receive Love from Me in unimaginably great measure!

The assurance of forevermore-pleasures awaiting you in heaven can help you endure your struggles in this world. I understand the difficulties you're facing, but remember: I am *your Strength and Song.* I am strong enough to carry you when you feel as if you can go no further. I even enable you to sing with Me—on good days *and* hard days. I, *your Song,* can fill you with Joy!

> *"Surely God is my salvation; I will trust and not be afraid. The LORD, the LORD, is my strength and my song; he has become my salvation." With joy you will draw water from the wells of salvation.*—ISAIAH 12:2–3

> *For you know the grace of our Lord Jesus Christ, that though he was rich, yet for your sakes he became poor, so that you through his poverty might become rich.*—2 CORINTHIANS 8:9

> *You will show me the path of life; in Your presence is fullness of joy; at Your right hand are pleasures forevermore.*—PSALM 16:11 NKJV

July 13

Sometimes you need help even to ask for My help. As you try to do several things at once, you find yourself moving faster and faster—interrupting one thing to do another. If your phone rings at such a time, your stress level rises even higher. The best way out of this turmoil is to STOP everything. Take a few deep breaths and whisper My Name. Acknowledge your need for My guidance through the moments of this day. I will lovingly lead you along *paths of righteousness—for My Name's sake.*

When you are preparing to do something challenging, you usually take time to enlist My help. But when you're facing everyday tasks, you tend to dive in unassisted—as if you can handle these matters alone. How much better it is to approach *everything* in humble dependence on Me! Whenever you find yourself in "diving" mode, ask Me to help you stop and seek Me—letting Me show you the way to go forward. *I will guide you along the best pathway for your life.*

> [The Lord] restores my soul. He guides me in paths
> of righteousness for his name's sake.—Psalm 23:3

> God did this so that men would seek him and perhaps reach out for him
> and find him, though he is not far from each one of us.—Acts 17:27

> The Lord says, "I will guide you along the best pathway for your
> life. I will advise you and watch over you."—Psalm 32:8 NLT

July 14

B<small>E STILL IN</small> M<small>Y</small> P<small>RESENCE</small>, *and wait patiently for Me to act.* Stillness is a rare commodity in this world. Many people judge themselves and their day by how much they have accomplished. Resting in My Presence is usually not one of those accomplishments. Yet how much blessing can be found in this holy rest!

Peace and Joy abound in My Presence, but it takes time for them to soak into your inner being. It also takes trust. Instead of fussing and fuming when your plans are thwarted, wait patiently for Me to act. You can *watch in hope for Me* because I am *God your Savior.* Be assured that *I will hear you.* I may not answer as soon as you would like, but I always respond to your prayers in the best way.

Don't worry about evil people or fret about their wicked schemes. I laugh at the wicked, for I know their day is coming. Rest in Me, beloved. *Be still, and know that I am God.*

> *Be still in the presence of the* L<small>ORD</small>, *and wait patiently for him to act. Don't worry about evil people who prosper or fret about their wicked schemes.* —P<small>SALM</small> 37:7 <small>NLT</small>

> *As for me, I watch in hope for the* L<small>ORD</small>, *I wait for God my Savior; my God will hear me.* —M<small>ICAH</small> 7:7

> *The Lord laughs at the wicked, for he knows their day is coming.* —P<small>SALM</small> 37:13

> *"Be still, and know that I am God; I will be exalted among the nations, I will be exalted in the earth!"* —P<small>SALM</small> 46:10 <small>NKJV</small>

July 15

My unfailing Love is better than life itself! There is no limit to My Love—in quality, quantity, or duration. It is infinitely better than anything this world offers, and it will never run out. *How priceless is My unfailing Love!*

Consider the parable of *the merchant looking for fine pearls. When he found one of great value, he sold everything he had and bought it.* My Love is like that pearl: so valuable that it is worth losing everything else to secure it forever.

Though gaining My Love is worth losing your life, it actually enriches your life. This glorious gift provides a foundation for you to build on, and it improves your relationships with other people. Knowing that you are perfectly and eternally loved helps you grow into the one I designed you to be. *Grasping how wide and long and high and deep is My Love* for you leads you into worship. *This* is where your intimacy with Me grows by leaps and bounds—as you joyously celebrate My magnificent Presence!

> Your unfailing love is better than life itself; how I praise you!—Psalm 63:3 nlt

> How priceless is your unfailing love! Both high and low among men find refuge in the shadow of your wings.—Psalm 36:7

> "Again, the kingdom of heaven is like a merchant looking for fine pearls. When he found one of great value, he went away and sold everything he had and bought it."—Matthew 13:45–46

> And I pray that you, being rooted and established in love, may have power, together with all the saints, to grasp how wide and long and high and deep is the love of Christ.—Ephesians 3:17–18

July 16

Proclaim My salvation day after day. You need to recall the truth of the gospel every single day: *By grace you have been saved through faith, and this is not your own doing; it's a gift—not a result of works.* This truth is very countercultural. The world tells you that you have to work at being good enough. Your own fallen mind and heart will agree with these messages unless you are vigilant. That's why Scripture warns you to *be alert*. The devil is *the accuser* of My followers. His accusations discourage and defeat many Christians, so remind yourself of gospel-truth frequently.

The best response to the glorious gift of grace is a thankful heart that delights in doing My will. It is vital to proclaim the gospel not only to yourself but to the world. *Declare My Glory to the nations!* Seek to share this good news—both near (to family, friends, coworkers) and far (to the nations). *All peoples* need to know the truth about Me. Let your thankfulness motivate you, energize you, and fill you with Joy!

Sing to the Lord, praise his name; proclaim his salvation day after day. Declare his glory among the nations, his marvelous deeds among all peoples.—Psalm 96:2–3

For by grace you have been saved through faith. And this is not your own doing; it is the gift of God, not a result of works, so that no one may boast.—Ephesians 2:8–9 ESV

Be self-controlled and alert. Your enemy the devil prowls around like a roaring lion looking for someone to devour.—1 Peter 5:8

Then I heard a loud voice in heaven say: "Now have come the salvation and the power and the kingdom of our God, and the authority of his Christ. For the accuser of our brothers, who accuses them before our God day and night, has been hurled down."—Revelation 12:10

July 17

Blessed are those who have learned to acclaim Me. The word "acclaim" means to express enthusiastic approval. This is not the natural inclination of mankind. It is something you need to learn—and practice. Begin with your thoughts. Instead of thinking of Me in boring, repetitive ways, ponder My glorious greatness! I spoke the world into existence. I formed people in My own image and gave them eternal souls. I created beauty in the world and throughout the universe. I am infinitely more brilliant than the greatest genius imaginable. My wisdom is *unsearchable,* and My Love is unfailing. Learn to think great thoughts of Me and to express them enthusiastically. The Psalms provide excellent instruction in this quest.

To acclaim Me also means to acknowledge My excellence publicly. *You are the light of the world* because you know Me as your Savior-God. I want you to *let your light shine before men*; tell them the wonders of who I am—and all I have done. *Proclaim the excellencies of Him who called you out of darkness into His marvelous Light.*

Blessed are those who have learned to acclaim you, who walk in the light of your presence, O Lord.—Psalm 89:15

Oh, the depth of the riches of the wisdom and knowledge of God! How unsearchable his judgments, and his paths beyond tracing out!—Romans 11:33

"You are the light of the world. A city set on a hill cannot be hidden; nor does anyone light a lamp and put it under a basket, but on the lampstand, and it gives light to all who are in the house. Let your light shine before men in such a way that they may see your good works, and glorify your Father who is in heaven."—Matthew 5:14–16 nasb

But you are a chosen race, *a* royal priesthood, a holy nation, a people for God's own possession, *so that you may proclaim the excellencies of Him who has called you out of darkness into His marvelous light.*—1 Peter 2:9 nasb

July 18

Rejoice always! This is one of the shortest verses in the Bible, but it is radiant with heavenly Light. I made you in My image, and I crafted you with the ability to choose Joy in the moments of your life. When your mind is going down an unpleasant, gloomy path, stop it in its tracks with this glorious command. See how many times each day you can remind yourself to rejoice.

It is important not only to be joyful but to think about specific reasons for rejoicing. They can be as simple as My daily provisions for you—food, shelter, clothing. Relationships with loved ones can also be a rich source of Joy. Since you are My beloved, your relationship with Me is an ever-present wellspring of gladness. These joyful thoughts will light up both your mind and your heart, enabling you to find more pleasure in your life.

Choosing to rejoice will bless you and those around you. It will also strengthen your relationship with Me.

Rejoice always.—1 Thessalonians 5:16 NKJV

So God created man in His own image; in the image of God He created him; male and female He created them.—Genesis 1:27 NKJV

Rejoice in the Lord always. I will say it again: Rejoice!—Philippians 4:4

July 19

I am your Help and your Shield. Pay special attention to the possessive pronoun *your.* I am not just *a* Help and *a* Shield. I am *yours*—for all time and throughout eternity. Let this forever-commitment strengthen and encourage you as you walk with Me through this day. *I will never leave you or forsake you.* You can depend on Me!

Because I am your Help, you don't need to fear your inadequacy. When the task ahead of you looks daunting, rejoice that I stand ready to assist you. Openly acknowledge your insufficiency, and trust in My infinite sufficiency. You and I *together* can accomplish anything, as long as it is My will.

You definitely need Me as your Shield. I protect you from many dangers—physical, emotional, and spiritual. Sometimes you're aware of My protective work on your behalf, but I also shield you from perils you never even suspect. Find comfort in this assurance of My powerful Presence watching over you. *Fear no evil,* My cherished one, *for I am with you.*

> *We wait in hope for the Lord; he is our help and our shield.* —Psalm 33:20

> *The Lord himself goes before you and will be with you; he will never leave you nor forsake you. Do not be afraid; do not be discouraged.* —Deuteronomy 31:8

> *I can do all things through Christ who strengthens me.* —Philippians 4:13 nkjv

> *Even though I walk through the valley of the shadow of death, I will fear no evil, for you are with me; your rod and your staff, they comfort me.* —Psalm 23:4

July 20

Cling to Me, beloved, for *My right hand supports you*. When you hold onto Me in childlike dependence, you are demonstrating your commitment to Me. I use difficult times to refine your faith and prove that it is genuine. As you cling to Me in the midst of adversity, your faith grows stronger and you are comforted. Having endured various trials, you gain confidence that you can cope with future hardships—with My help. You realize more and more that I will always be available to help you.

In the middle of the night or in the midst of tough times, remember that My right hand supports you. This hand that holds you up is strong and righteous; there's no limit to how much support it can provide. So when you're feeling overwhelmed, don't give up. Instead, *look to Me and My Strength*. Be assured that My powerful hand is also righteous; what it provides is good. *Do not fear, for I will strengthen you and help you. I will uphold you with My righteous right hand.*

My soul clings to you; your right hand upholds me.—Psalm 63:8

These have come so that your faith—of greater worth than gold, which perishes even though refined by fire—may be proved genuine and may result in praise, glory and honor when Jesus Christ is revealed.—1 Peter 1:7

Look to the Lord and his strength; seek his face always.—Psalm 105:4

"So do not fear, for I am with you; do not be dismayed, for I am your God. I will strengthen you and help you; I will uphold you with my righteous right hand."—Isaiah 41:10

July 21

THOSE WHO LOOK TO ME ARE RADIANT. I am the Sun that shines on continually, even when your circumstances are difficult and the way ahead looks dark. Because you know Me as Savior, you have a source of Light that overcomes the darkness. I designed you to *reflect My Glory*, and you do so by looking to Me—turning your face toward the Light. Take time to be still in My Presence, with your face upturned to absorb My radiance. The longer you stay in this Light-drenched atmosphere, the more I can bless and strengthen you.

While you are resting with Me, you may want to whisper the words of Jacob: *"Surely the Lord is in this place."* I am everywhere at every time, so this statement is always true—whether or not you sense My nearness.

Taking time to bask in My Love-Light, soaking in My radiance, can enhance your awareness of My Presence. Also, time spent with Me helps you to be a light in the world—radiating My Love to those around you.

Those who look to him are radiant; their faces are never covered with shame.—PSALM 34:5

And we, who with unveiled faces all reflect the Lord's glory, are being transformed into his likeness with ever-increasing glory, which comes from the Lord, who is the Spirit.—2 CORINTHIANS 3:18

When Jacob awoke from his sleep, he thought, "Surely the LORD is in this place, and I was not aware of it."—GENESIS 28:16

"Let your light so shine before men, that they may see your good works and glorify your Father in heaven."—MATTHEW 5:16 NKJV

July 22

You have received new birth into a living hope through My resurrection from the dead. I died on the cross to pay the penalty for the sins of all My followers. However, if I had remained dead, *your faith would be useless* and you would forever be spiritually dead—*still guilty of your sins.* Of course, it was impossible for My death to be permanent because I am God! As I stated clearly to those who questioned Me, *I and My Father are One.*

My resurrection is an extremely well-documented historical fact. This miraculous event opened the way for you to experience *new birth.* By confessing your sinfulness and trusting Me as your Savior, you have become one of My own—walking along a pathway to heaven. Because I am your living Savior, you walk along a way of *living hope!* The Light of My loving Presence shines upon you always, even in your darkest, most difficult moments. Look up to Me, beloved. Let My brilliant Love-Light pierce the darkness and fill your heart with Joy.

> *Praise be to the God and Father of our Lord Jesus Christ! In his great mercy he has given us new birth into a living hope through the resurrection of Jesus Christ from the dead.* —1 Peter 1:3

> *And if Christ has not been raised, then your faith is useless and you are still guilty of your sins.* —1 Corinthians 15:17 NLT

> *As for you, you were dead in your transgressions and sins.* —Ephesians 2:1

> *"I and My Father are one."* —John 10:30 NKJV

July 23

I AM GOD YOUR SAVIOR. No matter what is happening in the world, you can *be joyful in Me.* Your planet has been in a terribly fallen condition ever since Adam and Eve first disobeyed Me. They lost their first two sons in a heartbreaking way. Cain killed his younger brother Abel because he was jealous of him. Then God punished Cain by sentencing him to a life of *restless wandering on the earth.*

Ongoing effects of the Fall continue to make the world a dangerous, uncertain place. So the challenge before you each day is to be joyful in the midst of brokenness. Remind yourself often: "Jesus is with me and for me. *Nothing can separate me from His Love.*" Pour your energies into enjoying My Presence and looking for the good that remains on the earth. Use your gifts to shine My Light into places where I have given you access. *Have no fear of bad news,* for I am able to bring good out of evil. Train your heart to be *steadfast, trusting in Me,* your Savior.

Yet I will rejoice in the LORD, *I will be joyful in God my Savior.*—HABAKKUK 3:18

"When you work the ground, it will no longer yield its crops for you. You will be a restless wanderer on the earth."—GENESIS 4:12

Neither height nor depth, nor anything else in all creation, will be able to separate us from the love of God that is in Christ Jesus our Lord.—ROMANS 8:39

He will have no fear of bad news; his heart is steadfast, trusting in the LORD.—PSALM 112:7

July 24

Do not be afraid; do not be discouraged. You are looking ahead at uncertainties, letting them unnerve you. Fear and discouragement are waiting alongside your pathway into the future—ready to accompany you if you let them. *Yet I am always with you, holding you by your right hand.* Because I live beyond time, I am also on the path up ahead—shining brightly, beckoning you on, encouraging you to fix your gaze on Me. Cling tightly to My hand, and walk resolutely past those dark presences of fearfulness and despair. Keep looking toward My radiant Presence that beams out rays of *unfailing Love* and endless encouragement.

Your confidence comes from knowing I am continually with you *and* I am already in your future, preparing the way before you. Listen as I call back to you—words of warning and wisdom, courage and hope: *Do not fear, for I am with you. Do not be dismayed, for I am your God. I will strengthen you and help you; I will uphold you with My righteous right hand.*

> *The Lord himself goes before you and will be with you; he will never leave you nor forsake you. Do not be afraid; do not be discouraged.*—Deuteronomy 31:8

> *Yet I am always with you; you hold me by my right hand.*—Psalm 73:23

> *May your unfailing love be my comfort, according to your promise to your servant.*—Psalm 119:76

> *"So do not fear, for I am with you; do not be dismayed, for I am your God. I will strengthen you and help you; I will uphold you with my righteous right hand."*—Isaiah 41:10

July 25

It is in the present moment that you find Me ever near you. My Presence in the present is an endless source of Joy—*a continual feast*! I am training you to *rejoice in Me always*. This is a moment-by-moment choice. It is possible to find Joy in Me even during your most difficult times. I am always near, so I am constantly available to help you. I can even carry you through your hardest times.

Imagine a woman who has become engaged to a man she deeply loves and admires. Her heart overflows with pleasure whenever she thinks about her beloved. While he is on her mind, problems fade into the background, unable to dampen her enthusiasm and excitement. Similarly, when you remember that I am your Betrothed and you are promised to Me forever, you can find pleasure in Me even though you face many difficulties. The soul-satisfaction you find in Me helps you relate well to other people. As you enjoy My loving Presence, you are able to bless others with your Joy.

All the days of the afflicted are evil, but he who is of a merry heart has a continual feast.—Proverbs 15:15 nkjv

Rejoice in the Lord always. I will say it again: Rejoice! Let your gentleness be evident to all. The Lord is near.—Philippians 4:4–5

My soul will be satisfied as with the richest of foods; with singing lips my mouth will praise you.—Psalm 63:5

About Benjamin he said: "Let the beloved of the Lord rest secure in him, for he shields him all day long, and the one the Lord loves rests between his shoulders."—Deuteronomy 33:12

July 26

I BROADEN THE PATH BENEATH YOU so that your ankles do not turn. This shows how intricately I am involved in your life-journey. I know exactly what is before you, and I can alter the path ahead of you to make your way easier. Sometimes I enable you to see what I have done on your behalf. At other times you are blissfully unaware of the hardship I have spared you. Either way, My work to widen the way before you demonstrates how lovingly I am involved in your life.

From your perspective, My workings are often mysterious. I do not protect you—or anyone—from *all* adversity. Neither was *I* shielded from hardship during my thirty-three years of living in your world. On the contrary, I willingly suffered unimaginable pain, humiliation, and agony on the cross—for your sake! When My Father turned away from Me, I experienced unspeakable suffering. But because I was willing to endure that excruciating isolation from Him, you will *never* have to suffer alone. I have promised: *I am with you always!*

You broaden the path beneath me, so that my ankles do not turn. —PSALM 18:36

And about the ninth hour Jesus cried out with a loud voice, saying, "Eli, Eli, lama sabachthani?" that is, "My God, My God, why have You forsaken Me?" —MATTHEW 27:46 NKJV

". . . And teaching them to obey everything I have commanded you. And surely I am with you always, to the very end of the age." —MATTHEW 28:20

July 27

WHOEVER BELIEVES IN ME does not believe in Me only, but in the One who sent Me. When you look at Me, you see the One who sent Me. I came into the world not only to be your Savior but also to help you see the Father more clearly. He and I always work in perfect unity. As I proclaimed when I was teaching in the temple in Jerusalem: *"I and My Father are one."* So when you strive to live close to Me—*fixing your eyes on Me*—you are by no means ignoring My Father.

The Trinity, comprised of Father, Son, and Holy Spirit, is a great gift to you; it is also a mystery far beyond your comprehension. This blessing of three Persons in one greatly enriches your prayer life. You can pray to the Father in My Name; you can also speak directly to Me. And the Holy Spirit is continually available to help you with your prayers. Do not be perturbed by mysteries of the Godhead. Instead, respond to these wonders with joyous praise and adoration!

> Then Jesus cried out, "When a man believes in me, he does not believe in me only, but in the one who sent me. When he looks at me, he sees the one who sent me."—JOHN 12:44–45

> "I and My Father are one."—JOHN 10:30 NKJV

> Let us fix our eyes on Jesus, the author and perfecter of our faith, who for the joy set before him endured the cross, scorning its shame, and sat down at the right hand of the throne of God.—HEBREWS 12:2

> Let everything that has breath praise the LORD. Praise the LORD.—PSALM 150:6

July 28

I AM THE LIVING ONE *who sees you* always. I see into the very depths of your being. Not even one of your thoughts escapes My notice. My intimate awareness of everything about you means that you are never alone—in good times or in struggles. It also means that I want to cleanse your thoughts from their sinful tendencies.

When you find yourself thinking in a loveless, hurtful way, confess it to Me immediately. Ask Me not only to forgive you but to change you. You don't need to belabor your confession, as if you had to convince Me to extend grace to you. I went through torturous execution and utter separation from My Father so that I could *remove your sins as far from you as the east is from the west*. I delight in forgiving you!

Remember that even now I view you clothed in radiant garments—My perfect righteousness. And I can already see in you the glorious vision you will be when heaven becomes your home.

> *Therefore the well was called Beer-lahai-roi [A well to the Living One Who sees me]; it is between Kadesh and Bered.* —GENESIS 16:14 AMP

> *O LORD, you have searched me and you know me. You know when I sit and when I rise; you perceive my thoughts from afar.* —PSALM 139:1–2

> *God made him who had no sin to be sin for us, so that in him we might become the righteousness of God.* —2 CORINTHIANS 5:21

> *He has removed our sins as far from us as the east is from the west.* —PSALM 103:12 NLT

July 29

I AM TRAINING YOU in *patient endurance*. This lesson is not for the faint-hearted. However, it is a rich blessing—one aspect of sharing in My kingdom and My suffering.

Since My kingdom is eternal, it is of infinite value. And I have made it clear that *sharing in My sufferings* is necessary for *sharing in My Glory*. Moreover, this experience produces real benefits in the here and now—character.

Patient endurance can be developed only through hardship. So make every effort to welcome the very problem you dread. Bring it into My Presence with thanksgiving, and acknowledge your willingness to endure it as long as I deem necessary. Ask Me to take this dark, ugly thing and transform it into something lovely. I can weave bright, golden strands of Glory into the most heart-wrenching situation. It may take a long time for the lovely pattern to emerge, but this waiting can build patience. Rejoice, beloved, for I am polishing your character till it shines with the Light of My Glory!

> I, John, your brother and companion in the suffering and kingdom and patient endurance that are ours in Jesus, was on the island of Patmos because of the word of God and the testimony of Jesus.—REVELATION 1:9

> Now if we are children, then we are heirs—heirs of God and co-heirs with Christ, if indeed we share in his sufferings in order that we may also share in his glory.—ROMANS 8:17

> Do everything without complaining or arguing, so that you may become blameless and pure, children of God without fault in a crooked and depraved generation, in which you shine like stars in the universe.—PHILIPPIANS 2:14–15

July 30

Beloved, *My compassions never fail. They are new every morning.* So you can begin each day confidently, knowing that My vast reservoir of blessings is full to the brim. This knowledge helps you *wait for Me*, entrusting your long-unanswered prayers into My care and keeping. I assure you that not one of those petitions has slipped past Me unnoticed. I want you to drink deeply from My fountain of limitless Love and unfailing compassion. As you wait in My Presence, these divine nutrients are freely available to you.

Although many of your prayers are not yet answered, you can find hope in *My great faithfulness*. I keep all My promises in My perfect way and timing. I have promised to *give you Peace* that can displace the trouble and fear in your heart. If you become weary of waiting, remember that I also wait—*that I may be gracious to you and have mercy on you*. I hold back till you're ready to receive the things I have lovingly prepared for you. *Blessed are all those who wait for Me.*

Because of the Lord's great love we are not consumed, for his compassions never fail. They are new every morning; great is your faithfulness. I say to myself, "The Lord is my portion; therefore I will wait for him."—Lamentations 3:22–24

"Peace I leave with you; my peace I give you. I do not give to you as the world gives. Do not let your hearts be troubled and do not be afraid."—John 14:27

Therefore the Lord will wait, that He may be gracious to you; and therefore He will be exalted, that He may have mercy on you. For the Lord is a God of justice; blessed are all those who wait for Him.—Isaiah 30:18 nkjv

July 31

Before you call I will answer; while you are still speaking I will hear. I know you sometimes feel as if you're alone—in the dark. You continue praying because it's the right thing to do, but you wonder if your prayers make any difference. When you are feeling this way, it's good to stop and remember who I Am—*the King of Glory!* I transcend time. Past, present, and future all are alike to Me. This is why I can answer before you even call out to Me.

No prayer of yours is ever unheard or unanswered. However, sometimes My answer is "No" or "Not yet." At other times your prayers are answered in ways you cannot see. *My wisdom is unsearchable*—immeasurably beyond your understanding. Take time to think about the wonders of My infinite intelligence and to delight in My endless Love for you. If you persist in this intimate adoration, you will know beyond any doubt that you are *never* alone. You are Mine!

"Before they call I will answer; while they are still speaking I will hear."—Isaiah 65:24

Who is he, this King of glory? The Lord Almighty—he is the King of glory.—Psalm 24:10

Oh, the depth of the riches both of the wisdom and knowledge of God! How unsearchable are His judgments and His ways past finding out!—Romans 11:33 nkjv

August

*You have shown me the way of life,
and you will fill me with the joy of your presence.*

ACTS 2:28 NLT

August 1

Come eagerly into My ardent Presence, inviting Me to *satisfy you with My unfailing Love.* The best time to seek My Face is *in the morning,* soon after you awaken. Connecting with Me early sets the tone for the rest of the day. My endless Love is immensely satisfying: It helps you know you are treasured and significant. It reminds you that *together* you and I can handle the circumstances of your day. Knowing you are forever loved energizes you and gives you courage to persevere through difficulties.

Encountering My loving Presence in the morning equips you to *sing for Joy and be glad.* Think about the astonishing privilege of meeting with the One who is *King of kings and Lord of lords* in the privacy of your home. Rejoice that your name is written in *the Lamb's Book of Life*—with indelible ink! Take time to enjoy My Presence. Speak or sing praises; read Scripture and pray. Delight yourself in the wondrous truth that *nothing in all creation can separate you from My Love!*

Satisfy us in the morning with your unfailing love, that we may sing for joy and be glad all our days. —Psalm 90:14

And on His robe and on His thigh He has a name written, "KING OF KINGS, AND LORD OF LORDS." —Revelation 19:16 nasb

Nothing impure will ever enter it, nor will anyone who does what is shameful or deceitful, but only those whose names are written in the Lamb's book of life. —Revelation 21:27

Neither height nor depth, nor anything else in all creation, will be able to separate us from the love of God that is in Christ Jesus our Lord. —Romans 8:39

August 2

I AM YOUR LIVING LORD, your Rock, your Savior-God. Spend time pondering My greatness and My endless commitment to you. You live in a culture where vast numbers of people are leery of making commitments. Even those who say "I do" often change their minds later and leave. I, however, am your forever-Friend and the eternal Lover of your soul. You are utterly secure in My Love!

Instead of focusing on troubles in your life and in your world, remember who I Am. Not only am I your living Lord and unchanging Rock, I am also *God your Savior*. Because I am the everlasting God, my death on the cross for your sins *saves you to the uttermost*! So you don't need to worry that I'll stop loving you because your performance isn't good enough. It is *My* goodness and *My* righteousness that keep you secure in My Love. Let My unending commitment to you be a comfort as you journey through this trouble-filled world. Someday you will live with Me in paradise.

The LORD lives! Praise be to my Rock! Exalted be God my Savior!—PSALM 18:46

Therefore He is also able to save to the uttermost those who come to God through Him, since He always lives to make intercession for them.—HEBREWS 7:25 NKJV

For He made Him who knew no sin to be sin for us, that we might become the righteousness of God in Him.—2 CORINTHIANS 5:21 NKJV

August 3

WAIT IN MY PRESENCE. There are so many benefits—spiritual, emotional, and physical—to spending time with Me. Yet many of My children think this is a luxury they cannot afford. Even though they crave rest and quietness, they continue in their fast-paced lifestyle. I want *you* to arrange your priorities in such a way that you can have some restful times with Me. I will refresh your soul and strengthen you for the journey that lies ahead.

Be of good courage. Living in this very broken world requires bravery on your part. Since bravery is not the default setting in most human hearts, you will need My help to *be strong and courageous.* In spite of all the alarming events in the world, you don't have to be terrified or discouraged. Discipline yourself to *fix your thoughts on Me* again and again—and again! Find comfort in My promise to *be with you wherever you go.*

Continue your efforts to be courageous, and look to Me for help. *I will strengthen your heart.*

> *Wait on the L*ORD*; be of good courage, and He shall strengthen your heart; wait, I say, on the L*ORD*!* —PSALM 27:14 NKJV

> *"Have I not commanded you? Be strong and courageous. Do not be terrified; do not be discouraged, for the L*ORD *your God will be with you wherever you go."* —JOSHUA 1:9

> *Therefore, holy brothers, who share in the heavenly calling, fix your thoughts on Jesus, the apostle and high priest whom we confess.* —HEBREWS 3:1

August 4

Never underestimate the power of prayer! People who are feeling discouraged and hopeless often say something like, "There's nothing left to do but pray." The implication is that this is their last resort—and a feeble one at that. Nothing could be further from the truth!

I created mankind with the ability to communicate with Me. Since I am *the eternal, immortal, invisible King* of the universe, this is an astonishing privilege. Even when the human race became tainted with sin through Adam and Eve's disobedience, I did not withdraw this glorious privilege. And when I lived in your world as a flesh-and-blood man, I relied heavily on praying to My Father. I was keenly aware of how continuously I needed His help.

Persistent, heartfelt prayer will bless not only you but also your family, friends, church—even your country. Ask the Holy Spirit to help you pray effectively. Find others to join you in this venture of seeking My Face in humility and repentance. Beseech Me to *heal your land.*

> *For by Him all things were created that are in heaven and that are on earth, visible and invisible, whether thrones or dominions or principalities or powers. All things were created through Him and for Him.*—Colossians 1:16 nkjv

> *Now to the King eternal, immortal, invisible, the only God, be honor and glory for ever and ever. Amen.*—1 Timothy 1:17

> *And when He had sent the multitudes away, He went up on the mountain by Himself to pray. Now when evening came, He was alone there.*—Matthew 14:23 nkjv

> *"If my people, who are called by my name, will humble themselves and pray and seek my face and turn from their wicked ways, then I will hear from heaven and will forgive their sin and will heal their land."*—2 Chronicles 7:14

August 5

Look to Me and My strength; *seek My Face always*. I encourage you to *let your heart rejoice* whenever you are seeking Me.

Imagine an engaged couple—passionately in love. When the man goes to visit his betrothed, she doesn't open the door and blithely say, "Oh, it's you." Nor does he look past her as if she were invisible and ask, "Do you have anything to eat?" Instead, their hearts leap for joy because they are together. You are My betrothed, and I am the forever-Lover of your soul. Rejoice in the astonishing affection I have for you!

Glory in My holy Name; it's holy because it represents *Me*. This Name is *above every name*, yet you may use it freely to commune with Me and worship Me joyously. You are privileged to have such easy access to Me. Some people glory in their wealth, achievements, beauty, or fame. But I invite you to exult in *Me*—your Savior, Lord, and Lover. Glorifying Me will strengthen and delight you, bringing Power to your prayers and Joy to your heart.

> *Glory in his holy name; let the hearts of those who seek the Lord rejoice. Look to the Lord and his strength; seek his face always.*—1 Chronicles 16:10–11

> *I am jealous for you with a godly jealousy. I promised you to one husband, to Christ, so that I might present you as a pure virgin to him.*—2 Corinthians 11:2

> *"Greater love has no one than this, that he lay down his life for his friends."*—John 15:13

> *Therefore God also has highly exalted Him and given Him the name which is above every name, that at the name of Jesus every knee should bow, of those in heaven, and of those on earth, and of those under the earth.*—Philippians 2:9–10 nkjv

August 6

When planning and problems are preoccupying your mind, turn to Me and whisper My Name. Let the Light of My Presence shine on you as you rejoice in *My unfailing Love*. Thank Me for watching over you always and loving you eternally. Affirm your trust in Me; express your devotion to Me. Then ask Me to illuminate the way forward—helping you sort out what needs to be done today and what does not. Deal with problems as you must, but refuse to let worry or fear become central in your thoughts.

Keep returning your focus to Me as often as you can, and I will light up your perspective. Saturate your mind and heart with Scripture—reading it, studying it, and memorizing verses that are especially helpful to you. *My Word is a lamp to your feet and a Light for your path.*

If you follow these guidelines, your preoccupation with planning and problems will diminish. This leaves room in your life for more of Me. Delight in *the Joy of My Presence*!

> *Let them give thanks to the Lord for his unfailing love and his wonderful deeds for men. Let them sacrifice thank offerings and tell of his works with songs of joy.* —Psalm 107:21–22

> *Casting the whole of your care [all your anxieties, all your worries, all your concerns, once and for all] on Him, for He cares for you affectionately and cares about you watchfully.* —1 Peter 5:7 AMP

> *Your word is a lamp to my feet and a light for my path.* —Psalm 119:105

> *You have shown me the way of life, and you will fill me with the joy of your presence.* —Acts 2:28 NLT

August 7

I AM THE ONE who *keeps your lamp burning. I turn your darkness into Light.* Sometimes, when you are *weary and burdened,* you may feel as if your lamp is about to go out. It seems to be flickering and sputtering—on the verge of running out of fuel. Whenever this happens, call out to Me for help. Take some deep breaths in My Presence, and remember that *I am the One who fuels your lamp.* I am *your Strength*!

I am also your Light. Keep turning toward Me, letting the Glory of My Presence soak into you. My radiant beauty brightens your life and changes your perspective. When you turn away from Me and forget that I am with you, your world looks very dark. Indeed, there is much darkness in this deeply fallen world you inhabit. However, I am *the Light that shines on in the darkness.* So do not be afraid, My child. Trust Me wholeheartedly—no matter how gloomy things may appear—and I will *transform your darkness into Light.*

> *You, O Lord, keep my lamp burning; my God turns my darkness into light.* —Psalm 18:28

> *"Come to me, all you who are weary and burdened, and I will give you rest."* —Matthew 11:28

> *I love you, O Lord, my strength.* —Psalm 18:1

> *And the Light shines on in the darkness, for the darkness has never overpowered it [put it out or absorbed it or appropriated it, and is unreceptive to it].* —John 1:5 AMP

August 8

The fear of man is a snare. A snare is a kind of trap—something that entangles you, making it difficult for you to escape. "Fear of man" involves being overly concerned about what others think of you. It's an unhealthy, ungodly focus—seeing yourself through the eyes of others. This fear can be crippling, and it is full of distortions. Other people's views of you are distorted by their sinful nature. Furthermore, it's almost impossible to know what they really think about you. When you view yourself from others' perspectives, you add your own distortions to theirs. As you strive to present an acceptable "persona," you become trapped.

When you realize that fear of man is motivating you—controlling your thoughts and behavior—come to Me. At your request, I will forgive you for making others' views of you into an idol; I will help you break free from these entanglements. Affirm your trust in Me and take time to enjoy My Presence. As you forget about yourself and focus on Me, your loving Lord, you grow increasingly free!

The fear of man is a snare, but the one who trusts in the Lord is protected. —Proverbs 29:25 HCSB

If we confess our sins, He is faithful and just to forgive us our sins and to cleanse us from all unrighteousness. —1 John 1:9 NKJV

Now the Lord is the Spirit, and where the Spirit of the Lord is, there is freedom. —2 Corinthians 3:17

August 9

COME REST WITH ME, BELOVED. Though many tasks are calling to you, urging you to put them first, *I know what you need most: to be still in My Presence.* Take some deep breaths, and fix your gaze on Me. As you return your attention to Me, let your concerns roll off—like water off a duck's back. This enables you to relax and enjoy My nearness. I am never far from you!

Meditate on Scripture; search for Me in the Bible. Let these words of grace and truth soak into the depths of your soul and draw you closer to Me. *My Word is living and active,* so it can infuse fresh life into you.

When it is time to return to your tasks, bring Me into those activities. Include Me in your plans and problem-solving. I am relevant to everything you do, say, and think. Whisper My Name, "Jesus," in sweet remembrance of My nearness. *In everything you do, put Me first,* for I am the Lord of your life.

> "Be still, and know that I am God; I will be exalted among the nations, I will be exalted in the earth." —PSALM 46:10

> For the word of God is living and active, sharper than any two-edged sword, piercing to the division of soul and of spirit, of joints and of marrow, and discerning the thoughts and intentions of the heart. —HEBREWS 4:12 ESV

> In everything you do, put God first, and he will direct you and crown your efforts with success. —PROVERBS 3:6 TLB

August 10

I AM TRAINING YOU to be an overcomer—to find Joy in the midst of circumstances that previously would have defeated you. Your ability to transcend trouble is based on this rock-solid fact: *I have overcome the world*; I have already won the ultimate victory! Nonetheless, as I taught, *you will have trouble in this world*. So expect to encounter many difficulties as you journey through life. You inhabit a planet that is always at war, and the enemy of your soul never rests. But don't be afraid, because *He who is in you is greater than he who is in the world*. This is good reason to rejoice!

When you are in the midst of challenging circumstances, it is crucial to keep trusting Me. Whisper "I trust You, Jesus" as often as you need—remembering I am always near. Ask Me to help you learn all that I have for you in this trial. Look for flowers of Joy growing in the rich soil of adversity. The sunlight of *My Face is shining upon you*, beloved.

> *"I have told you these things, so that in me you may have peace. In this world you will have trouble. But take heart! I have overcome the world."*—JOHN 16:33

> *You are of God, little children, and have overcome them, because He who is in you is greater than he who is in the world.*—1 JOHN 4:4 NKJV

> *The LORD is near to all who call on him, to all who call on him in truth.*—PSALM 145:18

> *"The LORD make his face shine upon you and be gracious to you."*—NUMBERS 6:25

AUGUST 11

My Face is shining upon you, beloved. Take time to linger in My joyous Light, and seek to know Me as I truly am. I am always near you, closer than the air you're breathing. Awareness of My loving Presence is a rich blessing. However, the most important thing is to *trust* that I am with you regardless of what you are experiencing.

I am immanent—present throughout the entire universe. I am also transcendent—existing above and independent from the universe. I am *the King eternal, immortal, invisible, the only God. As the heavens are higher than the earth, so are My ways higher than your ways and My thoughts than your thoughts.* Therefore, don't expect to fully understand Me or My ways. When things don't go as you think they should, be willing to bow before My infinite *wisdom and knowledge. My judgments are unsearchable and My paths beyond tracing out,* but they are good. Remember the example of Job. When his family experienced multiple disasters, *he fell to the ground in worship.* I transcend all your troubles!

Now to the King eternal, immortal, invisible, the only God, be honor and glory for ever and ever. Amen.—1 Timothy 1:17

"For as the heavens are higher than the earth, so are My ways higher than your ways, and My thoughts than your thoughts."—Isaiah 55:9 nkjv

Oh, the depth of the riches of the wisdom and knowledge of God! How unsearchable his judgments, and his paths beyond tracing out!—Romans 11:33

At this, Job got up and tore his robe and shaved his head. Then he fell to the ground in worship.—Job 1:20

August 12

When you bump into massive difficulties on your life-path, I want you to *consider it pure Joy*. As you bounce off these "impossibilities," *My everlasting arms* are wide open—ready to catch you, calm you, and help you do what does not seem possible. You can be joyful in the midst of perplexing problems because I am *God your Savior*—and I have already accomplished the greatest miracle in your life: saving you from your sins. If you keep looking to Me, your resurrected Lord and King, your pessimism will eventually give way to courage. Though you are an earthbound creature, your soul shares in My eternal victory.

I have infinite Power, so "impossibilities" are My specialty. I delight in them because they display My Glory so vividly. They also help you live the way I intended: in joyful, trusting dependence on Me. The next time you face an "impossible" situation, turn to Me immediately with a hopeful heart. Acknowledge your total inadequacy and cling to Me—relying on My infinite sufficiency. *All things are possible with Me!*

Consider it pure joy, my brothers, whenever you face trials of many kinds, because you know that the testing of your faith develops perseverance.—James 1:2–3

The eternal God is your refuge, and underneath are the everlasting arms.—Deuteronomy 33:27 nkjv

Though the fig tree does not bud and there are no grapes on the vines, though the olive crop fails and the fields produce no food, though there are no sheep in the pen and no cattle in the stalls, yet I will rejoice in the Lord, I will be joyful in God my Savior.—Habakkuk 3:17–18

Jesus looked at them and said, "With man this is impossible, but with God all things are possible."—Matthew 19:26

August 13

No matter how you're feeling, remember that you are *not* on trial. *There is no condemnation for those who belong to Me*—those who know Me as Savior. You have already been judged "Not guilty!" in the courts of heaven.

I came to earth to set you free from bondage to sin. I long to see you living joyfully in that freedom. Learn to enjoy your guilt-free position in My kingdom, refusing to be weighed down or shackled. The world is in a fallen condition where sin and evil abound, but *I have overcome the world*!

The best response to the grace lavished on you is thankfulness—gratitude that fuels a desire to live according to My will. The closer you live to Me, the better you can discern My will; also, the more you can experience My Peace and Joy. Knowing Me intimately helps you trust Me enough to receive Peace from Me even in the midst of trouble. *Overflowing with thankfulness* has the delightful "side effect" of increasing your Joy. Live freely and joyously in My Presence, beloved!

Therefore, there is now no condemnation for those who are in Christ Jesus.—Romans 8:1

"If the Son sets you free, you will be free indeed."—John 8:36 esv

"I have told you these things, so that in me you may have peace. In this world you will have trouble. But take heart! I have overcome the world."—John 16:33

So then, just as you received Christ Jesus as Lord, continue to live in him, rooted and built up in him, strengthened in the faith as you were taught, and overflowing with thankfulness.—Colossians 2:6–7

August 14

I WILL RESTORE TO YOU *the Joy of My salvation*. When you confess your sins to Me with a humble heart, I gladly forgive you. But there is more: I restore *you*. *The salvation of your soul* is the source of *inexpressible and glorious Joy*! I want you to experience once again the rich, deep pleasure of a close relationship with Me. I desire to be your *First Love*.

Many people and things compete for your attention, so keeping Me first in your heart requires diligence. You have developed ways of seeking Me that are familiar and easy for you. But the danger of relying too much on routine is that it can become a tedious duty. When you realize this has happened, you need to stop—and try something new. Remember who I am: King of kings, Lord of lords, Creator-Sustainer of this vast, awesome universe! Take extra time to worship and adore Me before bringing Me your other prayers and petitions. This will awaken your heart to *My Glory*—and to the Joy of My Presence.

Restore to me the joy of Your salvation, and uphold me by Your generous Spirit.—PSALM 51:12 NKJV

Though you have not seen him, you love him; and even though you do not see him now, you believe in him and are filled with an inexpressible and glorious joy, for you are receiving the goal of your faith, the salvation of your souls.—1 PETER 1:8–9

"Yet I hold this against you: You have forsaken your first love."—REVELATION 2:4

"Father, I desire that they also whom You gave Me may be with Me where I am, that they may behold My glory which You have given Me; for You loved Me before the foundation of the world."—JOHN 17:24 NKJV

August 15

You will seek Me and find Me *when you search for Me with all your heart.* This is a delightful assignment, but it is also quite challenging. Spending time enjoying My Presence is a privilege reserved for those who know Me as Savior and Lord. To maximize the benefits of this precious experience, you need to seek Me wholeheartedly. However, your mind is often a tangled, unfocused mess. Enlist My Spirit to protect your mind and heart from distractions, distortions, deception, anxiety, and other entanglements. This will help you unscramble your thoughts and calm your heart—freeing you *to search for Me* unhindered.

I want you to seek Me not only in quiet times but also when you are engaged in other matters. Your astonishing brain is able to focus on Me even when you are busy. The simple prayer "Jesus, keep me aware of your Presence" can be like soft background music in your mind—playing continuously underneath your other mental activities. When *your mind is stayed on Me, I keep you in perfect Peace.*

> *"And you will seek Me and find Me, when you search for Me with all your heart."*—Jeremiah 29:13 nkjv

> *He will have no fear of bad news; his heart is steadfast, trusting in the* Lord.—Psalm 112:7

> *You will keep him in perfect peace, whose mind is stayed on You, because he trusts in You.*—Isaiah 26:3 nkjv

August 16

I will bless My people with Peace. This biblical promise is for everyone who trusts Me as Savior. So when you're feeling anxious, try praying: "Jesus, bless me with Your Peace." This short, simple prayer connects you with Me and opens you up to My help.

Peace and trust in Me are richly intertwined in My kingdom. The more you lean on Me in confident dependence, the less fearful you will be. If your *heart is steadfastly trusting in Me,* you need not be *afraid of bad news.* Because I am both sovereign and good, you can be confident that this world isn't spinning out of control. There *is* plenty of bad news in the world, but I'm not wringing My hands impotently. I am continually at work—even in the most devastating situations—bringing good out of evil.

My kingdom is about transformation, and I invite you to join Me in this endeavor. *Live as a child of the Light.* Together we will draw others out of darkness into the Light of My transforming Presence.

The Lord will give strength to His people; the Lord will bless His people with peace.—Psalm 29:11 NKJV

He will have no fear of bad news; his heart is steadfast, trusting in the Lord.—Psalm 112:7

For you were once darkness, but now you are light in the Lord. Live as children of light (for the fruit of the light consists in all goodness, righteousness and truth) and find out what pleases the Lord.—Ephesians 5:8–10

August 17

My chosen people are *holy and dearly loved.* I know that you are neither perfect nor sinless, but you are indeed *holy in My sight.* This is because I see you wrapped in the radiance of My righteousness. As My follower, you are covered with perfect righteousness forever!

You are also dearly loved. Let this transformational truth seep into the inner recesses of your heart, mind, and spirit. *Beloved* is your deepest, truest identity. When you look in the mirror, say to yourself, "I am my Beloved's." Repeat these four words throughout the day and just before you fall asleep.

Remembering you are perfectly loved by *the King of Glory* provides a solid foundation for your life. With your identity secure in Me, you can relate better to others. I want you to *clothe yourself with compassion, kindness, humility, gentleness, and patience.* Work on developing these qualities in your relationships with other people. The Holy Spirit will help you. He lives in you and delights to live through you—blessing others *and* you.

> *Therefore, as God's chosen people, holy and dearly loved, clothe yourselves with compassion, kindness, humility, gentleness and patience.*—Colossians 3:12

> *For he chose us in him before the creation of the world to be holy and blameless in his sight.*—Ephesians 1:4

> *I am my beloved's, and my beloved is mine. He feeds his flock among the lilies.*—Song of Songs 6:3 NKJV

> *Who is this King of glory? The Lord of hosts, He is the King of glory.*—Psalm 24:10 NKJV

August 18

You are feeling weighed down by yesterday's failures. You wish you could undo decisions you made that you now regret. However, the past is beyond the realm of change and cannot be undone. Even *I*, though I live in timelessness, respect the boundaries of time that exist in your world. So don't waste your energy bemoaning bad choices you have made. Instead, ask Me to forgive your sins and help you learn from your mistakes.

I hate to see My children weighed down by past failures, dragging them around like heavy chains attached to their legs. When you're feeling this way, try to imagine Me cutting the chains from your legs. I came to set My loved ones free. You are *free indeed*!

Rejoice that I redeem your failures—forgiving you and leading you along paths of newness. Talk with Me about your mistakes and be ready to *learn from Me*. Ask Me to show you the changes I want you to make. I will *guide you along right paths*.

"Come to me, all you who are weary and burdened, and I will give you rest. Take my yoke upon you and learn from me, for I am gentle and humble in heart, and you will find rest for your souls."—Matthew 11:28–29

"Therefore if the Son makes you free, you shall be free indeed."—John 8:36 nkjv

He renews my strength. He guides me along right paths, bringing honor to his name.—Psalm 23:3 nlt

August 19

Rejoice in your dependence on Me. This is a place of wonderful security! People who depend on themselves, others, or circumstances are building their lives on a foundation of sand. When storms come, they will realize how flimsy their foundation is; it will not be adequate to support them. You, on the other hand, are building your life *on the rock*. Your foundation will be more than sufficient to support you during life's storms.

I want you to depend on Me not only in stormy circumstances but when the skies of your life are calm. This is a daily discipline—preparing you for whatever lies ahead. It is also a source of great Joy. Relying on Me involves staying in communication with Me: an extraordinary privilege. This rich blessing provides you with strength, encouragement, and guidance. When you stay in touch with Me, you know you are not alone. As you *walk in the Light of My Presence*, I help you *rejoice in Me all day long*. Depending on Me is a most joyful way to live.

> "Therefore everyone who hears these words of mine and puts them into practice is like a wise man who built his house on the rock. The rain came down, the streams rose, and the winds blew and beat against that house; yet it did not fall, because it had its foundation on the rock. But everyone who hears these words of mine and does not put them into practice is like a foolish man who built his house on sand. The rain came down, the streams rose, and the winds blew and beat against that house, and it fell with a great crash."—Matthew 7:24–27

> *Blessed are those who have learned to acclaim you, who walk in the light of your presence, O Lord. They rejoice in your name all day long; they exult in your righteousness.*—Psalm 89:15–16

> *Be joyful always; pray continually.*—1 Thessalonians 5:16–17

August 20

FIND YOUR SECURITY IN ME. As the world you inhabit seems increasingly unsafe, turn your attention to Me more and more often. Remember that I am with you at *all* times, and I have already won the ultimate victory. Because *I am in you and you are in Me*, you have an eternity of perfect, stress-free life awaiting you. There will be no trace of fear or worry in heaven. Reverential worship of *the King of Glory* will flood you with unimaginable Joy!

Let this *future hope* strengthen and encourage you while you're living in this deeply fallen world. When you start to feel anxious about something you have seen, heard, or thought, bring that concern to Me. Remind yourself that *I* am the One who makes you secure—in all circumstances! If you find your mind gravitating toward an idolatrous way of feeling safe, tell yourself: "*That's* not what makes me safe." Then look trustingly to Me, and think about who I am: the victorious Savior-God who is your Friend forever. In Me you are absolutely secure!

> "On that day you will realize that I am in my Father, and you are in me, and I am in you."—JOHN 14:20

> *Lift up your heads, O you gates! And be lifted up, you everlasting doors! And the King of glory shall come in.*—PSALM 24:7 NKJV

> *There is surely a future hope for you, and your hope will not be cut off.*—PROVERBS 23:18

August 21

Put your trust in Me so you can discover *My unfailing Love* shining on in the midst of your troubles. When you are struggling with discouragement, you need to assert your trust in Me over and over again. It is vital to remember who I am: Creator and Sustainer of the universe, as well as your Savior, Lord, and Friend. You can count on Me because My Love for you is unfailing. It never runs out or grows dim, and it is not dependent on how well you're performing. Just as *I am the same yesterday, today, and forever,* so is My perfect Love.

Lift up your soul to Me—waiting in My Presence with no pretense and no demands. As you dedicate time to waiting and worshiping, I gradually transform you and open up the way before you. I will not necessarily reveal future things to you, but I will *show you the way* through this day—step by step. So trust Me wholeheartedly, beloved, for I am taking care of you wonderfully well!

> *Let the morning bring me word of your unfailing love, for I have put my trust in you. Show me the way I should go, for to you I lift up my soul.*—Psalm 143:8

> *In the past God spoke to our forefathers through the prophets at many times and in various ways, but in these last days he has spoken to us by his Son, whom he appointed heir of all things, and through whom he made the universe.*—Hebrews 1:1–2

> *Jesus Christ is the same yesterday, today, and forever.*—Hebrews 13:8 NKJV

August 22

I AM LIGHT; in Me there is no darkness at all. I, your God, am perfect in every way. There's not even an iota of badness in Me. You live in a world where evil and ungodliness run rampant. But remember: I am *the Light that keeps on shining in the darkness!* Nothing can extinguish—or even diminish—the perfection of My everlasting radiance. Someday you will be able to see My brilliance in all its Glory, and you will experience unimaginable Joy. For now, though, you must *live by faith, not by sight.*

When events in the world or in your private life are threatening to unnerve you, grasp My hand in trusting determination. Refuse to be intimidated by evil; instead, *overcome evil with good.* I am with you, and I have won the ultimate victory through My crucifixion and resurrection. *Nothing* will be able to undo these awesome events that punctured the darkness so that My dazzling brightness could break through and pour into the hearts of My followers. Spend time basking in this holy Light, for My Face is shining upon you.

> *This is the message we have heard from him and declare to you: God is light; in him there is no darkness at all.*—1 JOHN 1:5

> *And the Light shines on in the darkness, for the darkness has never overpowered it [put it out or absorbed it or appropriated it, and is unreceptive to it].*—JOHN 1:5 AMP

> *We live by faith, not by sight.*—2 CORINTHIANS 5:7

> *Do not be overcome by evil, but overcome evil with good.*—ROMANS 12:21

August 23

When tests and challenges come at you from all sides, consider it a joyful opportunity. Don't waste energy regretting the way things are or wishing you could go back to yesterday. Remember that I am sovereign, powerful, and loving; moreover, I am with you to help. Instead of being overwhelmed by all the difficulties, grasp My hand with confident trust. Though you are insufficient to handle your troubles by yourself, you and I *together* can handle anything! If you view your circumstances from this big-picture perspective, you can be joyful even in the midst of your struggles.

You have not only My Presence with you but My Spirit within you. He is always ready to help; seek His assistance as often as you need. One of the hardest parts of dealing with multiple trials is waiting for their resolution. Since patience is part of the Spirit's fruit, He can help you endure the waiting. Don't try to get out of hard times prematurely. Instead, persevere patiently, knowing that *perseverance must finish its work*—making you *mature and complete*.

Consider it a sheer gift, friends, when tests and challenges come at you from all sides.—James 1:2 msg

But the fruit of the Spirit is love, joy, peace, patience, kindness, goodness, faithfulness, gentleness and self-control. Against such things there is no law.—Galatians 5:22–23

Be joyful in hope, patient in affliction, faithful in prayer.—Romans 12:12

Perseverance must finish its work so that you may be mature and complete, not lacking anything.—James 1:4

August 24

COME TO ME, MY WEARY ONE, *and I will give you rest.* I know the depth and breadth of your weariness. Nothing is hidden from Me. There is a time to keep pushing yourself—when circumstances require it—and a time to rest. Even I, who have infinite energy, rested on the seventh day after completing My work of creation.

Seek My Face, and then just linger in My loving Presence while I shine upon you. Let favorite scriptures amble through your brain, refreshing your heart and spirit. If something comes to mind that you don't want to forget, jot it down; then return your attention to Me. As you relax with Me, My Love will soak into the depths of your being. You may want to express your love for Me—in whispers, in spoken words, in song.

I want you to know that I approve of you and I approve of rest. When you relax in My Presence, trusting in My finished work on the cross, both you and I are refreshed.

> "Come to me, all you who are weary and burdened, and I will give you rest."—MATTHEW 11:28

And on the seventh day God ended His work which He had done, and He rested on the seventh day from all His work which He had done.—GENESIS 2:2 NKJV

"The LORD make his face shine upon you and be gracious to you."—NUMBERS 6:25

August 25

I LIVE IN YOU! This four-word truth changes everything, wondrously improving your life both now and forever. Don't worry about whether you're an adequate home for Me. I joyfully move into believers' humble hearts, where I work patiently on renovating them. But I refuse to dwell in people who think they are "good enough" without Me. I have called such hypocrites *whitewashed tombs: beautiful on the outside* but putrid on the inside.

As you ponder the miraculous truth that *I live in you*, let your heart overflow with Joy! I am not a short-term tenant, indwelling you only as long as your behavior pleases Me. I have come to stay—permanently. I warn you, though, that My renovations can be quite painful at times. When My transforming work in you causes intense discomfort, cling trustingly to Me. *Live by faith in the One who loved you and gave Himself for you.* As you continue yielding to the changes I'm making, you'll become more and more fully the masterpiece I designed you to be.

> *I have been crucified with Christ and I no longer live, but Christ lives in me. The life I live in the body, I live by faith in the Son of God, who loved me and gave himself for me.*—GALATIANS 2:20

> *"Woe to you, teachers of the law and Pharisees, you hypocrites! You are like whitewashed tombs, which look beautiful on the outside but on the inside are full of dead men's bones and everything unclean."*—MATTHEW 23:27

> *For we are His workmanship, created in Christ Jesus for good works, which God prepared beforehand that we should walk in them.*—EPHESIANS 2:10 NKJV

August 26

No matter what is happening in your life, you can *be joyful in Me* because I am *your Savior*. When Habakkuk wrote about this, he was awaiting the invasion of his country by the Babylonians—*a ruthless, feared, and dreaded people*. Even as he pondered this terrifying prophecy, he was able to rejoice in his relationship with Me. This sort of Joy is supernatural—powered by the Holy Spirit, who lives in all My followers.

Joy and thankfulness are closely connected. *Give thanks to Me for My unfailing Love; tell of My wonderful works with songs of Joy.* My Love for you will never fail because I have already paid the full penalty for your sins. It doesn't depend on you! The more you thank Me—for your salvation, My Love, and other blessings—the more you will realize how blessed you really are. And a grateful attitude increases your Joy. You can nourish this gladness by thanking Me in your silent prayers, in your written, spoken, or whispered words, and through music. *Come before Me with joyful songs*!

Yet I will rejoice in the Lord, I will be joyful in God my Savior.—Habakkuk 3:18

"I am raising up the Babylonians, that ruthless and impetuous people, who sweep across the whole earth to seize dwelling places not their own. They are a feared and dreaded people; they are a law to themselves and promote their own honor."—Habakkuk 1:6–7

Let them give thanks to the Lord for his unfailing love and his wonderful deeds for men. Let them sacrifice thank offerings and tell of his works with songs of joy.—Psalm 107:21–22

Serve the Lord with gladness; come before Him with joyful songs.—Psalm 100:2 HCSB

August 27

I GIVE STRENGTH TO THE WEARY and increase the power of the weak. So do not be discouraged by your weakness. There are many kinds of weaknesses, and no one is exempt from all of them. I use them to keep My loved ones humble and to train them to wait on Me in trusting dependence. I have promised that *those who wait on Me will gain new strength.*

This waiting is not meant to be practiced only *sometimes*. I designed you to look to Me continually, knowing Me as *the Living One who sees you* always. Waiting on Me is closely related to trusting Me. The more time you spend focusing on Me, the more you will trust Me. And the more you trust Me, the more you will want to spend time with Me. Waiting on Me in the midst of your moments also increases your hope in Me. This hope blesses you in countless ways—lifting you above your circumstances, enabling you to *praise Me for the help of My Presence.*

He gives strength to the weary and increases the power of the weak. —ISAIAH 40:29

Though youths grow weary and tired, and vigorous young men stumble badly, yet those who wait for the LORD will gain new strength; they will mount up with wings like eagles, they will run and not get tired, they will walk and not become weary. —ISAIAH 40:30–31 NASB

Therefore the well was called Beer-lahai-roi [A well to the Living One Who sees me]; it is between Kadesh and Bered. —GENESIS 16:14 AMP

Why are you in despair, O my soul? And why have you become disturbed within me? Hope in God, for I shall again praise Him for the help of His presence. —PSALM 42:5 NASB

August 28

I AM WITH YOU and will watch over you wherever you go. There is an adventurous journey awaiting you, and you're anticipating it with mixed feelings. In some ways you are eager to step into this new adventure. You're even expecting to find abundant blessings along the way. However, part of you fears leaving your comfortable, predictable routine. When fearful thoughts assail you, remind yourself that I will be watching over you constantly—wherever you are. The comfort of My Presence is a forever-promise!

Your best preparation for the journey ahead is practicing My Presence each day. Tell yourself frequently: "Jesus is with me, taking good care of me." Visualize yourself holding onto My hand as you walk. Trust Me—your Guide—to show you the way forward as you go step by step. I have a perfect sense of direction, so don't worry about getting lost. Relax in My Presence, and rejoice in the wonder of sharing your whole life with Me.

> *"I am with you and will watch over you wherever you go, and I will bring you back to this land. I will not leave you until I have done what I have promised you."*—GENESIS 28:15

> *"Have I not commanded you? Be strong and courageous. Do not be frightened, and do not be dismayed, for the LORD your God is with you wherever you go."*—JOSHUA 1:9 ESV

> *For this God is our God for ever and ever; he will be our guide even to the end.*—PSALM 48:14

August 29

The Light of My Presence shines on every situation in your life—past, present, and future. I knew you *before the creation of the world*, and *I have loved you with an everlasting Love.* You are never alone, so look for Me in your moments. Search for Me as for hidden treasure.

Seek to "see" Me in the midst of all your circumstances; don't let them obscure your view of Me. Sometimes I display My Presence in grand, glorious ways. At other times I show Myself in simple, humble ways that make sense only to you. Ask Me to open your eyes and your heart to discern *all* My communications to you, beloved.

As you go through this day, remind yourself to look for the Light of My Presence shining on your life. Don't have such a narrow focus that you see only responsibilities and worldly concerns. Instead, expand your focus to include *Me* in your perspective. *You will seek Me and find Me when you search for Me with all your heart.*

> For he chose us in him before the creation of the world to be holy and blameless in his sight. —Ephesians 1:4

> The Lord appeared to us in the past, saying: "I have loved you with an everlasting love; I have drawn you with loving-kindness." —Jeremiah 31:3

> Blessed are those who have learned to acclaim you, who walk in the light of your presence, O Lord. —Psalm 89:15

> "And you will seek Me and find Me, when you search for Me with all your heart." —Jeremiah 29:13 NKJV

August 30

I make your feet like the feet of a deer. I enable you to stand on the heights. I created deer with the ability to climb steep mountains with ease and to stand on the heights with confidence. Your trust in Me can give you confidence to *walk and make progress upon your high places of trouble, responsibility, or suffering.*

It's crucial to remember that you live in a world where your spiritual enemies never declare a truce. So you need to stay alert and be ready for battle. Unlike warriors with servants to help them put on their gear, you must make the effort to armor yourself each day. No matter what happens, I want you to *be able to stand your ground, and after you have done everything, to stand.* When you're in the thick of battle, declare your trust in Me—your confidence that I am with you, helping you. You may feel as if you're losing the battle, but don't give up! Hold tightly to My hand, and just keep standing. This is victory.

> *He makes my feet like the feet of a deer; he enables me to stand on the heights.* —2 Samuel 22:34

> *The Lord God is my Strength, my personal bravery, and my invincible army; He makes my feet like hinds' feet and will make me to walk [not to stand still in terror, but to walk] and make [spiritual] progress upon my high places [of trouble, suffering, or responsibility]!* —Habakkuk 3:19 amp

> *Therefore put on the full armor of God, so that when the day of evil comes, you may be able to stand your ground, and after you have done everything, to stand.* —Ephesians 6:13

August 31

I AM YOUR TREASURE. I am immeasurably more valuable than anything you can see, hear, or touch. *Knowing Me* is the Prize above every other prize.

Earthly treasures are frequently hoarded, insured, worried over, or hidden for safekeeping. But the riches you have in Me can never be lost or stolen or damaged. On the contrary, as you freely share Me with others, you gain more of Me. Since I am infinite, there will always be more of Me to discover—and to love.

Your world often feels fragmented, with countless things—both large and small—vying for your attention. So much "stuff" keeps getting in the way of enjoying My Presence. *You are worried and troubled about many things, but only one thing is needed.* When you make Me that *one thing*, you choose what *will never be taken away from you*. Rejoice in My continual nearness, and let your knowledge of Me put everything else in perspective. I am the Treasure that can brighten all your moments!

I want to know Christ and the power of his resurrection and the fellowship of sharing in his sufferings, becoming like him in his death.—PHILIPPIANS 3:10

"Do not store up for yourselves treasures on earth, where moth and rust destroy, and where thieves break in and steal."—MATTHEW 6:19

And Jesus answered and said to her, "Martha, Martha, you are worried and troubled about many things. But one thing is needed, and Mary has chosen that good part, which will not be taken away from her."—LUKE 10:41–42 NKJV

September

*You guide me with your counsel,
leading me to a glorious destiny.
Whom have I in heaven but you?
I desire you more than anything on earth.*

PSALM 73:24–25 NLT

September 1

I AM YOUR STRENGTH. This truth about Me is especially precious on days when your inadequacies are screaming at you, telling you that you just can't go on. Knowing Me as your Strength is like having a guide who is always with you—showing you the way forward, clearing away obstacles, empowering you to take the next step. *I hold you by your right hand*, and *I guide you with My counsel*. Since I am omniscient, knowing everything, My counsel provides the best wisdom imaginable.

So don't fret about your weaknesses. They are training you to depend on My loving Presence—confident that I am with you and I will help you. Your world becomes less threatening when you throw off the pretense of being able to handle things by yourself. Furthermore, I meet you in your weaknesses and use them to draw other people to Me. My Light shines in and through your inadequacies when you keep looking to Me, your Strength. Let this Love-Light flow freely through you, filling you with Joy that overflows into others' lives.

> *O my Strength, I will sing praises to you, for you, O God, are my fortress, the God who shows me steadfast love.*—PSALM 59:17 ESV

> *Nevertheless I am continually with You; You hold me by my right hand. You will guide me with Your counsel, and afterward receive me to glory.*—PSALM 73:23–24 NKJV

> *If I must boast, I will boast of the things that show my weakness.*—2 CORINTHIANS 11:30

> *Be joyful in hope, patient in affliction, faithful in prayer.*—ROMANS 12:12

September 2

When people bare their souls to you, you are *on holy ground*. Your responsibility is to listen and love. If you jump in with both feet—trying to fix their problems—you pollute the holy terrain. Some people will retreat when this happens; others may be too wounded to realize they've been violated. Either way, you have spoiled a splendid opportunity.

To function effectively on holy ground, you need the help of the Holy Spirit. Ask Him to think through you, listen through you, love through you. As the Spirit's Love shines through you, My healing Presence goes to work in the other person. While you continue listening, your main role is to direct the person toward Me and My bountiful resources.

If you follow these guidelines, both you and others will be blessed. They will connect with *My unfailing Love* at soul-level, and I will *show them the way they should go*. As you listen and love in dependence on Me, My Spirit will flow through you like *streams of living water*, refreshing your soul.

> "Do not come any closer," God said. "Take off your sandals, for the place where you are standing is holy ground."—Exodus 3:5

> Let the morning bring me word of your unfailing love, for I have put my trust in you. Show me the way I should go, for to you I lift up my soul.—Psalm 143:8

> "The one who believes in Me, as the Scripture has said, will have streams of living water flow from deep within him." He said this about the Spirit. Those who believed in Jesus were going to receive the Spirit, for the Spirit had not yet been received because Jesus had not yet been glorified.—John 7:38–39 HCSB

September 3

If anything is excellent or praiseworthy, think about such things. This may sound easy, but it's actually quite countercultural. People who work in the media almost always shine their spotlights on what is wrong. They rarely bother to report good things that are happening—especially the many good things My people are doing.

Having a positive focus is not only countercultural; it's contrary to human nature. Your mind is a magnificent creation, but it is deeply fallen. When Adam and Eve rebelled against Me in the Garden of Eden, everything was damaged by the Fall. As a result, seeking to focus on excellent things does not come naturally to you. It requires persistent effort—making the right choice over and over again. Daily, moment by moment, you choose to look for what is good.

In spite of the massive problems in your world, much remains that is worthy of praise. Moreover, the One who is *most* praiseworthy is the One who is right beside you—closer than your thoughts. Rejoice in *Me*, beloved!

> *Finally, brothers, whatever is true, whatever is noble, whatever is right, whatever is pure, whatever is lovely, whatever is admirable—if anything is excellent or praiseworthy—think about such things.*—Philippians 4:8

When the woman saw that the fruit of the tree was good for food and pleasing to the eye, and also desirable for gaining wisdom, she took some and ate it. She also gave some to her husband, who was with her, and he ate it.—Genesis 3:6

> *How much better to get wisdom than gold, to choose understanding rather than silver!*—Proverbs 16:16

> *Nevertheless I am continually with You; You hold me by my right hand.*—Psalm 73:23 nkjv

September 4

I DISCIPLINE THE ONE I LOVE. Discipline is instruction intended to train; it's a course of action leading to a greater goal than immediate satisfaction. In fact, effective discipline can be unpleasant—even painful. So it's easy for you to feel unloved when I am leading you along a way that is difficult or confusing. In such a situation you have an important choice: to cling to Me in trusting dependence or to back away from Me and seek to go your own way.

When you are able to recognize My discipline as a facet of My Love for you, you can go through tough times joyfully—just as the early disciples did. You can come boldly into My Presence, asking Me to show you what I want you to learn and what changes you need to make. Tell Me also of your desire for reassurance of My Love. Take time to bask in the Light of My loving Presence. As you gaze at My Face, *the Light of the knowledge of My Glory* shines upon you!

> *For the Lord disciplines the one he loves, and chastises every son whom he receives.... For the moment all discipline seems painful rather than pleasant, but later it yields the peaceful fruit of righteousness to those who have been trained by it.*—HEBREWS 12:6, 11 ESV

> *So they departed from the presence of the council, rejoicing that they were counted worthy to suffer shame for His name.*—ACTS 5:41 NKJV

> *For God, who said, "Let light shine out of darkness," made his light shine in our hearts to give us the light of the knowledge of the glory of God in the face of Christ.*—2 CORINTHIANS 4:6

September 5

Joy is a choice. You may not have much control over your circumstances, but you can still choose to be joyful. I created you *a little lower than the heavenly beings*, and I gave you an amazing mind. Your ability to think things through and make decisions derives from your elevated position in My kingdom. Your thoughts are extremely important because emotions and behavior flow out of them. So endeavor to make good thought-choices.

Whenever you are feeling joyless, you need to pause and remember: *I am with you. I am watching over you* continuously. I love you with perfect, *unfailing Love*. I have given you My Spirit, and this Holy Helper within you has infinite Power. He can help you line up your thinking with the absolute truths of Scripture. My continual Presence is a biblical promise, so seek to see *Me* in the midst of your circumstances. At first you may perceive only your problems. But keep on looking till you can discern the Light of My Presence shining upon your difficulties, reflecting sparkles of Joy back to you.

Yet you have made him a little lower than the heavenly beings and crowned him with glory and honor.—Psalm 8:5 esv

"I am with you and will watch over you wherever you go, and I will bring you back to this land. I will not leave you until I have done what I have promised you."—Genesis 28:15

Let them give thanks to the Lord for his unfailing love and his wonderful deeds for men.—Psalm 107:8

You, however, are controlled not by the sinful nature but by the Spirit, if the Spirit of God lives in you. And if anyone does not have the Spirit of Christ, he does not belong to Christ.—Romans 8:9

September 6

I BROADEN THE PATH BENEATH YOU so that your ankles do not turn. I don't want you to focus overly much on what is ahead of you—wondering whether you'll be able to cope with it. Only *I* know what your future really holds. Moreover, I am the only One who fully understands what you are capable of. Finally, I can alter your circumstances—gradually or dramatically. In fact, I can widen the path you are walking on right now.

I want you to realize how intricately involved in your life I am. I delight in taking care of you—"tweaking" the situation you are in, to spare you from unnecessary hardship. Remember that I am *a shield for all who take refuge in Me*. Your part in this adventurous journey is to trust Me, communicate with Me, and walk with Me in steps of joyful dependence. I will not remove all adversity from your life, but I will widen the path you are traveling on—to *bless you and keep you from harm.*

You broaden the path beneath me, so that my ankles do not turn. —Psalm 18:36

As for God, his way is perfect; the word of the Lord is flawless. He is a shield for all who take refuge in him. —Psalm 18:30

"The Lord bless you and keep you." —Numbers 6:24 nkjv

September 7

I HAVE SEARCHED YOU *and known you. I am intimately acquainted with all your ways. Even before there is a word on your tongue, I know it all.* Beloved, you are indeed *fully known*! I have complete knowledge of everything about you—including your most secret thoughts and feelings. This transparency could be terrifying for you if you were not My follower. But you have nothing to fear because My perfect righteousness has been credited to you through your *faith in Me.* You're a cherished member of My family!

My intimate relationship with you is a powerful antidote to feelings of loneliness. Whenever you feel alone or afraid, voice your prayers to Me. I hear your silent prayers too, but whispering your words or uttering them out loud helps you think more clearly. Because I understand you perfectly, you don't have to explain things to Me. You can dive right in, seeking My help in your "here and now" circumstances. Spend a few moments relaxing with Me—breathing in *the Joy of My Presence.*

O LORD, *You have searched me and known me. You know when I sit down and when I rise up; You understand my thought from afar. You scrutinize my path and my lying down, and are intimately acquainted with all my ways. Even before there is a word on my tongue, behold, O* LORD, *You know it all.*—PSALM 139:1–4 NASB

For now we see indistinctly, as in a mirror, but then face to face. Now I know in part, but then I will know fully, as I am fully known.—1 CORINTHIANS 13:12 HCSB

This righteousness from God comes through faith in Jesus Christ to all who believe.—ROMANS 3:22

Surely you have granted him eternal blessings and made him glad with the joy of your presence.—PSALM 21:6

September 8

WHILE YOU WAIT WITH ME, I work on *renewing your mind*. As the Light of My Presence shines into your mind, darkness flees and deception is unmasked. However, there are many crevices where old thought patterns try to hide. My Spirit can search out and destroy those enemies, but He awaits your cooperation. Habitual ways of thinking do not die easily. When the Spirit's Light illuminates a hurtful thought, capture it by writing it down. Then bring it to Me so we can examine it together. I will help you identify the distortions and replace them with biblical truth.

The more you focus on Me and My Word, the more you can break free from painful, irrational thoughts. They usually have their roots in distressing experiences that wounded you, so the distortions are deeply etched into your brain. You may need to recapture the same thought multiple times before you can gain mastery over it. But all that effort leads to a marvelous result: increased ability to live freely and enjoy My Presence.

I wait for the LORD, my soul waits, and in his word I put my hope. —PSALM 130:5

Do not conform any longer to the pattern of this world, but be transformed by the renewing of your mind. Then you will be able to test and approve what God's will is—his good, pleasing and perfect will. —ROMANS 12:2

Again Jesus spoke to them, saying, "I am the light of the world. Whoever follows me will not walk in darkness, but will have the light of life." —JOHN 8:12 ESV

We demolish arguments and every pretension that sets itself up against the knowledge of God, and we take captive every thought to make it obedient to Christ. —2 CORINTHIANS 10:5

September 9

Your prayers are not cries in the dark; they rise to My kingdom of glorious Light. *Call to Me, and I will answer you and show you great and mighty things.* Mankind has long been plagued with eyes that do not see what is most important. People often fail to perceive the most obvious things. I can perform miracles before their very eyes, yet they see only mundane occurrences—or label them coincidences. Only *the eyes of your heart* can perceive spiritual realities.

I delight in people who have a *teachable* attitude. When you come to Me eager to learn *great things which you do not know,* I rejoice. A good teacher takes pleasure in a student who puts forth extra effort to discover new things. I am pleased with your desire to learn wondrous things from Me. Your openness to My teaching helps you understand *the hope to which I have called you, the riches of My glorious inheritance* in which you share. You can look forward to living with Me in the Holy City, where *the Glory of God provides Light.*

"Call to Me, and I will answer you, and show you great and mighty things, which you do not know."—Jeremiah 33:3 nkjv

I pray also that the eyes of your heart may be enlightened in order that you may know the hope to which he has called you, the riches of his glorious inheritance in the saints.—Ephesians 1:18

Teach me to do your will, for you are my God; may your good Spirit lead me on level ground.—Psalm 143:10

The city does not need the sun or the moon to shine on it, for the glory of God gives it light, and the Lamb is its lamp.—Revelation 21:23

September 10

As the world grows increasingly dark, remember that *you are the light of the world*. Don't waste energy lamenting bad things over which you have no control. Pray about these matters, but refuse to let them haunt your thoughts. Instead, focus your energies on doing what you can to brighten the place where I have put you. Use your time, talents, and resources to push back the darkness. Shine *My* Light into the world!

I am *the true Light that shines on in the darkness*—even in the most terrible conditions. Your light originates in Me and reflects from you. I have called you to *reflect My Glory*! You do this most effectively by becoming more and more fully the one I designed you to be. Spend ample time seeking My Face, beloved. Focusing on My Presence and My Word helps you to grow in grace and discern My will. Your time spent with Me nourishes your soul, providing comfort and encouragement. Thus I strengthen you and enable you to be a source of strength for others.

"You are the light of the world. A city that is set on a hill cannot be hidden."—Matthew 5:14 nkjv

The true light that gives light to every man was coming into the world.—John 1:9

And the Light shines on in the darkness, for the darkness has never overpowered it [put it out or absorbed it or appropriated it, and is unreceptive to it].—John 1:5 amp

And we, who with unveiled faces all reflect the Lord's glory, are being transformed into his likeness with ever-increasing glory, which comes from the Lord, who is the Spirit.—2 Corinthians 3:18

September 11

WITH THE THREAT OF TERRORISM looming over planet Earth, some people are saying—and feeling—that no place is really safe. In one sense, this is true. Evil people, especially terrorists, are unpredictable and ruthless. However, for Christian believers, there is no place that is actually *unsafe*. Your ultimate home is heaven, and no one can rob you of this glorious *inheritance that can never perish, spoil, or fade*. Furthermore, I am *sovereign* over everything, including your life and your loved ones. Nothing can happen to you—or to them—except what I allow.

The truth is, the world has been at war ever since Adam and Eve first sinned. The Fall in the Garden of Eden rendered the earth a dangerous place where good and evil contend against each other continually. So it's crucial to *be alert and self-controlled*. Remember that your ultimate enemy, the devil, has already been defeated. *I have overcome the world*, and you are on the winning side—*My* side. *In Me you have Peace*. In Me you are always safe.

> *Praise be to the God and Father of our Lord Jesus Christ! In his great mercy he has given us new birth into a living hope through the resurrection of Jesus Christ from the dead, and into an inheritance that can never perish, spoil or fade—kept in heaven for you.*—1 PETER 1:3–4

> *From birth I have relied on you; you brought me forth from my mother's womb. I will ever praise you.*—PSALM 71:6

> *Be self-controlled and alert. Your enemy the devil prowls around like a roaring lion looking for someone to devour.*—1 PETER 5:8

> *"These things I have spoken to you, that in Me you may have peace. In the world you will have tribulation; but be of good cheer, I have overcome the world."*—JOHN 16:33 NKJV

September 12

Your times are in My hands. So *trust in Me*, beloved. I am training you to feel secure in the midst of change and uncertainty. It can actually be a relief to realize you are not in control of your life. When you accept this human condition while resting in My sovereignty, you become increasingly free.

I am not telling you to be passive or fatalistic. It's important to use your energy and abilities, but I want you to do so prayerfully. Pray about everything, and search for Me in your moments. I am a God of surprises, so look for Me in unexpected places.

I invite you to *rejoice in this day that I have made*, asking Me to orchestrate its details and events. Since I am in control of *your times*, you don't have to be anxious about making things happen faster. Rushing and anxiety go hand in hand, and I have instructed you not to be anxious. If you let *Me* set the pace, I will bless you with *Peace that transcends all understanding*.

> But I trust in you, O Lord; I say, "You are my God." My times are in your hands; deliver me from my enemies and from those who pursue me.—Psalm 31:14–15

> This is the day the Lord has made; we will rejoice and be glad in it.—Psalm 118:24 nkjv

> Do not be anxious about anything, but in everything, by prayer and petition, with thanksgiving, present your requests to God. And the peace of God, which transcends all understanding, will guard your hearts and your minds in Christ Jesus.—Philippians 4:6–7

September 13

Your life is a precious gift from Me. Open your hands and your heart to receive this day gratefully. Relate to Me as your Savior and Friend, but remember I am also your Creator-God: *All things were created by Me.* As you go through this day that I've gifted to you, look for signs of My abiding Presence. *I am with you, watching over you continually.* On bright, joyful days, speak to Me about the pleasures I provide; as you thank Me for them, your Joy will expand abundantly. On dark, difficult days, grasp My hand in trusting dependence. *I will help you,* beloved.

Your physical life is an amazing gift, but your spiritual life is a treasure of infinite value! People who don't know Me as Savior will spend an eternity in terrible separation from Me. But because you belong to Me, you will live with Me forever, enjoying a glorified body that will never get sick or tired. Since I have saved you *by grace through faith,* let thankfulness for this indescribable gift fill you with overflowing Joy!

> *For by Him all things were created that are in heaven and that are on earth, visible and invisible, whether thrones or dominions or principalities or powers. All things were created through Him and for Him.*—Colossians 1:16 nkjv

> *"I am with you and will watch over you wherever you go, and I will bring you back to this land. I will not leave you until I have done what I have promised you."*—Genesis 28:15

> *"For I am the Lord, your God, who takes hold of your right hand and says to you, Do not fear; I will help you."*—Isaiah 41:13

> *For by grace you have been saved through faith, and that not of yourselves; it is the gift of God.*—Ephesians 2:8 nkjv

September 14

A LONG-TERM PROBLEM can become an idol. When you are troubled by a situation that just won't go away, it's important to monitor your thoughts. An ongoing difficulty can occupy more and more of your thinking, until it looms in idolatrous proportions—casting ugly shadows on the landscape of your mind. When you realize this has happened, confess it to Me. Pour out your feelings as you seek to break free from the hurtful preoccupation. Acknowledge your weakness in the face of this hardship, and *humble yourself under My mighty hand.*

A problem-preoccupation makes you anxious. So I urge you to *cast all your anxiety on Me*—trusting that *I care for you.* You may have to do this thousands of times daily, but don't give up! Each time you cast your worrisome concerns on Me, you are redirecting your attention from problems to My loving Presence. To strengthen these transactions, you can thank Me for caring so much for you. Remember that I not only died for you, *I live to make intercession for you.*

Dear children, keep yourselves from idols.—1 JOHN 5:21

Humble yourselves, therefore, under God's mighty hand, that he may lift you up in due time. Cast all your anxiety on him because he cares for you.—1 PETER 5:6–7

Therefore He is also able to save to the uttermost those who come to God through Him, since He always lives to make intercession for them.—HEBREWS 7:25 NKJV

September 15

I CAN SMOOTH OUT all the tangled-up places, including those in your mind and heart. So come to Me just as you are, with all your knotty problems and loose ends. Many of your difficulties are complicated by other people's perplexities. It can be hard to sort out how much of the mess is yours and how much is theirs. Be willing to take responsibility for your own mistakes and sin without feeling responsible for the sinful failures of others. I am here to help you untangle your complex problems and find the best way to go forward.

Christianity is all about transformation—a lifelong process. Some of the knots from your past are hard to untie, especially when they involve people who continue to hurt you. Beware of getting stuck in introspection or obsessing about how to fix things. Instead, keep turning toward Me, seeking My Face *and* My will. Wait with Me, trusting in My timing for unscrambling things and making your way clear. Be willing to live with unresolved problems, but don't let them be your focus. My Presence in the present is *your portion*—and your boundless blessing.

> *And we, who with unveiled faces all reflect the Lord's glory, are being transformed into his likeness with ever-increasing glory, which comes from the Lord, who is the Spirit.* —2 CORINTHIANS 3:18

> *Glory in his holy name; let the hearts of those who seek the LORD rejoice. Look to the LORD and his strength; seek his face always.* —1 CHRONICLES 16:10–11

> *I say to myself, "The LORD is my portion; therefore I will wait for him."* —LAMENTATIONS 3:24

September 16

Devote yourself to prayer with an alert mind and a thankful heart. For My followers, praying is a way of life—a way of staying connected with Me. But it's not easy. The evil one disdains your devotion to Me; his demonic underlings work to interrupt and weaken your communications with Me. So it's crucial for you to be committed to this discipline—determined to stay in touch with Me.

You can train yourself to call on Me even while you're engaging in other activities. This invites Me into your world, helping your work to go better and your life to be more fulfilling. It's also important to set aside some time to focus just on communicating with Me. This can be quite challenging! To pray effectively, you need an alert mind and a thankful heart. Ask My Spirit, *the Helper*, to empower your prayers—increasing your mental alertness and your thankfulness.

A wide-awake mind and a grateful heart will help you not only pray better but also live better. *Give thanks to Me and praise My Name.*

> *Devote yourselves to prayer with an alert mind and a thankful heart.*—Colossians 4:2 NLT

> "But when the Helper comes, whom I shall send to you from the Father, the Spirit of truth who proceeds from the Father, He will testify of Me."—John 15:26 NKJV

> *Enter his gates with thanksgiving and his courts with praise; give thanks to him and praise his name.*—Psalm 100:4

September 17

I delight in those who fear Me, who put their hope in My unfailing Love. "Fear of the Lord" is often misunderstood, but it is the foundation of spiritual wisdom and knowledge. It consists of reverential awe, adoration, and submission to My will. You submit to Me by exchanging *your* attitudes and goals for *Mine*. Since I am your Creator, aligning yourself with Me is the best way to live. When your lifestyle exhibits this biblical fear, I take delight in you. Seek to feel My pleasure shining on you at such times.

Living according to My will is not easy; there will be many ups and downs as you journey with Me. But no matter what is happening, you can find hope in My unfailing Love. In your world today, many people are feeling desperate. They've become disillusioned and cynical because they put their confidence in the wrong thing. But *My steadfast Love* will never let you down—it will never let you go! Cling to hope, beloved. It's a golden cord connecting you to Me.

The Lord delights in those who fear him, who put their hope in his unfailing love.—Psalm 147:11

The fear of the Lord is the beginning of knowledge, but fools despise wisdom and instruction.—Proverbs 1:7 nkjv

The steadfast love of the Lord never ceases; his mercies never come to an end; they are new every morning; great is your faithfulness.—Lamentations 3:22–23 esv

September 18

To infuse more Joy into your day, seek to increase your awareness that I am with you. An easy way to do this is to say: "Thank You, Jesus, for Your Presence." This is such a short, simple prayer that you can pray it frequently; it beautifully connects you to Me, expressing your gratitude. You don't have to *feel* My nearness in order to pray this way. However, the more you thank Me for My Presence, the more real I become to you. You align yourself—mind, heart, and spirit—with the reality that *in Me you live and move and have your being.*

You also increase your awareness by looking for signs of My unseen Presence around you. The beauties of nature and the pleasures of loved ones are reminders, pointing you to Me. You can also find Me in My Word, for I am the living Word. Ask My Spirit to illuminate Scripture to you—shining His Light in your heart, helping you see the Glory of My Presence.

"For in him we live and move and have our being." As some of your own poets have said, "We are his offspring."—Acts 17:28

In the beginning was the Word, and the Word was with God, and the Word was God. He was in the beginning with God.—John 1:1–2 nkjv

For God, who said, "Let light shine out of darkness," made his light shine in our hearts to give us the light of the knowledge of the glory of God in the face of Christ.—2 Corinthians 4:6

September 19

WHEN YOU ARE FEELING DOWNCAST, the best remedy is to *remember Me*. Think about who I am—*your Lord and your God*, your Savior and Shepherd, the Friend who *will never leave you*. I am fully aware of your every circumstance as well as all your thoughts and feelings. Everything about you is important to Me because you are so precious to Me. Remember the many ways I have taken care of you and helped you. Thank Me for each one that comes to mind, and relax in My loving Presence.

Tell Me about the things that are weighing you down. Though I know all about them, your voicing them to Me provides relief from the heavy load you've been carrying. In the Light of My Presence, you will see things more clearly. Together, you and I can sort out what is important and what is not. Moreover, as you linger with Me, My Face shines upon you—blessing, encouraging, and comforting you. I assure you that *you will again praise Me for the help of My Presence*.

My soul is downcast within me; therefore I will remember you from the land of the Jordan, the heights of Hermon—from Mount Mizar.—PSALM 42:6

Thomas answered and said to Him, "My Lord and my God!"—JOHN 20:28 NKJV

The LORD himself goes before you and will be with you; he will never leave you nor forsake you. Do not be afraid; do not be discouraged.—DEUTERONOMY 31:8

Why are you in despair, O my soul? And why have you become disturbed within me? Hope in God, for I shall again praise Him for the help of His presence.—PSALM 42:5 NASB

September 20

I AM GRACIOUS AND COMPASSIONATE, slow to anger and rich in Love. Explore the wonders of grace: unmerited favor lavished on you through My finished work on the cross. *By grace you have been saved through faith, and that not of yourself; it is the gift of God.* What's more, *My compassions never fail. They are new every morning.* So begin your day expectantly, ready to receive fresh compassions. Don't let yesterday's failures weigh you down. Learn from your mistakes and confess known sins, but don't let those become your focus. Instead, keep your eyes on Me.

I am *slow to anger.* So don't be quick to judge yourself—or others. Rather, rejoice that I am *rich in Love.* In fact, Love is at the very core of who I am. Your growth in grace involves learning to be more attentive to Me, more receptive to My loving Presence. This requires vigilant effort because the evil one despises your closeness to Me. Strive to stay alert, and remember: *There is no condemnation for those who belong to Me!*

> The Lord is gracious and compassionate, slow to anger and rich in love. The Lord is good to all; he has compassion on all he has made. —Psalm 145:8–9

> For by grace you have been saved through faith, and that not of yourselves; it is the gift of God. —Ephesians 2:8 NKJV

> Because of the Lord's great love we are not consumed; for his compassions never fail. They are new every morning; great is your faithfulness. —Lamentations 3:22–23

> Therefore, there is now no condemnation for those who are in Christ Jesus. —Romans 8:1

September 21

Come to Me, and rest in My Presence. I am *constantly thinking about you*, and I want you to become increasingly mindful of Me. Awareness of My Presence can *give you rest* even when you are quite busy. An inner peacefulness flows out of knowing *I am with you always*. This knowledge of Me permeates your heart, mind, and spirit—and it can fill you with deep Joy.

Many of My followers are so focused on the problems they see and the predictions they hear that they lose their Joy. It becomes buried under multiple layers of worry and fear. When you realize this has happened in your life, bring all your concerns to Me. Talk with Me about each one, seeking My help and guidance. Ask Me to remove the anxious layers that have buried your Joy. As you entrust your concerns into My care and keeping, your Joy will begin to emerge again. Nurture this gladness by speaking or singing praises to Me—*the King of Glory* who loves you eternally.

> "Come to me, all you who are weary and burdened, and I will give you rest."—Matthew 11:28

> *How precious it is, Lord, to realize that you are thinking about me constantly!*—Psalm 139:17 TLB

> "... And teaching them to obey everything I have commanded you. And surely I am with you always, to the very end of the age."—Matthew 28:20

> *Lift up your heads, O you gates! And be lifted up, you everlasting doors! And the King of glory shall come in.*—Psalm 24:7 NKJV

September 22

DON'T WORRY ABOUT YOUR INADEQUACY; instead, accept and embrace it. It's the perfect link to My limitless sufficiency. When your resources seem lacking, your natural inclination is to worry. The best way to resist this temptation is to openly acknowledge your insufficiencies and thank Me for them. This frees you from trying to be what you are not—your own Savior and Provider. Because you are weak and sinful, you need a Savior who is strong and perfect—a Provider who can *meet all your needs*.

You gain access to My boundless resources by being both still *and* active. Spending time alone with Me, waiting in My Presence, enhances your connection with Me. *I work for those who wait for Me*, doing for you what you cannot do for yourself. But there are many things you *can* do. When you go about your activities relying on *the strength that I supply, I am glorified* and you are blessed.

The next time you're feeling inadequate, turn to Me immediately. I lovingly meet you in the place of your neediness.

And my God will meet all your needs according to his glorious riches in Christ Jesus.—PHILIPPIANS 4:19

For since the world began, no ear has heard and no eye has seen a God like you, who works for those who wait for him!—ISAIAH 64:4 NLT

. . . Whoever speaks, as one who speaks oracles of God; whoever serves, as one who serves by the strength that God supplies—in order that in everything God may be glorified through Jesus Christ. To him belong glory and dominion forever and ever. Amen.—1 PETER 4:11 ESV

September 23

A bruised reed I will not break, and a dimly burning wick I will not extinguish. I know you sometimes feel as weak and helpless as a bent reed or a faintly burning flame. Accept your weakness and brokenness, beloved; let them open your heart to Me. You can be fully yourself with Me because I understand you perfectly. As you tell Me your troubles, I refresh you and offer you *Peace that surpasses all comprehension.* Instead of trying to figure everything out, *lean on Me* in confident trust. Go off-duty for a while, trusting that I'm watching over you and working on your behalf.

My healing work within you is most effective when you are resting in My watchful care. *Though the mountains be shaken and the hills be removed, yet My unfailing Love for you will not be shaken nor My covenant of Peace be removed—for I have compassion on you.* Whenever you're feeling weak and wounded, come confidently into My Presence to receive abundant Love and Peace.

> "A bruised reed He will not break and a dimly burning wick He will not extinguish; He will faithfully bring forth justice."—Isaiah 42:3 NASB

> Be anxious for nothing, but in everything by prayer and supplication with thanksgiving let your requests be made known to God. And the peace of God, which surpasses all comprehension, will guard your hearts and your minds in Christ Jesus.—Philippians 4:6–7 NASB

> Lean on, trust in, and be confident in the Lord with all your heart and mind and do not rely on your own insight or understanding.—Proverbs 3:5 AMP

> "Though the mountains be shaken and the hills be removed, yet my unfailing love for you will not be shaken nor my covenant of peace be removed," says the Lord, who has compassion on you.—Isaiah 54:10

September 24

You are a letter from Me, written not with ink but with the Spirit of the living God—on the tablet of your heart. Because you are one of My followers, the Holy Spirit is in you. He equips and empowers you to do far more than you could ever do on your own. So don't be intimidated by challenging circumstances or tough times. The third Person of the Godhead lives *inside* you! Ponder the implications of this glorious truth. You can do much more than you think possible when you walk in My ways, asking *the Helper* to strengthen you as you go step by step with Me.

The Spirit writes on the tablet of your heart not only to bless you but also to draw others to Me. When you are with people who don't know Me, He can make you a living letter from Me. One of the shortest but most effective prayers is: "Help me, Holy Spirit." Use this prayer as often as you need, inviting Him to bring gospel truths alive through you.

> *You show that you are a letter from Christ, the result of our ministry, written not with ink but with the Spirit of the living God, not on tablets of stone but on tablets of human hearts.* —2 Corinthians 3:3

> *You, however, are controlled not by the sinful nature but by the Spirit, if the Spirit of God lives in you. And if anyone does not have the Spirit of Christ, he does not belong to Christ.* —Romans 8:9

> *"But when the Helper comes, whom I shall send to you from the Father, the Spirit of truth who proceeds from the Father, He will testify of Me."* —John 15:26 nkjv

September 25

If it is possible, as far as it depends on you, live at peace with everyone. At times there will be someone who is determined to oppose you—without good cause. In this case, I don't hold you accountable for the conflict. More often, however, you have contributed something to the dissension. When this happens, you should repent of your part in the conflict and do whatever you can to restore a peaceful relationship. In *either* situation, you need to forgive the person who offended you. You may also need to forgive yourself.

Beloved, *be quick to listen, slow to speak, and slow to become angry.* Take time—not only to think through what you want to say but to *listen* to the other person. If you listen carefully and pause before responding, you will be much less likely to become angry.

Whenever you have failed to live at peace with others and you are at fault, do not despair. I paid the penalty for *all* your sins so you could have permanent Peace with Me.

> *If it is possible, as far as it depends on you,
> live at peace with everyone.* —Romans 12:18

> *My dear brothers, take note of this: Everyone should be quick
> to listen, slow to speak and slow to become angry.* —James 1:19

> *Therefore, since we have been justified through faith, we have
> peace with God through our Lord Jesus Christ.* —Romans 5:1

September 26

Don't be surprised by the many loose ends in your life. They will always be part of your experience in this fallen world. When I created Adam and Eve, I placed them in a perfect environment: the Garden of Eden. Since you are one of their descendants, your longing for perfection is natural. It is also supernatural. Because you are My follower, your ultimate destination is heaven—magnificent and glorious beyond anything you can imagine! Your longings will be completely satisfied there.

When the loose ends of this broken world are getting you down, stop and look up to Me. Remember that I, the Perfect One, am with you. Tell Me your troubles, and let Me help you with them. Seek My guidance in setting good priorities—according to My will for you. Take time to rest in My Presence and to worship Me. Praising Me directs your attention away from the world with all its brokenness, toward Me in all My Glory. While you're engaged in worshiping Me, you are participating in My Glory.

The Lord God took the man and put him in the Garden of Eden to work it and take care of it.—Genesis 2:15

Yet I am always with you; you hold me by my right hand. You guide me with your counsel, and afterward you will take me into glory.—Psalm 73:23–24

Give unto the Lord the glory due to His name; worship the Lord in the beauty of holiness.—Psalm 29:2 nkjv

September 27

To all who receive Me, to those who believe in My Name, I give the right to become children of God. There is a close connection between receiving Me and believing in My Name—the essence of who I am. Receiving a gift requires some measure of openness, and I am the best Gift imaginable! Recognizing Me as your Savior-God, you can believe that My offer of everlasting Life is real—and that it is for you.

Being a child of God is indescribably glorious! I am both your Savior and your constant Companion. As you journey through life in this dark world, I am with you each step of the way. I provide Light not only for your path but also for your mind and heart. I delight in giving you Joy—now and throughout eternity. Your brightest moment on earth will one day look quite dim in comparison with the Glory-Light of heaven! There you will *see My Face* in its brilliant splendor, and you will *be satisfied* with endless oceans of Love.

> *He was in the world, and though the world was made through him, the world did not recognize him. He came to that which was his own, but his own did not receive him. Yet to all who received him, to those who believed in his name, he gave the right to become children of God.*—John 1:10–12

> *"For God so loved the world that He gave His only begotten Son, that whoever believes in Him should not perish but have everlasting life."*—John 3:16 nkjv

> *And I—in righteousness I will see your face; when I awake, I will be satisfied with seeing your likeness.*—Psalm 17:15

September 28

When your world looks dark and threatening, come to Me. *Pour out your heart to Me*, knowing that I'm listening—and I care. Find comfort in My sovereignty: I'm in control even when global events look terribly out of control. Actually, many things are *not* as they should be, *not* as they were created to be. You do well to yearn for perfect goodness—someday those longings will be wondrously satisfied.

Consider the prophet Habakkuk as he awaited the Babylonian invasion of Judah. He knew the attack would be brutal, and he wrestled deeply with this prophetic knowledge. Finally, though, he wrote a hymn of absolute confidence in Me. After describing utterly desperate circumstances, he concluded: *"Yet I will rejoice in the Lord, I will be joyful in God my Savior."*

Feel free to wrestle with Me about your concerns. But remember that the goal is to come to a place of confident trust and transcendent Joy. You won't understand My mysterious ways, but you can find hope and help in My Presence. *I am your Strength*!

> *Trust in him at all times. Pour out your heart to him.*—Psalm 62:8 NLT

> *There will be no more night. They will not need the light of a lamp or the light of the sun, for the Lord God will give them light.*—Revelation 22:5

> *Though the fig tree does not bud and there are no grapes on the vines, though the olive crop fails and the fields produce no food, though there are no sheep in the pen and no cattle in the stalls, yet I will rejoice in the Lord, I will be joyful in God my Savior. The sovereign Lord is my strength; he makes my feet like the feet of a deer, he enables me to go on the heights.*—Habakkuk 3:17–19

> *Why are you in despair, O my soul? And why have you become disturbed within me? Hope in God, for I shall again praise Him for the help of His presence.*—Psalm 42:5 NASB

September 29

IF YOUR PRIMARY GOAL is pleasing yourself, your life will be filled with frustrations. The attitude that things should go your way is based on a faulty premise: that you are the center of your world. The truth is, *I* am the Center, and everything revolves around Me. So make your plans tentatively, *seeking My Face* and My will in all you do. This is a win-win situation: If things go according to your plans, rejoice and thank Me. When your desires are thwarted, communicate with Me and be ready to subordinate your will to Mine.

Remember that you belong to Me, beloved; *you are not your own.* This awareness that you belong to Another can be a great relief. It shifts your focus away from yourself and what you want. Instead of striving to make things go your way, your primary goal becomes pleasing *Me.* You might think this would be burdensome, but it is actually quite freeing. *My yoke is easy, and My burden is light.* Knowing that you belong to Me provides deep, satisfying *rest for your soul.*

Seek the LORD and His strength; seek His face continually.—PSALM 105:4 NASB

Don't you know that your body is a sanctuary of the Holy Spirit who is in you, whom you have from God? You are not your own.—1 CORINTHIANS 6:19 HCSB

So we make it our goal to please him, whether we are at home in the body or away from it.—2 CORINTHIANS 5:9

"Take my yoke upon you and learn from me, for I am gentle and humble in heart, and you will find rest for your souls. For my yoke is easy and my burden is light."—MATTHEW 11:29–30

September 30

The richest treasure I offer you is *the Light of the gospel of My Glory*. This is what makes the gospel such amazingly good news. It opens the way to My Glory!

When you trusted Me as your Savior, I set your feet on a pathway to heaven. Forgiveness of sins and a future in heaven are wondrous blessings, but I have even more for you. I have *made My Light shine in your heart to give you the Light of the knowledge of the Glory of My Face.* I want you to *seek My Face* wholeheartedly, so you can enjoy the radiant knowledge of My glorious Presence.

"Knowledge" is a very rich word. Some of its meanings are: *awareness acquired by experience or study* and *the sum of what has been perceived, discovered, or learned.* So knowing Me involves *awareness of Me*—experiencing My Presence. It also involves *perceiving* Me. *The god of this age has blinded the minds of unbelievers,* but you can know Me through perceiving the Light of My Glory!

The god of this age has blinded the minds of unbelievers, so that they cannot see the light of the gospel of the glory of Christ, who is the image of God.—2 Corinthians 4:4

For God, who said, "Let light shine out of darkness," made his light shine in our hearts to give us the light of the knowledge of the glory of God in the face of Christ.—2 Corinthians 4:6

When You said, "Seek My face," my heart said to You, "Your face, Lord, I will seek."—Psalm 27:8 nkjv

October

*Unfailing love surrounds those who trust the L*ORD.

PSALM **32:10** NLT

October 1

I WANT YOU TO RELAX and enjoy this day. It's easy for you to get so focused on your goals that you push yourself too hard—and neglect your need for rest. You tend to judge yourself on the basis of how much you've accomplished. There is certainly a time and place for being productive, using the opportunities and abilities I provide. Nonetheless, I want you to be able to like yourself as much when you're relaxing as when you're achieving.

Rest in the knowledge that you're a child of God, *saved by grace through faith* in Me. This is your ultimate—and foundational—identity. You hold a position of royalty in My eternal kingdom. Remember who you are!

When you're comfortable enough in your true identity to balance work with relaxation, you are more effective in My kingdom. A refreshed mind is able to think more clearly and biblically. A *restored soul* is more winsome and loving in interactions with others. So take time with Me, and let Me *lead you beside waters of rest.*

> *By the seventh day God had finished the work he had been doing; so on the seventh day he rested from all his work. And God blessed the seventh day and made it holy, because on it he rested from all the work of creating that he had done.*—GENESIS 2:2–3

> *For by grace you have been saved through faith, and that not of yourselves; it is the gift of God.*—EPHESIANS 2:8 NKJV

> *He makes me lie down in green pastures; He leads me beside quiet waters. He restores my soul; He guides me in the paths of righteousness for His name's sake.*—PSALM 23:2–3 NASB

October 2

I will judge the world in righteousness and the peoples in My truth. This promise is full of blessing and encouragement. It means that someday evil will be judged; My perfect justice will finally—and forever—prevail! Because you are My follower, clothed in My own righteousness, you have nothing to fear. But those who refuse to trust Me as Savior have *everything* to fear. Someday time will run out, and My wrath will be terrifying to all who persist in unbelief. They will even *call to the mountains and the rocks, "Fall on us and hide us from the face of Him who sits on the throne and from the wrath of the Lamb!"*

I will judge everyone in My truth. The concept of absolute truth is widely opposed, yet it is nonetheless rock-solid reality. Unbelievers will eventually bump up against this certainty whether they believe in it or not. For you—and all believers—My truth is a firm foundation on which you can live and work, play and praise. This is good reason to *sing for Joy!*

> *They will sing before the Lord, for he comes, he comes to judge the earth. He will judge the world in righteousness and the peoples in his truth.*—Psalm 96:13

> *I will greatly rejoice in the Lord, my soul shall be joyful in my God; for He has clothed me with the garments of salvation, He has covered me with the robe of righteousness, as a bridegroom decks himself with ornaments, and as a bride adorns herself with her jewels.*—Isaiah 61:10 nkjv

> *They called to the mountains and the rocks, "Fall on us and hide us from the face of him who sits on the throne and from the wrath of the Lamb!"*—Revelation 6:16

> *Come, let us sing for joy to the Lord; let us shout aloud to the Rock of our salvation.*—Psalm 95:1

October 3

MY JUDGMENTS ARE UNSEARCHABLE, *and My paths are beyond tracing out!* This is why trusting Me is your best response to My ways with you. My *wisdom and knowledge* are too deep for Me to explain Myself to you. This should not be surprising, since I am infinite and eternal. I have always existed—*from everlasting to everlasting I am God.*

I am also *the Word who became flesh and dwelt among you.* I identified with mankind to the full extent—taking on a human body and dying a terrible death to save sinners who believe in Me. My sacrificial life and death provide ample reason for you to trust Me even when you don't understand My ways. You can rejoice that your loving Savior and sovereign Lord is infinitely wise! And you can draw near Me at any time by lovingly whispering My Name. I am always within whispering-distance: now, throughout your lifetime, and for all eternity. I am *Immanuel—God with you*—and I will never leave you.

> *Oh, the depth of the riches of the wisdom and knowledge of God! How unsearchable his judgments, and his paths beyond tracing out!*—ROMANS 11:33

> *Before the mountains were born or you brought forth the earth and the world, from everlasting to everlasting you are God.*—PSALM 90:2

> *And the Word became flesh and dwelt among us, and we have seen his glory, glory as of the only Son from the Father, full of grace and truth.*—JOHN 1:14 ESV

> *"The virgin will be with child and will give birth to a son, and they will call him Immanuel"—which means, "God with us."*—MATTHEW 1:23

October 4

Do not let fear of mistakes immobilize you or make you anxious. In this life you *will* err sometimes because you're only human, with limited knowledge and understanding. When you're facing a major decision, learn as much as you can about the matter. *Seek My Face*—and My help. I will *guide you with My counsel* as you think things out in My Presence. When the time is right, go ahead and make the decision, even though the outcome is uncertain. Pray for My will to be done in this matter, and release the results to Me.

Fear has to do with punishment. If you have been punished unjustly or severely mistreated, it is natural for you to dread making mistakes. When choices need to be made, anxiety can cloud your thinking—perhaps even immobilizing you. The remedy is to remember that *I am with you* and for you—that you don't have to perform well for Me to keep loving you. Absolutely nothing, including your worst mistakes, *can separate you from My Love*!

When You said, "Seek My face," my heart said to You, "Your face, Lord, I will seek."—Psalm 27:8 nkjv

Yet I am always with you; you hold me by my right hand. You guide me with your counsel, and afterward you will take me into glory.—Psalm 73:23–24

There is no fear in love, but perfect love casts out fear. For fear has to do with punishment, and whoever fears has not been perfected in love.—1 John 4:18 esv

For I am convinced that neither death nor life, neither angels nor demons, neither the present nor the future, nor any powers, neither height nor depth, nor anything else in all creation, will be able to separate us from the love of God that is in Christ Jesus our Lord.—Romans 8:38–39

October 5

I WANT YOU TO *HAVE NO FEAR* of bad news. The only way to accomplish this feat is to have a *steadfast heart, trusting in Me.* There is an abundance of bad news in the world, but you don't need to be afraid of it. Instead, confidently rely on Me—*believe* in Me. Find encouragement in My sacrificial death on the cross and My miraculous resurrection. I, your living Savior, am Almighty God! I am *sovereign* over global events; I am still in control.

When things around you or in the world seem to be spinning out of control, come to Me and *pour out your heart.* Instead of fretting and fuming, put your energy into praying. Come to Me, not only for comfort but also for direction; I will help you find the way forward. Moreover, I take your prayers into account as I govern your planet—in ways far, far beyond your understanding.

Don't dread bad news or let it spook you. Instead, keep your heart steadfast and calm through confident trust in Me.

> *He will have no fear of bad news; his heart is steadfast, trusting in the* LORD. —PSALM 112:7

> *Yes, the Sovereign* LORD *is coming in power. He will rule with a powerful arm.* —ISAIAH 40:10 NLT

> *Trust in Him at all times, you people; pour out your heart before Him; God is a refuge for us.* —PSALM 62:8 NKJV

> *For to us a child is born, to us a son is given, and the government will be on his shoulders. And he will be called Wonderful Counselor, Mighty God, Everlasting Father, Prince of Peace.* —ISAIAH 9:6

October 6

ASK ME FOR WISDOM, BELOVED. I know how much you need it! King Solomon requested *a discerning heart*, and he received wisdom in magnificent abundance. This precious gift is also essential for you, especially when you're making plans and decisions. So come to Me for what you need, and *trust Me* to provide it in full measure.

One aspect of wisdom is recognizing your need for My help in all that you do. When your mind is sluggish, it's easy to forget about Me and simply dive into your tasks and activities. But eventually you bump into an obstacle. Then you face an important choice: to push ahead full throttle or to stop and ask Me for insight, understanding, and guidance. The closer to Me you live, the more readily and frequently you will seek My help.

The fear of the Lord is the beginning of wisdom. Though I am your Friend, remember who I am in My *great Power and Glory*! Godly fear—reverential awe and worshipful admiration—provides the best foundation for wisdom.

If any of you lacks wisdom, he should ask God, who gives generously to all without finding fault, and it will be given to him. But when he asks, he must believe and not doubt, because he who doubts is like a wave of the sea, blown and tossed by the wind.—JAMES 1:5–6

So give your servant a discerning heart to govern your people and to distinguish between right and wrong. . . . God gave Solomon wisdom and very great insight, and a breadth of understanding as measureless as the sand on the seashore.—1 KINGS 3:9, 4:29

The fear of the LORD is the beginning of knowledge, but fools despise wisdom and discipline.—PROVERBS 1:7

"Then they will see the Son of Man coming in the clouds with great power and glory."—MARK 13:26 NKJV

October 7

Train your mind to think great thoughts of Me! Many Christians are defeated by focusing mainly on less important things—the news, the weather, the economy, loved ones' problems, their own problems, and so on. Granted, *in this world you will have trouble*, but don't let troubles become your primary focus. Remind yourself that I am with you and *I have overcome the world*. I am nearer than the air you breathe, yet I am infinite God—*King of kings and Lord of lords*. I am also your loving Savior and faithful Friend.

One of the best ways to enhance awareness of My greatness is to worship Me. This connects you with the Godhead (Father, Son, and Spirit) in a glorious way. True worship expands My kingdom of Light in the world, pushing back the darkness. An exquisite way to praise Me is to read or sing the Psalms. Filling your mind with biblical truth will help you resist discouragement. When troubles assail you, exert yourself to think about who I am—your Savior and Friend who is Almighty God!

> "I have told you these things, so that in me you may have peace. In this world you will have trouble. But take heart! I have overcome the world."—John 16:33

> And on His robe and on His thigh He has a name written, "KING OF KINGS, AND LORD OF LORDS."—Revelation 19:16 nasb

> "I am the Alpha and the Omega, the Beginning and the End," says the Lord, "who is and who was and who is to come, the Almighty."—Revelation 1:8 nkjv

October 8

I WANT YOU TO BECOME increasingly preoccupied with Me. The default mode of most people is self-absorption. My followers are not immune to this affliction, and it hinders their growth in grace.

When a man and woman are deeply in love, they tend to be preoccupied with each other. So the way to become preoccupied with *Me* is to love Me more fully—*with all your heart and soul and mind*. This is *the greatest commandment*, and it is a most worthy goal. Of course, you cannot do it perfectly in this life. But the more you comprehend and delight in the wondrous, *unfailing Love* I have for you, the more ardently you can respond to Me. Ask My Spirit to help you in this glorious quest!

There are two parts to this adventure: learning to receive My Love in greater depth, breadth, and constancy; and responding by loving Me more and more. Thus you break free from the bondage of self-absorption and grow increasingly preoccupied with Me. I delight in setting you free!

Jesus replied, "'Love the Lord your God with all your heart and with all your soul and with all your mind.' This is the first and greatest commandment. And the second is like it: 'Love your neighbor as yourself.'"—MATTHEW 22:37–39

But I am like an olive tree flourishing in the house of God; I trust in God's unfailing love for ever and ever.—PSALM 52:8

We love Him because He first loved us.—1 JOHN 4:19 NKJV

"Therefore if the Son makes you free, you shall be free indeed."—JOHN 8:36 NKJV

October 9

BE CAREFUL not to attach your sense of worth to your performance. When you're dissatisfied with something you have said or done, talk with Me about it. Ask Me to help you sort out what is truly sinful and what is not. Confess any sins you're aware of, and receive My forgiveness gratefully. Then live in the freedom of being My beloved believer. Don't let your mistakes and sins diminish your sense of worth. Remember that you have been declared "Not Guilty" forever! *There is no condemnation for those who are in Me*—who belong to Me. You are precious to Me, and *I take delight in you*, so refuse to condemn yourself.

Your imperfect performance reminds you that you are human. It humbles you and helps you identify with flawed humanity. Since pride is such a deadly sin—the one that ultimately led to Satan's expulsion from heaven—being humbled is really a blessing. So thank Me for the circumstances that have diminished your pride, and draw nearer to Me. Receive *My priceless, unfailing Love* in full measure!

If we confess our sins, He is faithful and just to forgive us our sins and to cleanse us from all unrighteousness.—1 JOHN 1:9 NKJV

There is therefore now no condemnation for those who are in Christ Jesus.—ROMANS 8:1 ESV

"The LORD your God is with you, he is mighty to save. He will take great delight in you, he will quiet you with his love, he will rejoice over you with singing."—ZEPHANIAH 3:17

How priceless is your unfailing love! Both high and low among men find refuge in the shadow of your wings.—PSALM 36:7

October 10

A TROUBLESOME PROBLEM can become an idol in your mind. If you consistently think about something—pleasant or unpleasant—more than you think about Me, you are practicing a subtle form of idolatry. So it is wise to examine your thoughts.

Most people view idols as things that bring pleasure. But a chronic difficulty can captivate your mind, taking over increasingly more of your mental activity. Becoming aware of this bondage is a huge step toward breaking free from it. When you find yourself dwelling on a persistent problem, bring it to Me and confess the mental bondage you're experiencing. Request My help and My forgiveness, which I freely give. I will help you *take captive every thought to make it obedient to Me.*

I am teaching you to *fix your thoughts on Me* more and more. To achieve this goal, you need both discipline and desire. It's vital that you find pleasure in thinking of Me—rejoicing in My loving Presence. *Delight yourself in Me*, beloved; make Me the Desire of your heart.

> *All the prophets say it is true that all who believe in Jesus will be forgiven of their sins through Jesus' name.*—ACTS 10:43 NCV

> *We demolish arguments and every pretension that sets itself up against the knowledge of God, and we take captive every thought to make it obedient to Christ.*—2 CORINTHIANS 10:5

> *Therefore, holy brothers, who share in the heavenly calling, fix your thoughts on Jesus, the apostle and high priest whom we confess.*—HEBREWS 3:1

> *Delight yourself in the LORD; and He will give you the desires of your heart.*—PSALM 37:4 NASB

October 11

I AM YOUR STRENGTH AND YOUR SHIELD. I continually work—sometimes in wondrous ways—to invigorate you and protect you. The more fully you trust in Me, the more your heart can *leap for Joy!*

I want you to trust Me wholeheartedly—resting in My sovereign control over the universe. When circumstances seem to be spinning out of control, grab onto Me, believing that I know what I'm doing. I orchestrate every event of your life to benefit you in this world and the next.

While you are in the throes of adversity, your greatest challenge is to keep on trusting that I am both sovereign and good. Do not expect to understand My ways; *for as the heavens are higher than the earth, so are My ways and thoughts higher than yours.* When you respond to trouble with thanksgiving—convinced that I can bring good out of the most difficult situations—I am pleased. This act of faith encourages you and glorifies Me. I rejoice when My struggling children *give thanks to Me in song!*

> The LORD is my strength and my shield; my heart trusts in him, and I am helped. My heart leaps for joy and I will give thanks to him in song. —PSALM 28:7

> I love you, O LORD, my strength. The LORD is my rock, my fortress and my deliverer; my God is my rock, in whom I take refuge. —PSALM 18:1–2

> "For as the heavens are higher than the earth, so are My ways higher than your ways, and My thoughts than your thoughts." —ISAIAH 55:9 NKJV

October 12

Learn to lean on Me more and more. I know the full extent of your weakness, and that is where My powerful Presence meets you! My strength and your weakness fit together perfectly—in a wonderful synergy designed long before your birth. Actually, *My Power is most effective in weakness.* This is counterintuitive and mysterious, yet it is true.

It's important to lean on Me when you're feeling inadequate or overwhelmed. Remind yourself that you and I *together* are more than adequate. To sense my nearness, try closing your hand as if you're holding onto Mine. *For I take hold of your right hand and say to you, "Do not fear; I will help you."*

I want you to depend on Me even when you feel competent to handle things yourself. This requires awareness of both My Presence and your neediness. I am infinitely wise, so let Me guide your thinking as you make plans and decisions. Leaning on Me produces warm intimacy with Me—the One who *will never leave you or forsake you.*

> *But He said to me, My grace (My favor and loving-kindness and mercy) is enough for you [sufficient against any danger and enables you to bear the trouble manfully]; for My strength and power are made perfect (fulfilled and completed) and show themselves most effective in [your] weakness. Therefore, I will all the more gladly glory in my weaknesses and infirmities, that the strength and power of Christ (the Messiah) may rest (yes, may pitch a tent over and dwell) upon me!* —2 Corinthians 12:9 AMP

> *I can do all things through Christ who strengthens me.* —Philippians 4:13 NKJV

> *"For I am the Lord, your God, who takes hold of your right hand and says to you, Do not fear; I will help you."* —Isaiah 41:13

> *Be strong and courageous. Do not be afraid or terrified because of them, for the Lord your God goes with you; he will never leave you nor forsake you.* —Deuteronomy 31:6

October 13

Stay alert and be persistent in your prayers. With My Spirit's help, you can learn to be increasingly wide-awake to Me. This is not an easy assignment, because the world is rigged to pull your attention away from Me. Excessive noise and visual stimulation make it hard for you to find Me in the midst of your moments. Yet I am always nearby—as near as a whispered prayer.

People who are in love yearn to be alone together so they can concentrate intently on each other. I am the Lover of your soul, and I long for you to spend time alone with Me. When you shut out distractions to focus only on Me, I awaken your soul to *the Joy of My Presence*! This increases your love for Me and helps you stay spiritually alert. Praying becomes easier when you're aware of My radiant Presence.

Praying not only blesses you but provides an avenue for serving Me. Rejoice that you can collaborate with Me through prayer as I establish My kingdom on earth.

> *Pray in the Spirit at all times and on every occasion. Stay alert and be persistent in your prayers for all believers everywhere.* —Ephesians 6:18 NLT

> *God did this so that men would seek him and perhaps reach out for him and find him, though he is not far from each one of us. "For in him we live and move and have our being." As some of your own poets have said, "We are his offspring."* —Acts 17:27–28

> *Surely you have granted him eternal blessings and made him glad with the joy of your presence.* —Psalm 21:6

> *"Your kingdom come. Your will be done on earth as it is in heaven."* —Matthew 6:10 NKJV

October 14

I will be your Guide even to the end. Rejoice that the One who leads you through each day will never abandon you. I am the Constant you can always count on—the One who goes before you yet remains close beside you. I never let go of your hand. *I guide you with My counsel, and afterward I will take you into Glory.*

Many people are overly dependent on human leaders because they want someone to make their decisions for them. Unscrupulous people can manipulate their followers to do things they wouldn't freely choose to do. But everyone who trusts Me as Savior has a Leader who is completely trustworthy and dependable.

I guide you with My truth and teach you My precepts so that you can make good decisions. I've provided you with a wonderfully reliable map: the Bible. *My Word is a lamp to your feet and a light to your path.* Follow this Light, and follow *Me*—for I am the One who knows the best way for you to go.

> For this God is our God for ever and ever; he
> will be our guide even to the end.—Psalm 48:14

> Yet I am always with you; you hold me by my right hand. You guide me with
> your counsel, and afterward you will take me into glory.—Psalm 73:23–24

> Guide me in your truth and teach me, for you are God my
> Savior, and my hope is in you all day long.—Psalm 25:5

> Your word is a lamp to my feet and a light to my path.—Psalm 119:105 NKJV

October 15

I give you My shield of victory, and My right hand sustains you. I won the ultimate victory through My sacrificial crucifixion and My miraculous resurrection! I did this for *you,* for all who trust Me as Savior-God. I accomplished everything! Your part is just to *believe*: that you need a Savior to pay the penalty for your sins and that *I* am the only Way of salvation.

Your saving faith sets you on a path to heaven. Meanwhile, My victorious shield protects you as you journey through this world. Use *the shield of faith to stop the fiery arrows of the devil.* When you're in the thick of battle, call out to Me: "Help me, Lord! I trust in *You.*"

As you live in close dependence on Me, My right hand does indeed sustain you, holding you up. I have indescribably great Power! Yet I use My mighty right hand not only to protect you but to tenderly lead you and help you keep going. Sometimes I even *gather you in My arms and carry you close to My heart.*

> *You give me your shield of victory, and your right hand sustains me; you stoop down to make me great.* —Psalm 18:35

> *Jesus said to him, "I am the way, the truth, and the life. No one comes to the Father except through Me."* —John 14:6 nkjv

> *Hold up the shield of faith to stop the fiery arrows of the devil.* —Ephesians 6:16 nlt

> *He tends his flock like a shepherd: He gathers the lambs in his arms and carries them close to his heart; he gently leads those that have young.* —Isaiah 40:11

October 16

Challenging circumstances come and go, but I am constantly with you. I'm writing the storyline of your life through good times *and* hard times. I can see the big picture: from before your birth to beyond the grave. I know exactly what you will be like when heaven becomes your forever-home, and I'm continually working to transform you into this perfect creation. You are royalty in My kingdom!

The constancy of My Presence is a glorious treasure that is underrated by most Christians. They've been taught that *I am continually with them*, but they often think and act as if they're alone. How this grieves Me!

When you lovingly whisper My Name—drawing near Me even in tough times—both you and I are blessed. This simple prayer demonstrates your trust that I am indeed with you and I am taking care of you. The reality of My Presence outweighs the difficulties you are facing, no matter how heavy they seem. So *come to Me* when you're feeling *weary and heavy-laden. I will give you rest.*

But we ought always to thank God for you, brothers loved by the Lord, because from the beginning God chose you to be saved through the sanctifying work of the Spirit and through belief in the truth.—2 Thessalonians 2:13

Nevertheless I am continually with You; You hold me by my right hand.—Psalm 73:23 NKJV

"Come to Me, all who are weary and heavy-laden, and I will give you rest."—Matthew 11:28 NASB

October 17

I AM THE CHAMPION *who perfects your faith*. The more problem-filled your life becomes, the more important it is to *keep your eyes on Me*. If you gaze too long at your problems or at the troubles in this world, you will become discouraged. Whenever you're feeling weighed down or disheartened, break free by looking to Me. I am always with you, so you can communicate with Me at any time, in any situation. Instead of just letting your thoughts run freely, direct them to Me. This gives traction to your thinking and draws you closer to Me.

Rest in My embrace for a while, enjoying the nurturing protection of My Presence. As you survey the landscape of this broken world, rejoice that *nothing can separate you from My Love*! This promise applies to *anything* you could ever encounter. No matter how bleak things may look to you at this time, I am still in control. I—your Champion who fights for you—*scoff at* those who think they can defeat Me. Remember: *My unfailing Love surrounds you*!

> *Let us strip off every weight that slows us down, especially the sin that so easily trips us up. And let us run with endurance the race God has set before us. We do this by keeping our eyes on Jesus, the champion who initiates and perfects our faith. Because of the joy awaiting him, he endured the cross, disregarding its shame. Now he is seated in the place of honor beside God's throne.* —HEBREWS 12:1–2 NLT

> *For I am convinced that neither death nor life, neither angels nor demons, neither the present nor the future, nor any powers, neither height nor depth, nor anything else in all creation, will be able to separate us from the love of God that is in Christ Jesus our Lord.* —ROMANS 8:38–39

> *The One enthroned in heaven laughs; the Lord scoffs at them.* —PSALM 2:4

> *The LORD's unfailing love surrounds the man who trusts in him.* —PSALM 32:10

October 18

TRUST IN *MY UNFAILING LOVE*—thanking Me for the good you do not see. When evil seems to be flourishing in the world around you, it can look as if things are spinning out of control. But rest assured: I'm not wringing My hands helplessly, wondering what to do next. I am still in control, and there is behind-the-scenes goodness in the midst of the turmoil. So I urge you to thank Me not only for the blessings you can see but for the ones you cannot see.

My *wisdom and knowledge* are deeper and richer than words can express. *My judgments are unsearchable, and My paths beyond tracing out!* This is why trusting Me *at all times* is so crucial. You must not let confusing circumstances shake your faith in Me. When your world feels unsteady, the disciplines of trusting and thanking Me serve to stabilize you. Remember: *I am always with you. I guide you with My counsel, and afterward I will take you into Glory.* Let this hidden treasure—your heavenly inheritance—lead you into joyous thanksgiving!

> "Though the mountains be shaken and the hills be removed, yet my unfailing love for you will not be shaken nor my covenant of peace be removed," says the LORD, who has compassion on you.—ISAIAH 54:10

> *Oh, the depth of the riches of the wisdom and knowledge of God! How unsearchable his judgments, and his paths beyond tracing out!*—ROMANS 11:33

> *Trust in Him at all times, you people; pour out your heart before Him; God is a refuge for us.*—PSALM 62:8 NKJV

> *Yet I am always with you; you hold me by my right hand. You guide me with your counsel, and afterward you will take me into glory.*—PSALM 73:23–24

October 19

I want you to live close to Me, open to Me—aware of, attentive to, trusting, and thanking Me. I am always near you, so open yourself fully—heart, mind, and spirit—to My living Presence. Feel free to ask the Holy Spirit to help you in this endeavor.

Seek to stay aware of Me as you follow your path through this day. There is never a moment when I am not fully aware of you. Attentiveness involves being alert, listening carefully, and observing closely. I encourage you to be attentive not only to Me but to the people I bring into your life. Listening to others with full, prayerful attention blesses both them and you.

The Bible is full of instruction to trust Me and thank Me. Remember: I am totally trustworthy! So it is always appropriate to believe Me and My promises. I understand your weakness, and I will *help you overcome your unbelief.* Finally, thank Me throughout the day. This discipline of gratitude helps you receive My Joy in full measure!

"I am the Living One; I was dead, and behold I am alive for ever and ever! And I hold the keys of death and Hades."—Revelation 1:18

My dear brothers, take note of this: Everyone should be quick to listen, slow to speak and slow to become angry.—James 1:19

The father instantly cried out, "I do believe, but help me overcome my unbelief!"—Mark 9:24 nlt

The Lord is my strength and my shield; my heart trusts in him, and I am helped. My heart leaps for joy and I will give thanks to him in song.—Psalm 28:7

October 20

When the task before you looks daunting, refuse to be intimidated. Discipline your thinking to view the challenge as a privilege rather than a burdensome duty. Make the effort to replace your "I have to" mentality with an "I get to" approach. This will make all the difference in your perspective—transforming drudgery into delight. This is not a magic trick; the work still has to be done. But the change in your viewpoint can help you face the challenging chore joyfully and confidently.

As you go about your work, perseverance is essential. If you start to grow weary or discouraged, remind yourself: "I *get* to do this!" Then thank Me for giving you the ability and strength to do what needs to be done. Thankfulness clears your mind and draws you close to Me. Remember that My Spirit who lives in you is *the Helper*; ask Him to help you when you're perplexed. As you ponder problems and seek solutions, He will guide your mind. *Whatever you do, work at it with all your heart—as working for Me.*

Devote yourselves to prayer, being watchful and thankful. —Colossians 4:2

"I will pray the Father, and He will give you another Helper, that He may abide with you forever." —John 14:16 nkjv

Whatever you do, work at it with all your heart, as working for the Lord, not for men. —Colossians 3:23

October 21

Hold things with loose hands, but cling tightly and always to *My* hand. To be spiritually healthy, you must not be overly attached to your possessions. These are all blessings from Me, so receive them *with thankfulness*. But don't forget that ultimately *I* am the Owner of everything.

It's also important to hold *people* with open hands. Cherish your family and friends, yet beware of making them idols. If your life revolves around someone other than Me, you need to repent—changing your ways. Return to Me, beloved. Make Me *your First Love*, seeking to please Me above all else.

Another thing to hold loosely is control over your circumstances. When your life is flowing smoothly, it's easy to feel as if you're in control. Enjoy these peaceful times, but don't cling to them or think they are the norm. Instead, cling tightly to My hand—in good times, in hard times, at all times. Good times are better and hardship is more bearable when you're trustingly depending on Me. My abiding Presence is *your portion forever*!

> And now, just as you accepted Christ Jesus as your Lord, you must continue to follow him.—Colossians 2:6 nlt

> "But I have this against you, that you have left your first love. Therefore remember from where you have fallen, and repent and do the deeds you did at first; or else I am coming to you and will remove your lampstand out of its place—unless you repent."—Revelation 2:4–5 nasb

> Yet I am always with you; you hold me by my right hand. You guide me with your counsel, and afterward you will take me into glory. Whom have I in heaven but you? And earth has nothing I desire besides you. My flesh and my heart may fail, but God is the strength of my heart and my portion forever.—Psalm 73:23–26

October 22

Don't be afraid to tell Me how weak and weary—even overwhelmed—you feel at times. I am fully aware of the depth and breadth of your difficulties; nothing is hidden from Me.

Although I know everything, I wait to hear from you. *Pour out your heart to Me, for I am your Refuge.* There can be a peaceful intimacy in sharing your struggles with Me. You let down your guard and your pretense; you get real with Me—and with yourself. Then you rest in the safety of My Presence, trusting that I understand you perfectly and *love you with an everlasting Love.*

Relax deeply with Me; release yourself from striving to perform. *Be still*, letting My Presence refresh and renew you. When you are ready, ask Me to show you the way forward. Remember that I never leave your side; *I am holding you by your right hand.* This gives you courage and confidence to continue your journey. As you go along your path, hear Me saying, *"Do not fear; I will help you."*

> *Trust in him at all times, O people; pour out your hearts to him, for God is our refuge.* —Psalm 62:8

> *The Lord appeared to us in the past, saying: "I have loved you with an everlasting love; I have drawn you with loving-kindness."* —Jeremiah 31:3

> *"Be still, and know that I am God; I will be exalted among the nations, I will be exalted in the earth!"* —Psalm 46:10 NKJV

> *"For I am the Lord, your God, who takes hold of your right hand and says to you, Do not fear; I will help you."* —Isaiah 41:13

October 23

Do not despise suffering. It reminds you that you are on a pilgrimage to a far better place. I do provide some pleasures and comforts along the way, but they are temporary. When you reach your final destination—your home in heaven—I will shower you with *pleasures forevermore*. In that glorious place *there will be no more death or mourning or crying or pain*. The *fullness of Joy* you experience there will be permanent, never-ending.

Because you are My treasured follower, I can promise that your suffering will come to an end someday. Therefore, try to view your trouble as *momentary and light—producing for you an eternal weight of Glory beyond all measure and surpassing all comparisons!*

While you continue your journey through this world, be thankful for the comforts and pleasures I bless you with. And reach out to others who are suffering. *I comfort you in all your troubles so that you can comfort others.* Offering help to hurting people gives meaning to your suffering—and Glory to Me!

> *You will show me the path of life; in Your presence is fullness of joy; at Your right hand are pleasures forevermore.*—Psalm 16:11 NKJV

"He will wipe every tear from their eyes. There will be no more death or mourning or crying or pain, for the old order of things has passed away."—Revelation 21:4

For our light, momentary affliction (this slight distress of the passing hour) is ever more and more abundantly preparing and producing and achieving for us an everlasting weight of glory [beyond all measure, excessively surpassing all comparisons and all calculations, a vast and transcendent glory and blessedness never to cease!].—2 Corinthians 4:17 AMP

He comforts us in all our troubles so that we can comfort others. When they are troubled, we will be able to give them the same comfort God has given us.—2 Corinthians 1:4 NLT

October 24

LASTING JOY CAN BE FOUND only in Me. There are many sources of happiness in this world, and sometimes they spill over into Joy—especially when you share your pleasures with Me. I shower blessings into your life, and I rejoice when you respond to them with a glad, thankful heart. So come frequently to Me with thanksgiving, and the Joy of My Presence will multiply the pleasures of My blessings.

On days when Joy seems a distant memory, you need to *seek My Face* more than ever. Don't let circumstances or feelings weigh you down. Instead, tell yourself the ultimate truth: *I am continually with you, holding you by your right hand. I guide you with My counsel, and afterward I will receive you into Glory.* As you make your way through the debris of this broken world, hold onto these truths with all your might. Remember that I Myself am *the Truth*. Cling to Me; follow Me, for I am also *the Way*. The Light of My Presence is shining on you, illumining the path before you.

> *Look to the LORD and his strength; seek his face always.*—PSALM 105:4

> *Nevertheless I am continually with You; You hold me by my right hand. You will guide me with Your counsel, and afterward receive me to glory.*—PSALM 73:23–24 NKJV

> *Jesus answered, "I am the way and the truth and the life. No one comes to the Father except through me."*—JOHN 14:6

October 25

Let My unfailing Love be your comfort. "Comfort" eases grief and trouble; it also gives strength and hope. The best source of these blessings is My constant Love that will never, ever fail you. No matter what is happening in your life, this Love can console you and cheer you up. However, you must make the effort to turn to Me for help. I am always accessible to you, and I delight in giving you everything you need.

I have complete, perfect understanding of you and your circumstances. My grasp of your situation is far better than yours. So beware of being overly introspective—trying to figure things out by looking inward, leaving Me out of the equation. When you realize you have done this, turn to Me with a brief prayer: "Help me, Jesus." Remind yourself that *I* am the most important part of the equation of your life! Relax with Me awhile, letting My loving Presence comfort you. *In the world you will have trouble; but be of good cheer, I have overcome the world.*

May your unfailing love be my comfort, according to your promise to your servant.—Psalm 119:76

The Lord gives strength to his people; the Lord blesses his people with peace.—Psalm 29:11

Why are you in despair, O my soul? And why have you become disturbed within me? Hope in God, for I shall again praise Him for the help of His presence.—Psalm 42:5 nasb

"These things I have spoken to you, that in Me you may have peace. In the world you will have tribulation; but be of good cheer, I have overcome the world."—John 16:33 nkjv

October 26

Learn to be joyful when things don't go as you would like. Do not begin your day determined to make everything go your way. Each day you will bump up against at least one thing that doesn't yield to your will. It could be as trivial as the reflection you see in the mirror or as massive as a loved one's serious illness or injury. My purpose for you is *not* to grant your every wish or to make your life easy. My desire is that you learn to trust Me in all circumstances.

If you are intent upon having your way in everything, you will be frustrated much of the time. I don't want you to waste energy regretting things that have happened. The past cannot be changed, but you have My help in the present and My hope for the future. So try to relax—trusting in My control over your life. Remember: I am always close to you, and there is abundant *Joy in My Presence*. In fact, *My Face radiates with Joy* that shines upon you!

Trust in him at all times, O people; pour out your hearts to him, for God is our refuge.—Psalm 62:8

There is surely a future hope for you, and your hope will not be cut off.—Proverbs 23:18

You have made known to me the paths of life; you will fill me with joy in your presence.—Acts 2:28

"May the Lord's face radiate with joy because of you; may he be gracious to you."—Numbers 6:25 tlb

October 27

Come to Me, My weary one. Find rest in My refreshing Presence. I am always by your side, eager to help you—but sometimes you are forgetful of Me.

You are easily distracted by the demands of other people. Their expectations can be expressed in ways that are harsh or gentle, guilt-inducing or kind. But if these demands are numerous and weighty, they eventually add up to a crushing load.

When you find yourself sinking under *heavy burdens,* turn to Me for help. Ask Me to lift those weights from your shoulders and carry them for you. Talk with Me about the matters that concern you. Let the Light of My Presence shine on them so you can see the way forward. This same Light soothes and strengthens you as it soaks into the depths of your being.

Open your heart to My healing, holy Presence. *Lift up your hands* in joyful adoration, letting My blessings flow freely into you. Take time to rest with Me, beloved; relax while I *bless you with Peace.*

> Then Jesus said, "Come to me, all of you who are weary and carry heavy burdens, and I will give you rest."—Matthew 11:28 NLT

> Lift up your hands in the sanctuary and praise the Lord.—Psalm 134:2

> The Lord gives strength to his people; the Lord blesses his people with peace.—Psalm 29:11

October 28

Many people are selective about which parts of themselves they bring to Me in prayer. Some hesitate to approach Me about traits they consider shameful or embarrassing. Others are so used to living with painful feelings—loneliness, fear, guilt, shame—that it never occurs to them to ask for help in dealing with those things. Still others get so preoccupied with their struggles that they forget I'm even here. This is not My way for you, beloved.

There are hurting parts of you that I desire to heal. Some of them have been with you so long that you consider them facets of your identity. You carry them with you wherever you go, barely aware of their impact on your life. I want to help you learn to walk in freedom. However, you are so addicted to certain painful patterns that it will take time to break free from them. Only repeatedly exposing them to My loving Presence will bring you long-term healing. As you grow increasingly free, you'll be released to experience My Joy in greater and greater measure!

Therefore, there is now no condemnation for those who are in Christ Jesus.—Romans 8:1

In my anguish I cried to the Lord, and he answered by setting me free.—Psalm 118:5

The Lord has done great things for us, and we are filled with joy.—Psalm 126:3

October 29

Do not be overcome by evil, but overcome evil with good. Sometimes you feel bombarded with all the bad things happening in the world. News reports are alarming, and people are *calling evil good and good evil.* All of this can be overwhelming unless you stay in communication with Me. I am saddened but not surprised by the horrors you see around you. I know fully the deceitful, wicked condition of human hearts. Unless people are redeemed through saving faith in Me, their potential for doing wrong is unlimited.

Instead of being disheartened by the condition of the world, I want My followers to be lights shining in the darkness. When evil appears to be winning, be more determined than ever to accomplish *something* good. Sometimes this will involve working directly against the bad things that upset you. At other times it will be a matter of doing whatever you can to promote biblical goodness—according to your gifts, abilities, and circumstances. Either way, you focus less on bemoaning evil and more on working to create something that is good.

Do not be overcome by evil, but overcome evil with good.—Romans 12:21

Woe to those who call evil good and good evil, who put darkness for light and light for darkness, who put bitter for sweet and sweet for bitter.—Isaiah 5:20

"The heart is deceitful above all things, and desperately wicked; who can know it?"—Jeremiah 17:9 NKJV

October 30

WALK WITH ME in close, trusting Love-bonds of joyful dependence. The companionship I offer you sparkles with precious promises from the Bible. I love you with perfect, *everlasting Love.* I am always with you—every nanosecond of your life. I know everything about you, and I have already paid the penalty for all your sins. Your inheritance—*kept in heaven for you—can never perish, spoil, or fade.* I guide you through your life, and *afterward I will take you into Glory*!

Dependence is an inescapable trait of the human condition. Many people despise their neediness and work hard to create the illusion of self-sufficiency in their lives. However, I designed you to need Me constantly and to be joyful about your reliance on Me. Recognizing and accepting your dependence increases your awareness of My loving Presence. This draws you closer to Me and helps you enjoy My company.

I invite you to commune with Me, your devoted Companion, in more and more of your moments. Walk joyfully with Me along the pathway of your life.

> *The LORD has appeared of old to me, saying: "Yes, I have loved you with an everlasting love; therefore with lovingkindness I have drawn you."*—JEREMIAH 31:3 NKJV

> *Praise be to the God and Father of our Lord Jesus Christ! In his great mercy he has given us new birth into a living hope through the resurrection of Jesus Christ from the dead, and into an inheritance that can never perish, spoil or fade—kept in heaven for you.*—1 PETER 1:3–4

> *You guide me with your counsel, and afterward you will take me into glory.*—PSALM 73:24

October 31

I AM A SHIELD FOR ALL who take refuge in Me. When your world is feeling unsafe and threatening, ponder this precious promise. I personally shield and protect *all* who make Me their refuge—their safe place in the midst of trouble.

Finding shelter in Me involves *trusting in Me* and *pouring out your heart to Me.* No matter what is going on in your life, it is always the right time to tell Me that you trust Me. However, sometimes it will be necessary to attend to the demands of your circumstances before you pause to pour out your heart. Whisper your trust—and wait till you find the right time and place for expressing your deep emotions to Me. Then, when circumstances permit, speak freely in My Presence. This rich communication will provide real relief; it will also strengthen your relationship with Me and help you find the way forward.

My shielding Presence is continually available to you. Whenever you're feeling fearful, turn to Me and say: "Jesus, I take refuge in You."

> *As for God, his way is perfect; the word of the LORD is flawless. He is a shield for all who take refuge in him.*—2 SAMUEL 22:31

> *God is our refuge and strength, always ready to help in times of trouble.*—PSALM 46:1 NLT

> *Trust in him at all times, O people; pour out your hearts to him, for God is our refuge.*—PSALM 62:8

November

*Trust in him at all times.
Pour out your heart to him,
for God is our refuge.*

Psalm 62:8 NLT

November 1

I AM THE GOD WHO MAKES YOU STRONG, who makes your pathway safe. Come to Me just as you are—with all your sins and weaknesses. Confess your sins, and ask Me to remove them from you *as far as the east is from the west.* Then stay in My Presence with your inadequacies in full view. Ask Me to infuse strength into you, seeing your weaknesses as "jars" that are ready to be filled with My Power. Thank Me for your insufficiency that helps you keep depending on Me. Rejoice in My infinite sufficiency!

I am the One who makes your pathway safe. This includes protection from worry and excessive planning. Instead of gazing into the unknown future, try to be mindful of Me as you journey through this day. Remain in communication with Me, letting My guiding Presence keep you on course. I will go before you as well as beside you—clearing away obstacles on the path up ahead. Trust Me to make conditions on your pathway the very best for you.

> *He is the God who makes me strong, who makes my pathway safe.* —PSALM 18:32 GNT

> *As far as the east is from the west, so far has he removed our transgressions from us.* —PSALM 103:12

> *But he said to me, "My grace is sufficient for you, for my power is made perfect in weakness." Therefore I will boast all the more gladly about my weaknesses, so that Christ's power may rest on me.* —2 CORINTHIANS 12:9

> *But we have this treasure in jars of clay to show that this all-surpassing power is from God and not from us.* —2 CORINTHIANS 4:7

November 2

When anxiety is great within you, turn to Me for *consolation.* Other words for "consolation" are *comfort, compassion, empathy, help, encouragement, reassurance,* and *relief.* I gladly provide all of this—and much more—for My children. Yet your natural tendency when you're feeling anxious is to focus on yourself or your problems. The more you do this, the more you forget about Me and all the help I can supply. This worldly focus only increases your anxiety! Let the discomfort you feel at such times alert you to your neglect of Me. Whisper My Name, and invite Me into your difficulties.

Seek My Face, finding comfort in My compassion and empathy. Look to Me for encouragement, reassurance, and help. I know all about your problems, and I also know the best way to deal with them. As you relax in My loving Presence, I strengthen you and provide relief from your anxiety. I reassure you that *nothing in all creation can separate you from My Love.* My consolation is full of blessings, beloved; *it brings Joy to your soul.*

When anxiety was great within me, your consolation brought joy to my soul.—Psalm 94:19

When You said, "Seek My face," my heart said to You, "Your face, Lord, I will seek."—Psalm 27:8 nkjv

For I am convinced that neither death nor life, neither angels nor demons, neither the present nor the future, nor any powers, neither height nor depth, nor anything else in all creation, will be able to separate us from the love of God that is in Christ Jesus our Lord.—Romans 8:38–39

November 3

GIVE UP THE ILLUSION of being in control of your life. When things are going smoothly, it's easy to feel as if you're in charge. The more you perceive yourself as your own master, and the more comfortable you become in this role, the harder you will fall.

I want you to enjoy times of smooth sailing and be thankful for them. But don't become addicted to this sense of mastery over your life, and don't consider it the norm. Storms *will* come, and uncertainties will loom on the horizon. If you cling to control and feel entitled to having things go your way, you are likely to sink when difficulties come.

I am training you to *trust in Me at all times—for I am your Refuge*. I use adversity to set you free from the illusion of being in control. When your circumstances and your future are full of uncertainties, look to Me. Find your security in *knowing Me*, the Master who is sovereign over the storms of your life—over everything.

> Now listen, you who say, "Today or tomorrow we will go to this or that city, spend a year there, carry on business and make money." Why, you do not even know what will happen tomorrow.—JAMES 4:13–14

> Trust in him at all times, O people; pour out your hearts to him, for God is our refuge.—PSALM 62:8

> "And this is eternal life, that they may know You, the only true God, and Jesus Christ whom You have sent."—JOHN 17:3 NKJV

November 4

LIVING IN CLOSE COMMUNICATION with Me can be a foretaste of heaven. It is wonderful, but it requires a level of spiritual and mental concentration that is extremely challenging. In the Psalms, David wrote about this wonderful way of living, declaring that *he had set Me always before him.* As a shepherd, he had plenty of time to seek My Face and enjoy My Presence. He discovered the beauty of days lived with Me always before him and beside him. I am training you to live this way too. It is an endeavor that requires persistent effort and determination. Yet rather than detracting from what you are doing, your closeness to Me will fill your activities with vibrant Life.

Whatever you do, do it for Me—with Me, through Me, in Me. Even menial tasks glow with the Joy of My Presence when you do them for Me. Ultimately, *nothing in all creation will ever be able to separate you from Me.* So this delightful you-and-I-together adventure can continue throughout eternity!

I have set the LORD always before me. Because he is at my right hand, I will not be shaken. —PSALM 16:8

Whatever you do, work at it with all your heart, as working for the Lord, not for men, since you know that you will receive an inheritance from the Lord as a reward. It is the Lord Christ you are serving. —COLOSSIANS 3:23–24

No power in the sky above or in the earth below—indeed, nothing in all creation will ever be able to separate us from the love of God that is revealed in Christ Jesus our Lord. —ROMANS 8:39 NLT

November 5

D0 NOT BE AFRAID, *for I am close beside you, guarding, guiding all the way.* Though I am always with you, you are often unaware of My Presence.

Fear can provide a wake-up call to your heart, alerting you to reconnect with Me. When you feel your anxiety rising, take time to relax and let the Light of My Presence shine upon you—and within you. As you rest in the warmth of My Love-Light, that cold, hard fear will start to melt away. Respond to My Love by affirming your love for Me and your trust in Me.

Remember that I am a *guarding, guiding* God. If you knew how much harm I protect you from, you would be astonished! The most important protection I provide is to guard your soul, which is eternal. Because you are My follower, your soul is secure in Me; *no one can snatch you out of My hand.* Moreover, I lead you as you go along your pathway toward heaven. *I will be your Guide even to the end.*

> *Even when walking through the dark valley of death I will not be afraid, for you are close beside me, guarding, guiding all the way.* —PSALM 23:4 TLB

> *"I give them eternal life, and they shall never perish; no one can snatch them out of my hand."* —JOHN 10:28

> *For this God is our God for ever and ever; he will be our guide even to the end.* —PSALM 48:14

November 6

Love is patient. In the apostle Paul's long list of characteristics of Christian love, the very first one is "patience." This is the ability to endure adversity calmly—not becoming upset when waiting a long time or dealing with difficult people or problems. Paul's emphasis on patience is countercultural, and it is often overlooked by My followers. This vital virtue rarely comes first in people's minds when they think about love. However, there is one common exception to this rule: a devoted mother or father. The demands of babies and young children help develop patience in good parents. They put aside their own needs to focus on their children—tenderly taking care of their needs.

I want My followers to lace their love for one another with plenty of patience. This virtue is the fourth trait listed in the fruit of the Spirit. Therefore, My Spirit can equip you to succeed in this challenging endeavor. Remember that I love you with perfect, *unfailing Love*. Ask the Holy Spirit to help you care for others with My bountiful, patient Love.

Love is patient, love is kind. It does not envy, it does not boast, it is not proud.—1 Corinthians 13:4

Rejoice in hope; be patient in affliction; be persistent in prayer.—Romans 12:12 hcsb

But the fruit of the Spirit is love, joy, peace, patience, kindness, goodness, faithfulness, gentleness, self-control; against such things there is no law.—Galatians 5:22–23 nasb

The Lord delights in those who fear him, who put their hope in his unfailing love.—Psalm 147:11

November 7

Each day has enough trouble of its own. A logical implication of this truth is that you can expect to encounter *some* trouble every day. I want to help you handle calmly and confidently the difficulties that come your way. Events that surprise you do *not* surprise Me, because I know everything. I am *the Beginning and the End.* Moreover, I am fully available to you—to guide and comfort you as you go through turbulent times.

Having *enough* trouble in each day can help you live in the present. Your active mind seeks challenges to chew on. Without enough to occupy your mind today, you are more likely to worry about the future. I am training you to keep your focus on My Presence in the present.

Difficulties need not deter you from enjoying My Presence. On the contrary, they draw you closer to Me when you collaborate with Me in handling them. As we deal with your problems *together,* you gain confidence in your ability to cope. And the pleasure of My Company greatly increases your Joy!

> "Therefore do not worry about tomorrow, for tomorrow will worry about itself. Each day has enough trouble of its own."—Matthew 6:34

> And He said to me, "It is done! I am the Alpha and the Omega, the Beginning and the End. I will give of the fountain of the water of life freely to him who thirsts."—Revelation 21:6 nkjv

> Be joyful in hope, patient in affliction, faithful in prayer.—Romans 12:12

November 8

Beware of loving praise from men more than praise from *Me*. One of the effects of the Fall is that people are overly concerned about what others think of them—their social or professional performance, their physical attractiveness. Advertisements for cosmetics and fashionable clothes can feed this hurtful tendency to be focused on one's image.

I don't want you to be preoccupied with how other people view you. I have lovingly shielded you from being able to read the minds of others. What they think of you is really "none of your business." People's thoughts are unreliable—distorted by their sinfulness, weaknesses, and insecurities. Even if they praise you to your face, some of their thoughts about you will be quite different.

I am the only One who sees you as you truly are. Although you are far from perfect, I view you radiantly clothed in My perfect righteousness. Instead of seeking *praise from men*, seek to see Me looking at you. My loving approval of you is shining from My Face.

For they loved praise from men more than praise from God. —John 12:43

I delight greatly in the Lord; my soul rejoices in my God. For he has clothed me with garments of salvation and arrayed me in a robe of righteousness, as a bridegroom adorns his head like a priest, and as a bride adorns herself with her jewels. —Isaiah 61:10

"The Lord make His face to shine upon and enlighten you and be gracious (kind, merciful, and giving favor) to you; the Lord lift up His [approving] countenance upon you and give you peace (tranquility of heart and life continually)." —Numbers 6:25–26 AMP

November 9

TRUST ME TO LEAD YOU step by step through this day. I provide sufficient Light for only one day at a time. If you try to look into the future, you will find yourself peering into darkness. *My Face shines upon you only in the present!* This is where you find My unfailing, unquenchable Love. My Love for you is even stronger than the bond between a mother and her baby. *Though she may forget the baby at her breast, I will not forget you!* You are so precious to Me that *I have engraved you on the palms of My hands.* Forgetting you is out of the question.

I want you to *really come to know—practically, through experience—My Love, which far surpasses mere knowledge.* The Holy Spirit, who lives in your innermost being, will help you. Ask Him to fill you up completely with My fullness so that you may have *the richest measure of the divine Presence*: becoming *a body wholly filled and flooded* with Me! Thus you can experience My Love in full measure.

> "The LORD make His face shine upon you,
> and be gracious to you."—NUMBERS 6:25 NKJV

Many waters cannot quench love, nor can the floods drown it.—SONG OF SONGS 8:7 NKJV

"Can a mother forget the baby at her breast and have no compassion on the child she has borne? Though she may forget, I will not forget you! See, I have engraved you on the palms of my hands; your walls are ever before me."—ISAIAH 49:15–16

[That you may really come] to know [practically, through experience for yourselves] the love of Christ, which far surpasses mere knowledge [without experience]; that you may be filled [through all your being] unto all the fullness of God [may have the richest measure of the divine Presence, and become a body wholly filled and flooded with God Himself]!—EPHESIANS 3:19 AMP

November 10

I WANT YOU TO COMFORT OTHERS *with the comfort you have received from Me.* No matter what circumstances you are enduring, My Presence and comfort are sufficient for your needs. As a Christian, everything you endure has meaning and purpose. Suffering can build your character and prepare you to help others who are struggling. So talk freely with Me about the difficulties in your life, and ask Me to use them for My purposes. Of course, you can seek relief from hardship, but be careful not to overlook the blessings hidden in it.

When you draw closer to Me during tough times—seeking My help—you grow in maturity and wisdom. This equips you to help others as they endure adversity. Your empathy for hurting people will spill over into their lives. You will find that you're the most effective at comforting those who are enduring trials you've already been through.

You can grow in peacefulness though the discipline of hardship. Though it is painful at the time, *later it yields the peaceful fruit of righteousness.*

> *Praise be to the God and Father of our Lord Jesus Christ, the Father of compassion and the God of all comfort, who comforts us in all our troubles, so that we can comfort those in any trouble with the comfort we ourselves have received from God.*—2 CORINTHIANS 1:3–4

> *And my God will meet all your needs according to his glorious riches in Christ Jesus.*—PHILIPPIANS 4:19

> *For the moment all discipline seems painful rather than pleasant, but later it yields the peaceful fruit of righteousness to those who have been trained by it.*—HEBREWS 12:11 ESV

November 11

THANKFULNESS IS THE BEST ANTIDOTE to a sense of entitlement—the poisonous attitude that "the world owes me." This misconception is epidemic in the work world, and it is contrary to biblical teaching. The apostle Paul commanded Christians to "keep away from every brother who is idle." Paul also taught by example—*working day and night to make himself a model for others to follow.* He even gave this rule: "If a man will not work, he shall not eat."

One definition of entitlement is *the feeling or belief that you deserve to be given something.* Thankfulness is the opposite: a grateful attitude for what you *already* have. If I gave you what you deserved, your ultimate destination would be hell—you would have no hope of salvation. So be thankful that I am *rich in mercy; it is by grace you have been saved.*

Thinking that you deserve more than you currently have will make you miserable, but a grateful attitude will fill you with Joy. Moreover, when you are thankful, you *worship Me acceptably with reverence and awe.*

Keep away from every brother who is idle and does not live according to the teaching you received from us. For you yourselves know how you ought to follow our example. We were not idle when we were with you. . . . We worked night and day, laboring and toiling so that we would not be a burden to any of you. We did this . . . in order to make ourselves a model for you to follow. For even when we were with you, we gave you this rule: "If a man will not work, he shall not eat." —2 THESSALONIANS 3:6–10

God, who is rich in mercy, made us alive with Christ even when we were dead in transgressions—it is by grace you have been saved. —EPHESIANS 2:4–5

Oh, give thanks to the LORD, for He is good! For His mercy endures forever. —PSALM 107:1 NKJV

Let us be thankful, and so worship God acceptably with reverence and awe. —HEBREWS 12:28

November 12

I AM *FULL OF GRACE AND TRUTH*. "Grace" refers to the undeserved favor and Love I have for you. Receiving something you don't deserve is humbling, and that's a good thing—protecting you from pride. Grace is a gift of boundless worth, for it secures your eternal salvation. Because you know Me as Savior, I will always be favorable toward you, beloved. My Love for you is undeserved, unearned, and unfailing; so you can't lose it! Just *trust in My unfailing Love, and rejoice in My salvation.*

I am not only full of truth, but *I am the Truth*. People today are barraged by news and messages laced with spin and lies. As a result, cynicism abounds in the world. But in Me and in the Bible, you find absolute, unchanging Truth! Knowing Me *sets your feet on a rock and gives you a firm place to stand.* This secure foundation for your life makes you a bright beacon in a dark, relativistic world. *Let your light shine* so that *many will see and put their trust in Me*.

> *And the Word became flesh and dwelt among us, and we have seen his glory, glory as of the only Son from the Father, full of grace and truth.* —JOHN 1:14 ESV

> *Jesus said to him, "I am the way, the truth, and the life. No one comes to the Father except through Me."* —JOHN 14:6 NKJV

> *But I trust in your unfailing love; my heart rejoices in your salvation. I will sing to the LORD, for he has been good to me.* —PSALM 13:5–6

> *"Let your light shine before men, that they may see your good deeds and praise your Father in heaven."* —MATTHEW 5:16

November 13

I want you to have quiet confidence in Me, your living God. As the prophet Isaiah wrote: *In quietness and confidence is your strength.* Sometimes people use loud voices or preposterous promises to gain power over others. These noisy speakers may appear to be strong—offering health and wealth to people who give them money—but they are actually just parasites. They survive by sucking precious resources out of others.

True strength comes from quietly trusting in *Me* and *My* promises. Rejoice that I am a *living* God—not a lifeless idol. *I am the Living One; I was dead, and behold I am alive for ever and ever.* My Power is infinite, yet I approach you gently and lovingly. Spend time with Me, cherished one, relating to Me in confident trust. As you relax with Me, I strengthen you—preparing you for challenges you will encounter on the road ahead. While you are focusing on My Presence, use Scripture to help you pray. You can draw near Me by whispering: *"I love You, O Lord, my strength."*

> This is what the Sovereign Lord, the Holy One of Israel, says:
> "Only in returning to me and resting in me will you be saved.
> In quietness and confidence is your strength."—Isaiah 30:15 nlt

> "I am the Living One; I was dead, and behold I am alive for ever and ever! And I hold the keys of death and Hades."—Revelation 1:18

> I love You, O Lord, my strength.—Psalm 18:1 nasb

November 14

I AM ALWAYS WITH YOU, beloved, whether you're aware of My Presence or not. Sometimes the place you are in seems desolate—devoid of My loving companionship. But you can call out to Me and *know* that I am by your side, eager to help. *I am near to all who call on Me.* Whisper My Name in tender trust, casting your doubts to the wind. Tell Me your troubles and seek My guidance; then change the subject. Praise Me for My greatness and glory, My power and majesty! Thank Me for the good things I have done and am doing in your life. You will find Me richly present in your praise and thanksgiving.

Taste and see that I am good! The more you focus on Me and My blessings, the better you can taste My goodness. Delight in the sweetness of *My unfailing Love*. Savor the hearty flavor of My strength. Satisfy the hunger of your heart with the Joy and Peace of My Presence. *I am with you and will watch over you wherever you go.*

> *The LORD is near to all who call on him, to all who call on him in truth.*—PSALM 145:18

> *Oh, taste and see that the LORD is good; blessed is the man who trusts in Him!*—PSALM 34:8 NKJV

> *"Though the mountains be shaken and the hills be removed, yet my unfailing love for you will not be shaken nor my covenant of peace be removed," says the LORD, who has compassion on you.*—ISAIAH 54:10

> *"I am with you and will watch over you wherever you go, and I will bring you back to this land. I will not leave you until I have done what I have promised you."*—GENESIS 28:15

November 15

COME TO ME, and rest in My Presence. I am the *Prince of Peace*. You need My Peace continually, just as you need *Me* at all times. When things are going smoothly in your life, you tend to forget how dependent on Me you really are. Later, when you encounter bumps in the road, you become anxious and upset. Eventually you return to Me and seek My Peace. I gladly give you this glorious gift, though it's hard for you to receive it till you calm down. How much better it is to stay close to Me at *all* times.

Remember that I, your Prince, am royalty! *All authority in heaven and on earth has been given to Me.* When you're experiencing hard times in your life, come to Me and tell Me your troubles. But remember who I Am! Don't shake your fist at Me or demand that I do things your way. Instead, pray these encouraging words of David: *"But I trust in You, O LORD; I say, 'You are my God.' My times are in Your hands."*

"Come to me, all you who are weary and burdened, and I will give you rest." —MATTHEW 11:28

For to us a child is born, to us a son is given, and the government will be on his shoulders. And he will be called Wonderful Counselor, Mighty God, Everlasting Father, Prince of Peace. —ISAIAH 9:6

Then Jesus came to them and said, "All authority in heaven and on earth has been given to me." —MATTHEW 28:18

But I trust in you, O LORD; I say, "You are my God." My times are in your hands; deliver me from my enemies and from those who pursue me. —PSALM 31:14–15

November 16

You are safe, secure, and complete in Me. So stop your anxious striving, and come to Me with the things that concern you. Trust Me enough to be open and honest as you talk about these matters that weigh you down. *Give all your worries and cares to Me, for I care about you*—I am taking care of you! Then rest for a while *in the shelter of My Presence*.

When you wander away and leave Me out of your life, you no longer feel complete. The restlessness you experience at such times is a gift from Me, reminding you to return to your *First Love*. I want to be central in your thoughts and feelings, your plans and actions. This helps you live meaningfully, according to My will.

You are on a pathway to heaven, and I am your constant Companion. You *will* encounter trouble as you journey with Me, *but take heart! I have overcome the world*. In Me you are indeed safe, secure, and complete.

Give all your worries and cares to God, for he cares about you.—1 Peter 5:7 nlt

How great is your goodness, which you have stored up for those who fear you, which you bestow in the sight of men on those who take refuge in you. In the shelter of your presence you hide them from the intrigues of men.—Psalm 31:19–20

"Yet I hold this against you: You have forsaken your first love."—Revelation 2:4

"I have told you these things, so that in me you may have peace. In this world you will have trouble. But take heart! I have overcome the world."—John 16:33

November 17

The very essence of My words is truth—absolute, unchanging, eternal Truth! More and more people are falling for the lie that truth is either relative or nonexistent. They are too cynical or too wounded to see things that are *true, noble, right, pure, lovely, admirable.* They tend to focus on what is false, wrong, impure, and ugly. This hurtful focus leads many to despair and self-destructive behavior. *The god of this age has blinded the minds of unbelievers so that they cannot see the Light of the gospel of My Glory.*

The gospel radiates pure, powerful Light that illuminates My Glory—the wonder of who I am and what I have done! This good news has unlimited Power to transform lives from despair to delight. All My children, filled with My Spirit, are well equipped to be Light-bearers, shining gospel brightness into the lives of others. I want *you* to join in this glorious venture, using your gifts and the opportunities I provide. I know you are weak, but that fits My purposes perfectly. My Power is *most effective in your weakness.*

The very essence of your words is truth.—Psalm 119:160 NLT

Whatever is true, whatever is noble, whatever is right, whatever is pure, whatever is lovely, whatever is admirable—if anything is excellent or praiseworthy—think about such things.—Philippians 4:8

The god of this age has blinded the minds of unbelievers, so that they cannot see the light of the gospel of the glory of Christ.—2 Corinthians 4:4

My grace (My favor and loving-kindness and mercy) is enough for you [sufficient against any danger and enables you to bear the trouble manfully]; for My strength and power are made perfect (fulfilled and completed) and show themselves most effective in [your] weakness. Therefore, I will all the more gladly glory in my weaknesses and infirmities, that the strength and power of Christ (the Messiah) may rest . . . upon me!—2 Corinthians 12:9 AMP

November 18

I, THE LORD, AM YOUR STRENGTH. On days when you are feeling strong, this truth may not speak powerfully to you. However, it is a lifeline full of encouragement and hope, and it is always available to you. Whenever you're feeling weak, your lack of strength can help you look to Me and cling to this secure lifeline. You may call out to Me at any time, *"Lord, save me!"*

Let *My unfailing Love be your comfort.* When you seem to be sinking in your struggles, it's crucial to hold onto something that will not fail you, something you can trust with your very life. My powerful Presence not only strengthens you; it holds you close and doesn't let go. I have a firm grip on you, beloved.

Because I am always near, there's no need to fear being weak. In fact, *My Strength comes into its own in your weakness*; the two fit together perfectly. So, thank Me for your weaknesses—trusting in My ever-present Strength.

O my strength, I sing praise to you; you, O God, are my fortress, my loving God.—PSALM 59:17

But when [Peter] saw the wind, he was afraid and, beginning to sink, cried out, "Lord, save me!"—MATTHEW 14:30

May your unfailing love be my comfort, according to your promise to your servant.—PSALM 119:76

And then he told me, My grace is enough; it's all you need. My strength comes into its own in your weakness. Once I heard that, I was glad to let it happen. I quit focusing on the handicap and began appreciating the gift. It was a case of Christ's strength moving in on my weakness.—2 CORINTHIANS 12:9 MSG

November 19

DON'T BE AFRAID to face your sins. Except for Me, there has never been a sinless person. *If you claim to be without sin, you deceive yourself* and evade *the truth*. It's actually quite freeing to *confess your sins*, knowing that *I will forgive you and purify you from all unrighteousness*. The good news is that I have redeemed you—paid the full penalty for all your sins. When you confess your wrongdoings, you are aligning yourself with the truth. Since I Myself *am the Truth*, your confession draws you closer to Me. It also *sets you free* from nagging guilt feelings.

When you realize you have sinned in your thoughts, words, or actions, admit it immediately. Your confession need not be lengthy or eloquent. It can be as simple as: "Forgive me and cleanse me, Lord." I have already done the hard part—dying on the cross for your sins. Your part is to live in the Light of the Truth. I, your Savior, *am the Light of the world*.

> *If we claim to be without sin, we deceive ourselves and the truth is not in us. If we confess our sins, he is faithful and just and will forgive us our sins and purify us from all unrighteousness.* —1 JOHN 1:8–9

> *Jesus said to him, "I am the way, the truth, and the life. No one comes to the Father except through Me."* —JOHN 14:6 NKJV

> *"Then you will know the truth, and the truth will set you free."* —JOHN 8:32

> *When Jesus spoke again to the people, he said, "I am the light of the world. Whoever follows me will never walk in darkness, but will have the light of life."* —JOHN 8:12

November 20

Let Me teach you how to spend more of your time in the present. The future, as most people conceptualize it, does not really exist. When you gaze into your tomorrows, making predictions, you are simply exercising your imagination. I alone have access to what is "not yet" because I am not limited by time. As you go step by step through each day, I unfurl the future before you. However, while you're moving forward through time, you never set foot on anything but the present moment. Recognizing the futility of gazing into yet-to-come times can set you free to live more fully in the present.

Becoming free is a demanding process because your mind is accustomed to wandering into the future at will. When you find yourself caught up in such thoughts, recognize that you are roaming in a fantasyland. Awakening yourself to this truth helps you return to the present, where I eagerly await you, ready to enfold you in *My unfailing Love.*

Since no man knows the future, who can tell him what is to come?—Ecclesiastes 8:7

"I am the Alpha and the Omega," says the Lord God, "who is, and who was, and who is to come, the Almighty."—Revelation 1:8

Many are the woes of the wicked, but the Lord's unfailing love surrounds the man who trusts in him.—Psalm 32:10

November 21

When you are thankful, you *worship Me acceptably—with reverence and awe.* Thanksgiving is not just a holiday celebration once a year. It's an attitude of the heart that produces Joy; it is also a biblical command. You cannot worship Me acceptably with an ungrateful heart. You may go through the motions, but your ingratitude will hold you back.

Whenever you're struggling spiritually or emotionally, pause and check your "thankfulness gauge." If the reading is low, ask Me to help you increase your level of gratefulness. Search for reasons to thank Me; jot them down if you like. Your perspective will gradually shift from focusing on all that is wrong to rejoicing in things that are right.

No matter what is happening, you can *be joyful in God your Savior.* Because of My finished work on the cross, you have a glorious future that is guaranteed forever! Rejoice in this free gift of salvation—for you, for *all* who trust Me as Savior. Let your heart overflow with thankfulness, and I will fill you with My Joy.

> *Therefore, since we are receiving a kingdom that cannot be shaken, let us be thankful, and so worship God acceptably with reverence and awe.*—Hebrews 12:28

> *Enter into His gates with thanksgiving, and into His courts with praise. Be thankful to Him, and bless His name.*—Psalm 100:4 nkjv

> *Love does not delight in evil but rejoices with the truth.*—1 Corinthians 13:6

> *Though the fig tree does not bud and there are no grapes on the vines, though the olive crop fails and the fields produce no food, though there are no sheep in the pen and no cattle in the stalls, yet I will rejoice in the Lord, I will be joyful in God my Savior.*—Habakkuk 3:17–18

November 22

THANK ME for the glorious gift of grace! *For by grace you have been saved through faith. And this is not your own doing; it is the gift of God, not a result of works, so that no one may boast.* Through My finished work on the cross and your belief in Me as your Savior, you have received the greatest gift of all: *eternal Life*. Even the faith needed to receive salvation is a gift. The best response to such amazing generosity is a grateful heart. You can never thank Me too much or too frequently for grace.

During this Thanksgiving season, ponder what it means to have all your sins forgiven. It means you are no longer on a pathway to hell; your destination is *a new heaven and a new earth*. It also means that every day of your life is valuable. As you go through this day, thank Me often for the amazing gift of grace. Let this gratitude for grace fill you with Joy and increase your thankfulness for the many *other* blessings I provide.

> *For by grace you have been saved through faith. And this is not your own doing; it is the gift of God, not a result of works, so that no one may boast.*—EPHESIANS 2:8–9 ESV

> "For God so loved the world that he gave his one and only Son, that whoever believes in him shall not perish but have eternal life."—JOHN 3:16

> "Do not be afraid of those who kill the body but cannot kill the soul. Rather, be afraid of the One who can destroy both soul and body in hell."—MATTHEW 10:28

> *Now I saw a new heaven and a new earth, for the first heaven and the first earth had passed away. Also there was no more sea.*—REVELATION 21:1 NKJV

November 23

Give thanks to Me, for I am good; My Love endures forever. I want you to set aside time to think about the many blessings I have provided for you. Thank Me for the gift of life—yours and those you love. Be grateful also for everyday provisions: food and water, shelter, clothing, and so on. Then remember the greatest gift of all: everlasting Life for everyone who knows Me, the Savior.

As you ponder all I have done for you, delight also in who *I Am*. I am one hundred percent Good! There has never been, and there will never be, even a speck of darkness in Me. *I am the Light of the world*! Moreover, My Love for you will go on and on—throughout eternity.

Even now, you are enveloped in My loving Presence. Regardless of what is happening, I am always close to My followers. So don't worry about whether or not you can sense My Presence. Simply *trust* that I am with you, and find comfort in *My unfailing Love.*

Give thanks to the Lord, for he is good; his love endures forever.—Psalm 107:1

Jesus replied, I assure you, most solemnly I tell you, before Abraham was born, I Am.—John 8:58 amp

Then Jesus again spoke to them, saying, "I am the Light of the world; he who follows Me will not walk in the darkness, but will have the Light of life."—John 8:12 nasb

Let them give thanks to the Lord for his unfailing love and his wonderful deeds for men.—Psalm 107:8

November 24

Receive joyfully and thankfully the blessings I shower on you, but do not cling to them. Hold them loosely—ready to release them back to Me. At the same time, I want you to enjoy fully the good things I give you. The best way to do this is to live in the present, refusing to worry about tomorrow. *Today* is the time to delight in the blessings I have provided. Since you don't know what tomorrow will bring, make the most of what you have today: family, friends, talents, possessions. And look for opportunities to be a blessing to others.

When I remove from you something or someone you treasure, it's healthy to grieve your loss. It is also important to draw closer to Me during this time. Cling to Me, beloved, for your relationship with Me will never be taken away from you. Let Me be *your Rock, in whom you take refuge*. Often I provide unexpected *new* blessings to comfort you and lead you forward. Be on the lookout for all that I have for you!

> "Therefore do not worry about tomorrow, for tomorrow will worry about its own things. Sufficient for the day is its own trouble."—Matthew 6:34 NKJV

> "Martha, Martha," the Lord answered, "you are worried and upset about many things, but only one thing is needed. Mary has chosen what is better, and it will not be taken away from her."—Luke 10:41–42

> The Lord is my rock, my fortress and my deliverer; my God is my rock, in whom I take refuge. He is my shield and the horn of my salvation, my stronghold.—Psalm 18:2

> "See, I am doing a new thing! Now it springs up; do you not perceive it? I am making a way in the desert and streams in the wasteland."—Isaiah 43:19

November 25

I CREATED YOU TO GLORIFY ME. Make this precept your focal point as you find your way through this day. Thanksgiving, praise, and worship are means of glorifying Me. Thank Me frequently; be on the lookout for My blessings, searching for them as for hidden treasure. Praise Me not only in prayer and song but in your words to other people. Tell them about My marvelous deeds; declare how great I am! Join with others to worship Me at church, where the weight of My Glory can be palpable.

When you need to make decisions, consider what would glorify Me and bring Me pleasure. This can help you to choose wisely and stay more aware of My Presence. Instead of getting stuck in introspection, ask Me to guide your mind as you think things out. I know everything about you and your situation. The better you know Me, the more effectively I can guide your choices; so endeavor to enhance your knowledge of Me. *My Word is a lamp to your feet and a light for your path.*

Give thanks in all circumstances; for this is the will of God in Christ Jesus for you. —1 THESSALONIANS 5:18 ESV

Declare his glory among the nations, his marvelous deeds among all peoples. —PSALM 96:3

For our light affliction, which is but for a moment, is working for us a far more exceeding and eternal weight of glory, while we do not look at the things which are seen, but at the things which are not seen. For the things which are seen are temporary, but the things which are not seen are eternal. —2 CORINTHIANS 4:17–18 NKJV

Your word is a lamp to my feet and a light for my path. —PSALM 119:105

November 26

THANKING ME AWAKENS YOUR HEART and sharpens your mind, helping you enjoy My Presence. So when you're feeling out of focus or out of touch with Me, make the effort to thank Me for *something*. There is always an abundance of things to choose from: eternal gifts—such as salvation, grace, and faith—as well as ordinary, everyday blessings. Think back over the past twenty-four hours, and make note of all the good things I've provided in that short block of time. Not only will this lift your spirits, it will wake up your mind so you can think more clearly.

Remember that *your enemy the devil prowls around like a roaring lion, looking for someone to devour*. This is why it's so important to *be self-controlled and alert*! When you let your mind drift out of focus, you are much more vulnerable to the evil one. However, the remedy is simple. As soon as you realize what has happened, you can drive away the enemy by thanking and praising Me. This is worship warfare—and it works!

For it is by grace you have been saved, through faith—and this not from yourselves, it is the gift of God—not by works, so that no one can boast. —EPHESIANS 2:8–9

Be self-controlled and alert. Your enemy the devil prowls around like a roaring lion looking for someone to devour. —1 PETER 5:8

Thanks be to God for His indescribable gift! —2 CORINTHIANS 9:15 NKJV

November 27

THANKFULNESS AND TRUST are like close friends who are always ready to help you. When your day looks bleak and the world seems scary, it's time to rely on these faithful friends. Stop for a moment and take some deep breaths. Look around you—searching for beauty and blessings—and thank Me for what you find. This connects you with Me in a wonderful way. Speak to Me in glowing terms about the many good gifts I've provided. Make the effort to thank Me with enthusiasm, regardless of how you're feeling. As you persist in expressing your gratitude, you'll find yourself becoming joyful.

It's also helpful to frequently voice your trust in Me. This reminds you that I am with you and I am absolutely reliable! There are always areas of your life where you need to trust Me more fully. When hard times come, view them as opportunities to expand the scope of your trust—*living by faith* in these challenging seasons. Don't waste the opportunities; use them to come closer to Me. I welcome you warmly, with open arms!

It is good to give thanks to the LORD, and to sing praises to Your name, O Most High; to declare Your lovingkindness in the morning, and Your faithfulness every night. —PSALM 92:1–2 NKJV

You are my God, and I will give you thanks; you are my God, and I will exalt you. —PSALM 118:28

We live by faith, not by sight. —2 CORINTHIANS 5:7

Come near to God and he will come near to you. —JAMES 4:8

November 28

You love Me because I first loved you. The truth is that *you were dead in your sins*—completely unable to love Me—until My Spirit worked in the depths of your being to make you spiritually alive. This enabled you to repent of your sinfulness and receive not only eternal Life but also everlasting Love. As you ponder this miraculous gift of salvation, let gratitude rise up within you and fill you with Joy.

Thankfulness is so very important for your growth in grace. It opens your heart and mind to My Word, enabling you to increase in wisdom and understanding. A thankful attitude helps you discover the myriad blessings I shower upon you—even in the midst of hard times. A grateful heart protects you from discouragement and self-pity. It heightens your awareness of My continual Presence and helps you grasp more fully the vast dimensions of My Love for you. So nurture well your thankfulness, beloved. Your gratitude will nourish your love for Me—making it grow bright and strong!

We love Him because He first loved us.—1 John 4:19 nkjv

As for you, you were dead in your transgressions and sins.—Ephesians 2:1

I pray that out of his glorious riches he may strengthen you with power through his Spirit in your inner being, so that Christ may dwell in your hearts through faith. And I pray that you, being rooted and established in love, may have power, together with all the saints, to grasp how wide and long and high and deep is the love of Christ.—Ephesians 3:16–18

November 29

The prospect of the righteous is Joy. This means your prospects are excellent, for I have clothed you with My *robe of righteousness.* So begin each day eager to receive the Joy I have in store for you.

Some of My followers fail to find the pleasures I have prepared for them because they focus too much on problems in their lives and trouble in the world. Instead of living *to the full,* they live cautiously, seeking to minimize pain and risk. In doing so, they also minimize their Joy and their effectiveness in My kingdom. This is *not* My way for you.

As you awaken each morning, seek My Face with hopeful anticipation. Invite Me to prepare you not only for any difficulties on the road ahead but also for the pleasures I've planted alongside your path. Then take My hand as you begin your journey through the day, and let Me share in everything you encounter along the way—including all the Joy!

The prospect of the righteous is joy, but the hopes of the wicked come to nothing.—Proverbs 10:28

I will greatly rejoice in the Lord, my soul shall be joyful in my God; for He has clothed me with the garments of salvation, He has covered me with the robe of righteousness, as a bridegroom decks himself with ornaments, and as a bride adorns herself with her jewels.—Isaiah 61:10 nkjv

"The thief comes only to steal and kill and destroy; I have come that they may have life, and have it to the full."—John 10:10

November 30

JOY IS A CHOICE—one that you face many times each day as long as you live in this world. When you graduate to heaven, indescribably glorious Joy will be yours—effortlessly. You won't have to exert your will to be joyful. It will come naturally and be constant.

While you journey through this fallen world, I want to help you make increasingly wise choices. You need to become aware—and stay aware—that you can choose to be positive and hopeful moment by moment. Make it your goal to find Joy in the midst of your day. If you notice that you're experiencing discouragement, frustration, or other negative feelings, let those prickly emotions prod you into remembering Me. *Seek My Face* and talk with Me. You can pray something like, "Jesus, I choose to be joyful because You are *God My Savior* and nothing can separate me from Your loving Presence."

Live victoriously, beloved, by seeking to find Me in more and more of your moments.

When You said, "Seek My face," my heart said to You, "Your face, LORD, I will seek."—PSALM 27:8 NKJV

Yet I will rejoice in the LORD, I will be joyful in God my Savior.—HABAKKUK 3:18

For I am convinced that neither death nor life, neither angels nor demons, neither the present nor the future, nor any powers, neither height nor depth, nor anything else in all creation, will be able to separate us from the love of God that is in Christ Jesus our Lord.—ROMANS 8:38–39

December

*Therefore you will joyously draw water
from the springs of salvation.*

ISAIAH 12:3 NASB

December 1

Whatever you do, work at it with all your heart, as working for Me, not for men. Half-heartedness is not pleasing to Me, nor is it good for you. It's tempting to rush through routine tasks and do them sloppily, just to get them done. But this negative attitude will pull you down and lower your sense of worth. If you do the same tasks with a thankful heart, you can find pleasure in them and do a much better job.

It's helpful to remember that every moment of your life is a gift from Me. Instead of feeling entitled to better circumstances, make the most of whatever I provide—including your work. When I put Adam and Eve in the Garden of Eden, I instructed them to *work it and take care of it*. Even though it was a perfect environment, it was not a place of idleness or total leisure.

Whatever you do, beloved, you are *working for Me.* So give Me your best efforts, and I will give you Joy.

> *Whatever you do, work at it with all your heart, as working for the Lord, not for men.* —Colossians 3:23

> *The Lord God took the man and put him in the Garden of Eden to work it and take care of it.* —Genesis 2:15

> *We hear that some among you are idle. They are not busy; they are busybodies. Such people we command and urge in the Lord Jesus Christ to settle down and earn the bread they eat.* —2 Thessalonians 3:11–12

December 2

To the one who is thirsty I will give water free of charge from the spring of the water of Life. Drink deeply from this spring so that I can live abundantly in you. Let the water of Life soak into the depths of your being, refreshing and renewing you. Since this Life-water is free, you can have as much of it as you want—as much of *Me* as you want. I am *Christ in you, the hope of Glory*!

I long for you to *thirst for Me, your God*, more and more. Thirst is a very powerful appetite; this is necessary because drinking sustains life even more than eating. Pure water is a much healthier choice than canned drinks full of sugar or chemicals. Similarly, thirsting for Me first and foremost is crucial for your spiritual health. Though other things may seem to satisfy you for a while, they will not slake the thirst of your soul.

Rejoice that what you need most is free of charge! *Joyously draw water from the springs of salvation.*

> He also said to me, "It is done! I am the Alpha and the Omega, the beginning and the end. To the one who is thirsty I will give water free of charge from the spring of the water of life."—Revelation 21:6 net

> To them God has chosen to make known among the Gentiles the glorious riches of this mystery, which is Christ in you, the hope of glory.—Colossians 1:27

> O God, you are my God; earnestly I seek you; my soul thirsts for you; my flesh faints for you, as in a dry and weary land where there is no water.—Psalm 63:1 esv

> Therefore you will joyously draw water from the springs of salvation.—Isaiah 12:3 nasb

December 3

Even though you do not see Me, you believe in Me. I am far more real—complete, unchanging, unlimited—than the things you can see. When you believe in Me, you are trusting in rock-solid Reality. I am the indestructible *Rock* on which you can keep standing, no matter what your circumstances may be. And because you belong to Me, I am devoted to you. Beloved, I encourage you to *take refuge in Me.*

Believing in Me has innumerable benefits. The most precious one is *the salvation of your soul*—forever and ever. Your belief in Me also enhances your present life immensely, making it possible for you to know who you are and Whose you are. As you stay in communication with Me, I help you find your way through this fallen world with hope in your heart. All of this enlarges your capacity for Joy. The more you seek Me and the more fully you know Me, the more I can fill you with *inexpressible and glorious Joy*!

> *Though you have not seen him, you love him; and even though you do not see him now, you believe in him and are filled with an inexpressible and glorious joy, for you are receiving the goal of your faith, the salvation of your souls.*—1 Peter 1:8–9

> *The Lord is my rock, my fortress and my deliverer; my God is my rock, in whom I take refuge. He is my shield and the horn of my salvation, my stronghold.*—Psalm 18:2

> *But if we hope for what we do not see, we eagerly wait for it with perseverance.*—Romans 8:25 nkjv

December 4

I want you to trust Me enough to relax and enjoy My Presence. I did not design you to live in a state of hyper-vigilance—feeling and acting as if you are constantly in the midst of an emergency. Your body is wonderfully crafted to "gear up" when necessary and then to "gear down" when the crisis is over. But because you live in such a broken world, you find it difficult to let down your guard and relax. I want you to remember that I am with you all the time and that I am totally worthy of your confidence. *Pour out your heart to Me*, committing all the things that are troubling you into My sovereign care.

The more you *lean on Me*, the more fully you can enjoy My Presence. As you relax in My healing Light, I shine Peace into your mind and heart. Your awareness of My Presence with you grows stronger, and *My unfailing Love* soaks into your inner being. *Trust in Me*, beloved, *with all your heart and mind*.

Trust in him at all times, O people; pour out your hearts to him, for God is our refuge.—Psalm 62:8

But I am like an olive tree flourishing in the house of God; I trust in God's unfailing love for ever and ever.—Psalm 52:8

Lean on, trust in, and be confident in the Lord with all your heart and mind and do not rely on your own insight or understanding.—Proverbs 3:5 AMP

December 5

I CREATED YOU *IN MY IMAGE*—with the amazing capacity to communicate with Me. As My image-bearer, you are capable of choosing the focus of your mind. Many of your thoughts come and go unbidden, but you can control them more than you realize. The Holy Spirit inspired Paul to write, *"Whatever is true, whatever is noble, whatever is right . . . think about such things."* I wouldn't instruct you to think in this way unless it was possible for you to do so.

Because the world contains both good and evil, you can choose to focus on *excellent, praiseworthy* things or on terrible, upsetting matters. Sometimes you have to deal with the brokenness around you, but each day offers moments when you are free to ponder *pure, lovely* things. When your mind is idle, it often moves toward a negative focus—regretting things in the past, worrying about the future. Meanwhile, I am *with you* in the present, waiting for you to recall My Presence. Train yourself to turn toward Me frequently. This brightens even your hardest times, increasing your Joy.

So God created man in his own image, in the image of God he created him; male and female he created them.—GENESIS 1:27

Finally, brothers, whatever is true, whatever is noble, whatever is right, whatever is pure, whatever is lovely, whatever is admirable—if anything is excellent or praiseworthy—think about such things.—PHILIPPIANS 4:8

"Behold, the virgin shall be with child, and bear a Son, and they shall call His name Immanuel," which is translated, "God with us."—MATTHEW 1:23 NKJV

You have made known to me the paths of life; you will fill me with joy in your presence.—ACTS 2:28

December 6

Trust Me, beloved. Every time you have an anxious, fearful thought, you need to take multiple looks at Me. Speak My Name to remind yourself I am near, ready to help you. Quote Scripture back to Me: *"I trust in You, O Lord; I say, 'You are my God.' My times are in Your hands."* Express your love to Me, saying: *"I love You, O Lord, my Strength."* Remember that I—your Savior and King—*take great delight in you*. You're a cherished member of My royal family forever!

Connecting with Me interrupts the negative thoughts that tend to course through your mind. So the more consistently you communicate with Me, the freer you will become. Since *I am the Truth*, living close to Me helps you recognize and break free from distortions and lies.

Trusting and loving Me are at the very core of your relationship with Me. These beautiful ways of drawing near Me protect you from being too focused on yourself and your fears. Turn to Me over and over again—secure in My sheltering Presence.

> *But I trust in you, O Lord; I say, "You are my God." My times are in your hands; deliver me from my enemies and from those who pursue me.*—Psalm 31:14–15

> *I love you, O Lord, my strength.*—Psalm 18:1

> *"The Lord your God is in your midst; he is a warrior who can deliver. He takes great delight in you; he renews you by his love; he shouts for joy over you."*—Zephaniah 3:17 net

> *Jesus said to him, "I am the way, the truth, and the life. No one comes to the Father except through Me."*—John 14:6 nkjv

December 7

I WANT YOU TO LEARN to *be joyful always* by connecting your Joy to Me first and foremost. One way of doing this is to remember that I love you at all times and in all circumstances. *Though the mountains be shaken and the hills be removed, My unfailing Love for you will not be shaken.* So don't give in to the temptation to doubt My Love when things don't go as you would like or when you have failed in some way. My loving Presence is the solid rock on which you can always stand—knowing that in *Me* you are eternally secure. I am *the Lord who has compassion on you!*

Another way of increasing your Joy is to *give thanks in all circumstances.* Ask My Spirit to help you view your life through the lens of gratitude. Search for blessings scattered along your pathway—even during your hardest times—and thank Me for each one. I encourage you to look steadily through your lens of gratefulness by *thinking about things that are excellent and worthy of praise.*

> *Be joyful always; pray continually; give thanks in all circumstances, for this is God's will for you in Christ Jesus.* —1 THESSALONIANS 5:16–18

> *"Though the mountains be shaken and the hills be removed, yet my unfailing love for you will not be shaken nor my covenant of peace be removed," says the* LORD, *who has compassion on you.* —ISAIAH 54:10

> *And now, dear brothers and sisters, one final thing. Fix your thoughts on what is true, and honorable, and right, and pure, and lovely, and admirable. Think about things that are excellent and worthy of praise.* —PHILIPPIANS 4:8 NLT

December 8

I AM THE LORD OF PEACE—the only source of genuine Peace. I give you this gift, not as something separate from Myself, but as part of who I am. You cannot just grab this blessing on the run. You need to set aside time for focusing on Me and enjoying My Presence.

You live in the midst of intense spiritual warfare, and My Peace is an essential part of your armor. To stay on your feet during the battles, you must wear sturdy combat boots—*the Gospel of Peace*. This good news assures you that I love you and I am *for you*.

Many of My followers forfeit Peace because they think I am always scrutinizing them through critical eyes. On the contrary, I gaze at you through eyes of perfect Love. Instead of punishing yourself when you've failed, remember that My death on the cross covers *all* your sins. I love you *with unfailing Love*—simply because you're Mine! Rejoice in this Gospel-Peace; it is yours to enjoy *at all times and in every way.*

Now may the Lord of peace himself give you peace at all times and in every way. The Lord be with all of you. —2 THESSALONIANS 3:16

. . . And having shod your feet in preparation [to face the enemy with the firm-footed stability, the promptness, and the readiness produced by the good news] of the Gospel of peace. —EPHESIANS 6:15 AMP

What then shall we say to these things? If God is for us, who can be against us? —ROMANS 8:31 NKJV

Satisfy us in the morning with your unfailing love, that we may sing for joy and be glad all our days. —PSALM 90:14

December 9

As you journey through life with Me, see the hope of heaven shining on your path—lighting up your perspective. Remember that you are one of My *chosen people, belonging to Me. I called you out of darkness into My wonderful Light.* Savor the richness of these concepts: *I chose you before the creation of the world*, so nothing can separate you from Me. You belong to Me forever! I drew you out of the darkness *of sin and death* into the exquisite Light of eternal Life.

The brightness of My Presence helps you in multiple ways. The closer to Me you live, the more clearly you can see the way forward. As you soak in this Love-drenched Light, *I give you strength and bless you with Peace.* My radiance blesses not only you but also other people as it permeates your whole being. This time spent focusing on Me helps you become more like Me, enabling you to shine into the lives of others. I'm continually drawing My loved ones out of darkness into My glorious Light.

> *You are a chosen people, a royal priesthood, a holy nation, a people belonging to God, that you may declare the praises of him who called you out of darkness into his wonderful light.* —1 Peter 2:9

> *For he chose us in him before the creation of the world to be holy and blameless in his sight.* —Ephesians 1:4

> *For the law of the Spirit of life has set you free in Christ Jesus from the law of sin and death.* —Romans 8:2 esv

> *The Lord will give strength to His people; the Lord will bless His people with peace.* —Psalm 29:11 nkjv

December 10

Be still in My Presence, and wait patiently for Me to act. Spending quality time with Me is so good for you, beloved. I rejoice when you push back the many things clamoring for your attention and focus wholeheartedly on Me. I know how hard it is for you to sit quietly with Me, and I don't expect perfection from you. Instead, I treasure your persistence in seeking My Face. My loving approval shines on you as you *seek Me with all your heart.* This intimate connection between us helps you wait trustingly for Me to act.

Don't worry about evil people who prosper or fret about their wicked schemes. Trust that I'm still in control and that justice will ultimately prevail. *I will judge the world in righteousness and the peoples in My truth.* Meanwhile, look for ways to advance My kingdom in this world. Keep your eyes on Me as you go through today, and be willing to follow wherever I lead. *Do not be overcome* or discouraged *by evil, but overcome evil with good*!

> *Be still in the presence of the Lord, and wait patiently for him to act. Don't worry about evil people who prosper or fret about their wicked schemes.* —Psalm 37:7 NLT

> *"You will seek me and find me when you seek me with all your heart."* —Jeremiah 29:13

> *Let the fields be jubilant, and everything in them. Then all the trees of the forest will sing for joy; they will sing before the Lord, for he comes, he comes to judge the earth. He will judge the world in righteousness and the peoples in his truth.* —Psalm 96:12–13

> *Do not be overcome by evil, but overcome evil with good.* —Romans 12:21 NKJV

December 11

I AM THE ROCK that is higher than you and your circumstances. I am *your* Rock in whom you can take refuge—any time, any place. Come to Me, beloved; rest in the Peace of My Presence. Take a break from trying to figure everything out. Admit that many, many things are beyond your understanding—and your control. *My ways and thoughts are higher than yours, as the heavens are higher than the earth.*

When the world around you looks confusing and evil appears to be winning, remember this: I am the Light that keeps on shining in all situations. And light *always* overcomes darkness whenever these two opposites meet face to face.

Since you are My follower, I want you to shine brightly in this troubled world. Whisper My Name; sing songs of praise. Tell others *good tidings of great Joy*—that I am the *Savior, who is Christ the Lord*! I am also the One who is with you continually. Keep looking to Me, and My Presence will illuminate your path.

> *From the ends of the earth I call to you, I call as my heart grows faint; lead me to the rock that is higher than I.* —PSALM 61:2

> *The LORD is my rock, my fortress and my deliverer; my God is my rock, in whom I take refuge. He is my shield and the horn of my salvation, my stronghold.* —PSALM 18:2

> *"As the heavens are higher than the earth, so are my ways higher than your ways and my thoughts than your thoughts."* —ISAIAH 55:9

> *Then the angel said to them, "Do not be afraid, for behold, I bring you good tidings of great joy which will be to all people. For there is born to you this day in the city of David a Savior, who is Christ the Lord."* —LUKE 2:10–11 NKJV

December 12

When I entered your world as the God-Man, *I came to that which was My own.* Everything belongs to Me! Most people think their possessions are their own, but the truth is, you—and everything you possess—belong to Me. Though you may feel isolated and alone at times, this is only an illusion. I bought you at an astronomical price, so you are Mine—My treasure. The colossal price I paid shows how precious you are to Me! Ponder this powerful truth whenever you start to doubt your worth. You are My cherished one, *saved by grace through faith* in Me, your Savior.

Because you are precious to Me, I want you to take good care of yourself: spiritually, emotionally, and physically. Make time for pondering Scripture in your mind and heart. Protect yourself, both emotionally and physically, from those who would take advantage of you. Remember that *your body is the Holy Spirit's temple*. I also want you to help others discover the glorious good news—the free gift of *eternal Life for all who believe in Me.*

He came to that which was his own, but his own did not receive him. —John 1:11

For it is by grace you have been saved, through faith—and this not from yourselves, it is the gift of God—not by works, so that no one can boast. —Ephesians 2:8–9

Do you not know that your body is a temple of the Holy Spirit, who is in you, whom you have received from God? You are not your own; you were bought at a price. Therefore honor God with your body. —1 Corinthians 6:19–20

"For God so loved the world that he gave his one and only Son, that whoever believes in him shall not perish but have eternal life." —John 3:16

December 13

Everyone on the side of truth listens to Me. I am Truth incarnated. The reason I was born and came into your world was *to testify to the truth.*

Many people believe that there are no absolutes and that everything is relative. Unscrupulous people capitalize on this prevailing view by manipulating information in false ways—to promote their own agendas. They present evil things as good, and vice versa. This is abhorrent to Me! As I said about all unrepentant liars, *their place will be in the fiery lake of burning sulfur.*

Remember that *the devil is a liar and the father of lies.* The more you listen to Me, especially through the reading of Scripture, the more you will treasure truth and take delight in Me—the living Truth. The Holy Spirit is *the Spirit of Truth*; ask Him to give you discernment. He will help you navigate your way through this world where spin and outright lies are commonplace. Strive to stay *on the side of truth* so you can live close to Me and enjoy My Presence.

> "For this reason I was born, and for this I came into the world, to testify to the truth. Everyone on the side of truth listens to me."—John 18:37

> "But the cowardly, the unbelieving, the vile, the murderers, the sexually immoral, those who practice magic arts, the idolaters and all liars—their place will be in the fiery lake of burning sulfur."—Revelation 21:8

> "You belong to your father, the devil. . . . He was a murderer from the beginning, not holding to the truth, for there is no truth in him. When he lies, he speaks his native language, for he is a liar and the father of lies."—John 8:44

> "However, when He, the Spirit of truth, has come, He will guide you into all truth; for He will not speak on His own authority, but whatever He hears He will speak; and He will tell you things to come."—John 16:13 NKJV

December 14

DO NOT GROW WEARY AND LOSE HEART. When you are dealing with difficulties that go on and on, it's easy to get so tired that you feel like giving up. Chronic problems can wear you out and wear you down. If you focus too much on these troubles, you're in danger of sliding into a black hole of self-pity or despair.

There are several kinds of weariness. Unrelieved physical tiredness makes you vulnerable to emotional exhaustion and spiritual fatigue—losing heart. However, I have equipped you to transcend your troubles by *fixing your eyes on Me*. I paid dearly for this provision by *enduring the cross* for you. Pondering My willingness to suffer so much can strengthen you to endure your own hardships.

Worshiping Me is a wonderful way to renew your strength in My Presence. When you take steps of faith by praising Me in the midst of difficulties, My glorious Light shines upon you. As you persevere in focusing on Me, you *reflect My Glory* to others, and you're *transformed into My likeness with ever-increasing Glory*.

> *Let us fix our eyes on Jesus, the author and perfecter of our faith, who for the joy set before him endured the cross, scorning its shame, and sat down at the right hand of the throne of God. Consider him who endured such opposition from sinful men, so that you will not grow weary and lose heart.* —HEBREWS 12:2–3

> *For we walk by faith, not by sight.* —2 CORINTHIANS 5:7 NKJV

> *And we, who with unveiled faces all reflect the Lord's glory, are being transformed into his likeness with ever-increasing glory, which comes from the Lord, who is the Spirit.* —2 CORINTHIANS 3:18

December 15

In Isaiah's prophecy about My birth, he referred to Me as *Eternal Father*. There is unity of essence in the Trinity, even though it is comprised of three Persons. When the Jews were questioning Me in the temple, I went so far as to say: *"I and the Father are one."* Later, when Philip asked Me to show the Father to the disciples, I said: *"Anyone who has seen Me has seen the Father."* So never think of Me as just a great teacher. I am God, and the Father and I live in perfect unity.

As you come to know Me in greater depth and breadth, realize that you are also growing closer to the Father. Don't let the mysterious richness of the Trinity confuse you. Simply come to Me, recognizing that I am everything you could ever need Me to be. I—your only Savior—am sufficient for you.

In the midst of this busy Advent season, keep bringing your focus back to My holy Presence. Remember that *Immanuel* has come, and rejoice!

> *For a child will be born to us, a son will be given to us; and the government will rest on His shoulders; and His name will be called Wonderful Counselor, Mighty God, Eternal Father, Prince of Peace.* —Isaiah 9:6 nasb

> *"I and the Father are one."* —John 10:30

> *Jesus answered: "Don't you know me, Philip, even after I have been among you such a long time? Anyone who has seen me has seen the Father. How can you say, 'Show us the Father'?"* —John 14:9

> *"Behold, the virgin shall be with child, and bear a Son, and they shall call His name Immanuel," which is translated, "God with us."* —Matthew 1:23 nkjv

December 16

When an angel announced My birth to *shepherds living out in the fields* near Bethlehem, he told them: *Do not be afraid. I bring you good news of great Joy.* The instruction to not be afraid is repeated in the Bible more than any other command. It is a tender, merciful directive—and it is for you! I know how prone to fear you are, and I do not condemn you for it. However, I *do* want to help you break free from this tendency.

Joy is a powerful antidote to fear! And the greater the Joy, the more effective an antidote it is. The angel's announcement to the shepherds was one of *great* Joy. Don't ever lose sight of what amazingly *good news* the gospel is! You repent of your sins and trust Me as Savior. I forgive *all* your sins, changing your ultimate destination from hell to heaven. Moreover, I give you *Myself*—lavishing My Love upon you, promising you My Presence forever. Take time to ponder the angel's glorious proclamation to the shepherds. *Rejoice in Me*, beloved.

> *And there were shepherds living out in the fields nearby, keeping watch over their flocks at night. An angel of the Lord appeared to them, and the glory of the Lord shone around them, and they were terrified. But the angel said to them, "Do not be afraid. I bring you good news of great joy that will be for all the people."*—Luke 2:8–10

> *How great is the love the Father has lavished on us, that we should be called children of God! And that is what we are! The reason the world does not know us is that it did not know him.*—1 John 3:1

> *Rejoice in the Lord always. Again I will say, rejoice!*—Philippians 4:4 nkjv

December 17

Sing for Joy to Me, your Strength. Christmas music is one of the best blessings of the season, and it doesn't have to cost you anything. You can sing the carols at church or in the privacy of your home—or even in your car. As you are making a joyful noise, pay close attention to the words. They are all about Me and My miraculous entrance into your world through the virgin birth. Singing from your heart increases both your Joy and your energy. It also blesses Me.

I created you to glorify Me and enjoy Me forever. So it's not surprising that you feel more fully alive when you glorify Me through song. I want you to learn to enjoy Me in more and more aspects of your life. Before you arise from your bed each morning, try to become aware of My Presence with you. Say to yourself: *"Surely the Lord is in this place."* This will awaken your awareness to the wonders of My continual nearness. *I will fill you with Joy in My Presence.*

> *Sing for joy to God our strength; shout aloud to the God of Jacob!* —Psalm 81:1

> *But let all who take refuge in you rejoice; let them sing joyful praises forever. Spread your protection over them, that all who love your name may be filled with joy.* —Psalm 5:11 NLT

> *When Jacob awoke from his sleep, he thought, "Surely the Lord is in this place, and I was not aware of it."* —Genesis 28:16

> *You have made known to me the paths of life; you will fill me with joy in your presence.* —Acts 2:28

December 18

I, YOUR SAVIOR, AM *MIGHTY GOD*! Much of the focus during Advent is on the Baby in the manger. I did indeed begin My life on earth in this humble way. I set aside My Glory and took on human flesh. But I continued to be God—able to live a perfect, sinless life and perform mighty miracles. *I, your God, am with you—mighty to save*! Be blessed by this combination of My tender nearness and My majestic Power.

When I entered the world, *I came to that which was My own*, because everything was made through Me. *But My own did not receive Me. Yet to all who received Me, to those who believed in My Name, I gave the right to become children of God.* This gift of salvation is of infinite value. It gives meaning and direction to your life—and makes heaven your final destination. During this season of giving and receiving presents, remember that the ultimate present is eternal Life. Respond to this glorious gift by *rejoicing in Me always!*

> For unto us a Child is born, unto us a Son is given; and the government will be upon His shoulder. And His name will be called Wonderful, Counselor, Mighty God, Everlasting Father, Prince of Peace.—ISAIAH 9:6 NKJV

> "The LORD your God is with you, he is mighty to save. He will take great delight in you, he will quiet you with his love, he will rejoice over you with singing."—ZEPHANIAH 3:17

> He came to that which was his own, but his own did not receive him. Yet to all who received him, to those who believed in his name, he gave the right to become children of God.—JOHN 1:11–12

> Rejoice in the Lord always. I will say it again: Rejoice!—PHILIPPIANS 4:4

December 19

I AM IMMANUEL—*God with you* at all times. This promise provides a solid foundation for your Joy. Many people try to pin their pleasure to temporary things, but My Presence with you is eternal. Rejoice greatly, beloved, knowing that your Savior *will never leave you or forsake you.*

The nature of time can make it difficult for you to enjoy your life. On rare days when everything is going well, your awareness that the ideal conditions are fleeting can dampen your enjoyment of them. Even the most delightful vacation must eventually come to an end. Seasons of life also come and go, despite your longing at times to "stop the clock" and keep things just as they are.

Do not look down on temporary pleasures, but *do* recognize their limitations—their inability to quench the thirst of your soul. Your search for lasting Joy will fail unless you make *Me* the ultimate goal of your quest. *I will show you the way of Life. In My Presence is fullness of Joy.*

> *"The virgin will be with child and will give birth to a son, and they will call him Immanuel"—which means, "God with us."*—MATTHEW 1:23

> *The LORD himself goes before you and will be with you; he will never leave you nor forsake you. Do not be afraid; do not be discouraged.*—DEUTERONOMY 31:8

> *You will show me the path of life; in Your presence is fullness of joy; at Your right hand are pleasures forevermore.*—PSALM 16:11 NKJV

December 20

No matter how lonely you may feel, you are never alone. Christmas can be a hard time for people who are separated from loved ones. The separation may be a result of death, divorce, distance, or other causes. The holiday merriment around you can intensify your sense of aloneness. But all My children have a resource that is more than adequate to help them: My continual Presence.

Remember this prophecy about Me: "*The virgin . . . will give birth to a Son, and they will call Him Immanuel*"—which means "God with us." Long before I was born, I was proclaimed to be the God who is *with you*. This is rock-solid truth that nobody and no circumstance can take away from you.

Whenever you're feeling lonely, take time to enjoy My Presence. Thank Me for *wrapping you with a robe of righteousness* to make you righteous. Ask Me—*the God of hope*—to *fill you with Joy and Peace*. Then, through the help of My Spirit, you can *overflow with hope* into the lives of other people.

> *Therefore the Lord himself will give you a sign: The virgin will be with child and will give birth to a son, and will call him Immanuel.*—Isaiah 7:14

> *I will rejoice greatly in the Lord, my soul will exult in my God; for He has clothed me with garments of salvation, He has wrapped me with a robe of righteousness, as a bridegroom decks himself with a garland, and as a bride adorns herself with her jewels.*—Isaiah 61:10 nasb

> *For He made Him who knew no sin to be sin for us, that we might become the righteousness of God in Him.*—2 Corinthians 5:21 nkjv

> *May the God of hope fill you with all joy and peace as you trust in him, so that you may overflow with hope by the power of the Holy Spirit.*—Romans 15:13

December 21

I became poor so that you might become rich. My incarnation—the essence of Christmas—was a gift of infinitely great value. However, it impoverished Me immeasurably! I gave up the majestic splendors of heaven to become a helpless baby. My parents were poor, young, and far away from home when I was born in a stable in Bethlehem.

I performed many miracles during My lifetime, but they were for the benefit of others, not Myself. After fasting forty days and nights in the wilderness, I was tempted by the devil to *turn stones into bread.* But I refused to do this miracle, even though I was so hungry. I lived as a homeless man for years.

Because I was willing to experience a life of poverty, you are incredibly rich! My life, death, and resurrection opened the way for My followers to become *children of God* and heirs of glorious, eternal riches. My abiding Presence is also a precious gift. Celebrate all these amazing gifts with gratitude and overflowing Joy!

> *For you know the grace of our Lord Jesus Christ, that though he was rich, yet for your sakes he became poor, so that you through his poverty might become rich.* —2 Corinthians 8:9

> *Jesus was led up by the Spirit into the wilderness to be tempted by the devil. And when He had fasted forty days and forty nights, afterward He was hungry. Now when the tempter came to Him, he said, "If You are the Son of God, command that these stones become bread." But He answered and said, "It is written, 'Man shall not live by bread alone, but by every word that proceeds from the mouth of God.'"* —Matthew 4:1–4 nkjv

> *Yet to all who received him, to those who believed in his name, he gave the right to become children of God.* —John 1:12

> *Behold, I bring you good news of great joy that will be for all the people.* —Luke 2:10 esv

December 22

I AM THE LIGHT OF THE WORLD! Many people celebrate Advent season by illuminating their homes with candles and decorated trees. This is a way of symbolizing My coming into the world—eternal Light breaking through the darkness and opening up the way to heaven. Nothing can reverse this glorious plan of salvation. All who trust Me as Savior are adopted into My royal family forever!

My Light shines on in the darkness, for the darkness has never overpowered it. No matter how much evil and unbelief you see in this dark world, I continue to shine brightly—a beacon of hope to those who have eyes that really see. So it's crucial to look toward the Light as much as possible. *Fix your eyes on Me*, beloved! Through thousands of good thought-choices, you can find Me—"see" Me—as you journey through this life. My Spirit can help you persevere in the delightful discipline of keeping your eyes on Me. *Whoever follows Me will never walk in darkness but will have the Light of Life.*

When Jesus spoke again to the people, he said, "I am the light of the world. Whoever follows me will never walk in darkness, but will have the light of life."—JOHN 8:12

God decided in advance to adopt us into his own family by bringing us to himself through Jesus Christ. This is what he wanted to do, and it gave him great pleasure.—EPHESIANS 1:5 NLT

And the Light shines on in the darkness, for the darkness has never overpowered it [put it out or absorbed it or appropriated it, and is unreceptive to it].—JOHN 1:5 AMP

Let us fix our eyes on Jesus, the author and perfecter of our faith, who for the joy set before him endured the cross, scorning its shame, and sat down at the right hand of the throne of God.—HEBREWS 12:2

December 23

Those who wait upon Me will gain new strength. Spending time alone with Me is so good for you, but it is increasingly countercultural. Multitasking and staying busy have become the norm. During the Advent season, there are even *more* things to be done and places to go. So I encourage you to break free from all the activity and demands for a while. *Seek My Face* and enjoy My Presence, remembering that Christmas is all about *Me*.

Waiting upon Me is an act of faith—trusting that prayer really does make a difference. *Come to Me with your weariness and burdens*, being candid and real with Me. *Rest* in My Presence, and tell Me about your concerns. Let Me lift the burdens from your aching shoulders. Trust that *I am able to do exceedingly abundantly above all you ask or think*.

As you arise from these quiet moments, hear Me whispering "I am with you" throughout the day. Rejoice in the *new strength* you have gained through spending time with Me.

> Yet those who wait for the Lord will gain new strength; they will mount up with wings like eagles, they will run and not get tired, they will walk and not become weary.—Isaiah 40:31 nasb

> When You said, "Seek My face," my heart said to You, "Your face, Lord, I will seek."—Psalm 27:8 nkjv

> "Come to me, all you who are weary and burdened, and I will give you rest."—Matthew 11:28

> Now to Him who is able to do exceedingly abundantly above all that we ask or think, according to the power that works in us . . . —Ephesians 3:20 nkjv

December 24

Prepare your heart for the celebration of My birth. Listen to the voice of John the Baptist: *"Prepare the way for the Lord; make straight paths for Him."*

Christmas is the time to exult in My miraculous incarnation, when *the Word became flesh and dwelt among you*. I identified with mankind to the ultimate extent—becoming a Man and taking up residence in your world. Don't let the familiarity of this astonishing miracle dull its effect on you. Recognize that I am the Gift above all gifts, and *rejoice in Me*!

Clear out clutter and open up your heart by pondering the wonders of My entrance into human history. View these events from the perspective of the shepherds, who were keeping watch over their flocks at night. They witnessed first one angel and then *a multitude* of them lighting up the sky, proclaiming: *"Glory to God in the highest, and on earth Peace among those with whom He is pleased!"* Gaze at the Glory of my birth, just as the shepherds did, and respond with childlike wonder.

"Prepare the way for the Lord, make straight paths for him."—Mark 1:3

And the Word became flesh and dwelt among us, and we have seen his glory, glory as of the only Son from the Father, full of grace and truth.—John 1:14 ESV

Rejoice in the Lord always. Again I will say, rejoice!—Philippians 4:4 NKJV

And suddenly there was with the angel a multitude of the heavenly host praising God and saying, "Glory to God in the highest, and on earth peace among those with whom he is pleased!"—Luke 2:13–14 ESV

December 25

I AM THE WORD THAT BECAME FLESH. I have always been, and I will always be. *In the beginning was the Word, and the Word was with God, and the Word was God.* As you think about Me as a baby, born in Bethlehem, do not lose sight of My divinity. This baby who grew up and became a Man-Savior is also God Almighty! It could not have been otherwise. My sacrificial life and death would have been insufficient if I were not God. So rejoice that *the Word*, who entered the world as a helpless infant, is the same One who brought the world into existence.

Though I was rich, for your sake I became poor, so that you might become rich. No Christmas present could ever compare with the treasure you have in Me! I remove your sins *as far as the east is from the west*—freeing you from all condemnation. I gift you with unimaginably glorious Life that will never end! The best response to this astonishing Gift is to embrace it joyfully and gratefully.

In the beginning was the Word, and the Word was with God, and the Word was God.... The Word became flesh and made his dwelling among us. We have seen his glory, the glory of the One and Only, who came from the Father, full of grace and truth.—JOHN 1:1, 14

In the past God spoke to our forefathers through the prophets at many times and in various ways, but in these last days he has spoken to us by his Son, whom he appointed heir of all things, and through whom he made the universe.—HEBREWS 1:1–2

For you know the grace of our Lord Jesus Christ, that though He was rich, yet for your sake He became poor, so that you through His poverty might become rich.—2 CORINTHIANS 8:9 NASB

As far as the east is from the west, so far has He removed our transgressions from us.—PSALM 103:12 NKJV

December 26

I am the greatest Gift imaginable! When you have *Me*, you have everything you need—for this life and the next. I have promised to *meet all your needs according to My glorious riches*. Yet My loved ones sometimes fail to enjoy the riches I provide because of an ungrateful attitude. Instead of rejoicing in all that they have, they long for what they do not have. As a result, they become discontented.

I'm training you to practice *the sacrifice of thanksgiving*—thanking Me *in all circumstances*. First, give thanks for the blessings you can see in your life. Then stop and ponder the awesome gift of knowing Me. I am your living God, your loving Savior, your constant Companion. No matter how much or how little you have in this world, your relationship with Me makes you immeasurably rich. So whenever you are counting your blessings, be sure to include the infinite wealth you have in Me. Add Me into the equation, and your gratitude will grow exponentially. Whatever you have + Me = an incalculable fortune!

And my God will meet all your needs according to his glorious riches in Christ Jesus. —Philippians 4:19

I will offer to You the sacrifice of thanksgiving, and will call upon the name of the Lord. —Psalm 116:17 NKJV

Give thanks in all circumstances, for this is God's will for you in Christ Jesus. —1 Thessalonians 5:18

December 27

I GIVE YOU JOY that is independent of circumstances; I give you Myself! *All the treasures of wisdom and knowledge are hidden in Me.* Because I am infinitely wise and all-knowing, you will never run out of treasures to search for.

I am a wellspring of Joy—eager to overflow into your life. Open wide your heart, mind, and spirit to receive Me in full measure. My Joy is not of this world; it can coexist with the most difficult circumstances. No matter what is happening in your life, *the Light of My Presence* continues to shine upon you. Look up to Me with a trusting heart. If you persist in searching for Me, My Joy-Light can break through the darkest storm clouds. Let this heavenly Light soak into you, brightening your perspective and filling you with transcendent delight.

Remember that you have *an inheritance in heaven that can never perish, spoil, or fade.* Since *you believe in Me, inexpressible, glorious Joy is yours*—now and forever!

> *. . . In whom are hidden all the treasures of wisdom and knowledge.*—COLOSSIANS 2:3

> *Blessed are those who have learned to acclaim you, who walk in the light of your presence, O LORD. They rejoice in your name all day long; they exult in your righteousness.*—PSALM 89:15–16

> *Praise be to the God and Father of our Lord Jesus Christ! In his great mercy he has given us new birth into a living hope through the resurrection of Jesus Christ from the dead, and into an inheritance that can never perish, spoil or fade—kept in heaven for you. . . . Though you have not seen him, you love him; and even though you do not see him now, you believe in him and are filled with an inexpressible and glorious joy.*—1 PETER 1:3–4, 8

December 28

How priceless is My unfailing Love! This is truly a gift of heavenly proportions. Remember the unspeakable price I paid to secure this gift for you: I endured torture, humiliation, and death. My willingness to suffer so much for you demonstrates how extravagantly I love you.

I want you to comprehend how astonishingly rich you are in Me. I have given you the priceless treasure of My eternal Love! This gift makes you far wealthier than a multibillionaire, even if you own very little of this world's goods. So stand tall as you journey through your life, knowing that this glorious inner treasure is your portion each step of the way.

Rejoice that My Love is both priceless *and* unfailing. You can always count on it because it's even more reliable than the rising of the sun. Let My unfailing Love fill you with exuberant Joy as you walk along *the path of Life* with Me.

> *How priceless is your unfailing love! Both high and low among men find refuge in the shadow of your wings.*—Psalm 36:7

> *But we have this treasure in jars of clay to show that this all-surpassing power is from God and not from us.*—2 Corinthians 4:7

> *You will show me the path of life; in Your presence is fullness of joy; at Your right hand are pleasures forevermore.*—Psalm 16:11 NKJV

December 29

Let My Peace rule in your heart, and be thankful. And let My Spirit help you in this challenging endeavor. The Spirit lives in you, so His fruit—*Love, Joy, Peace*—is always accessible to you. A simple way to request His help is to pray: "Holy Spirit, fill me with Your Peace." Try sitting in a quiet place until you feel relaxed and calm. When you are thoroughly relaxed, it is easier to seek My Face and enjoy My Presence.

While you rest in My Presence, take time to thank Me for the many good things I give you. As you focus on Me and My bountiful blessings, let your heart swell with gratitude and even *leap for Joy*. One of the most precious gifts imaginable is My *robe of righteousness*—to cover your sins. This glorious *garment of salvation* is a priceless blessing for all who trust Me as Savior. The gift of eternal righteousness, purchased through My blood, provides a firm foundation for both Peace and Joy.

> *Let the peace of Christ rule in your hearts, since as members of one body you were called to peace. And be thankful.*—Colossians 3:15

> *But the fruit of the Spirit is love, joy, peace, longsuffering, kindness, goodness, faithfulness, gentleness, self-control. Against such there is no law.*—Galatians 5:22–23 nkjv

> *The Lord is my strength and my shield; my heart trusts in him, and I am helped. My heart leaps for joy and I will give thanks to him in song.*—Psalm 28:7

> *I delight greatly in the Lord; my soul rejoices in my God. For he has clothed me with garments of salvation and arrayed me in a robe of righteousness, as a bridegroom adorns his head like a priest, and as a bride adorns herself with her jewels.*—Isaiah 61:10

December 30

I am the Alpha and the Omega, the Beginning and the End. My perspective is unlimited by time. Because I am infinite, I am able to see and understand everything at once. This makes Me the ideal Person to be in charge of your life. I know the ending of your earth-life as well as I know its beginning—and I know everything in between. You are finite and fallen; your understanding is limited and far from perfect. So trusting in Me rather than relying *on your own understanding* is the most reasonable way to live; it is also the most joyful.

The end of your life is not to be feared. It's simply the last step of your journey to heaven. I can see that event as clearly as I see you right now. Moreover, because I am the Omega—the End—I am already there. I will be awaiting you when you reach this glorious destination. So whenever you're feeling the strain of your journey through this world, fix your eyes on *the End*—and rejoice!

> *And He said to me, "It is done! I am the Alpha and the Omega, the Beginning and the End. I will give of the fountain of the water of life freely to him who thirsts."*—Revelation 21:6 nkjv

> *Trust in the Lord with all your heart, and do not lean on your own understanding.*—Proverbs 3:5 esv

> *You guide me with your counsel, and afterward you will take me into glory.*—Psalm 73:24

> *Let us fix our eyes on Jesus, the author and perfecter of our faith, who for the joy set before him endured the cross, scorning its shame, and sat down at the right hand of the throne of God.*—Hebrews 12:2

December 31

As you come to the end of this year, take some time to look back—and also to look ahead. Ask Me to help you review the highlights of this year: hard times as well as good times. Try to see *Me* in these memories, for I have been close beside you—every step of the way.

When you were clinging to Me for help in the midst of tough times, I comforted you with My loving Presence. I was also richly present in circumstances that filled you with great Joy. I was with you on the mountain peaks, in the valleys, and everywhere in between.

Your future stretches out before you all the way into eternity. I am the Companion who will never leave you, the Guide who knows every step of the way ahead. The Joy that awaits you in paradise is *inexpressible and full of Glory*! As you prepare to step into a new year, let heaven's Light shine upon you and brighten the path just before you.

> "For I am the Lord, your God, who takes hold of your right hand and says to you, Do not fear; I will help you." —Isaiah 41:13

> *You will show me the path of life; in Your presence is fullness of joy; at Your right hand are pleasures forevermore.* —Psalm 16:11 nkjv

> *For this God is our God for ever and ever; he will be our guide even to the end.* —Psalm 48:14

> *Though you have not seen Him, you love Him, and though you do not see Him now, but believe in Him, you greatly rejoice with joy inexpressible and full of glory, obtaining as the outcome of your faith the salvation of your souls.* —1 Peter 1:8–9 nasb

About the Author

Sarah Young's devotional writings are personal reflections from her daily quiet time of Bible reading, praying, and writing in prayer journals. With sales of more than 16 million books worldwide, *Jesus Calling*® has appeared on all major bestseller lists. Sarah's writings include *Jesus Calling*®, *Jesus Today*®, *Jesus Lives*™, *Dear Jesus*, *Jesus Calling*® *for Little Ones*, *Jesus Calling*® *My First Bible Storybook*, *Jesus Calling*® *Bible Storybook*, *Jesus Calling*®: *365 Devotions for Kids*, *Jesus Today*®: *Devotions for Kids*, and *Peace in His Presence*—each encouraging readers in their journey toward intimacy with Christ. Sarah and her husband were missionaries in Japan and Australia for many years. They currently live in the United States. *Jesus Calling*® was written to help people connect not only with Jesus, the living Word, but also with the Bible—the only infallible, inerrant Word of God.

Sarah endeavors to keep her devotional writing consistent with that unchanging standard. Many readers have shared that Sarah's books have helped them grow to love God's Word. As Sarah states in the introduction to *Jesus Calling*®, "The devotions . . . are meant to be read slowly, preferably in a quiet place—with your Bible open."

Sarah is biblically conservative in her faith and reformed in her doctrine. She earned a master's degree in biblical studies and counseling from Covenant Theological Seminary in St. Louis. She is a member of the Presbyterian Church in America (PCA), where her husband,

Stephen, is an ordained minister. Stephen and Sarah continue to be missionaries with Mission to the World, the PCA mission board.

Sarah spends a great deal of time in prayer, reading the Bible, and memorizing Scripture. She especially enjoys praying daily for readers of all her books.

If you liked reading this book, you may enjoy these other titles by *Sarah Young*

Jesus Calling
Enjoying Peace in His Presence
ISBN 9781591451884

Jesus Today
Experience Hope Through His Presence
ISBN 9781400320097

Jesus Lives
Seeing His Love in Your Life
ISBN 9781400320943

Dear Jesus
Seeking His Light in Your Life
ISBN 9781404104952

Learn more at JesusCalling.com

More than 20 million lives have been impacted by the words of

Sarah Young

Connect with others who are reading Sarah Young devotionals

- Hear moving stories about how lives have been changed
- Download free discussion guides
- Catch the latest news on products
- Read what others are saying
- Share your own story

LEARN MORE AT JESUSCALLING.COM

Go Deeper with Jesus Always

The Jesus Always
52-Week Discussion Guide

This discussion guide is designed to help an individual or group gain a deeper understanding of "Embracing Joy in His Presence."

Download your free copy at www.jesuscalling.com/books/jesus-always/

ENJOY JESUS' PRESENCE.
FIND COMFORT
IN HIS PEACE.

FAVORITE QUOTATIONS *from* Jesus Calling

PEACE in HIS PRESENCE

Sarah Young

Selected quotes and scriptures from *Jesus Calling* along with inspiring images will encourage you to worship and find comfort in the peace of the Lord.

www.jesuscalling.com

THOMAS NELSON
Since 1798